JULIA FOR

DATA SCIENCE

first edition

Zacharias Voulgaris, PhD

Published by:

2 Lindsley Road
Basking Ridge, NJ 07920 USA

https://www.TechnicsPub.com

Cover design by John Fiorentino
Edited by Lauren McCafferty

ISBN, print ed.   9781634621304
ISBN, Kindle ed.   9781634621311
ISBN, ePub ed.   9781634621328

First Printing 2016

Library of Congress Control Number: 2016944030

Dedicated to the memory of my father, Nicholas C. Voulgaris

Contents at a Glance

Table of Contents

I discovered Julia a few years back, and I've been intrigued by its potential and its power ever since. Julia's user-friendly Integrated Development Environment (IDE) made it very accessible, and its high level logic (very similar to Matlab and other high level languages) and performance made it powerful. However, I was more involved in other, more established platforms such as R and Java, and unable to give Julia my full attention.

As such, I didn't delve much further beyond the basics, including the applications of the tutorial that was available at the time. Besides, I knew that there are constantly new and interesting languages being developed, most of which never become mainstream.

So, why am I bothering with Julia now? Well, for one, it remained relevant as the years went by; the number of attendees at the Julia conference has been growing considerably every year. Even though I had been familiar with its basics, when I revisited Julia I discovered that I still had a lot to learn, as it had evolved considerably since I'd first encountered it.

Most importantly, it had crossed the pond and made its presence known to people in Europe, one of whom had created a series of exercises and videos about this fairly new language.

After playing around with Version 0.2, I began to wonder if I could actually do something useful with it, beyond factoring numbers quickly or calculating the nth Fibonacci number. However, the few packages that were available with Version 0.2 were poorly documented. There were only a handful of videos introducing the language, most of which were talks from a Python conference. Still, I kept Julia installed on my machine and would use it to write a script from time to time, usually tackling a programming challenge from Project Euler, Programming Praxis, or some similar site. I was a program manager at the time, so I didn't have much incentive to master a new programming language. Everything I did was a labor of love.

A few months later, though, I started working with data science again; I became more seriously involved with Julia programming. I quickly found that it was easier to code with than Python, for instance, which required a bunch of packages to complete basic data engineering tasks.

After enough casual use, I decided to tackle an entire data science project solely with Julia. Despite the inevitable learning curve and growing pains, I managed to complete it. It wasn't my best work, but it was proof that with a little practice and trial-and-error, Julia could handle serious data science problems and do so efficiently.

In writing this book I will share this and many other subsequent experiences, exploring how Julia can be integrated into various parts of the data science pipeline. Although there are other books that touch on Julia, there is not a single volume that comprehensively illustrates how Julia can be useful in the realm of data science. I considered waiting for the arrival of such a book, but given the experience I had built in years of experimenting with Julia, I decided to simply write it myself.

I understand that it is a big risk to write a book on a language that's still in its relative infancy, but it very well may be the case that Julia never stops evolving. If I waited for the language to reach homeostasis, this book would never get written.

I do not expect you to know anything about Julia or to be an established data scientist. If you have the desire to expand your skill-set, the drive to learn new ways of solving old problems, and the discipline to apply yourself throughout this book, you can make Julia an effective part of your data analytics ecosystem.

CHAPTER 1
Introducing Julia

There are dozens of programming languages out there: some generic, some focused on specific niches, each claiming to be better than the rest. The most powerful languages–the ones capable of rapidly performing complex calculations–tend to be difficult to learn (and even more difficult to master). Their audience is thus limited to those "hardcore" programmers who usually have some innate talent for this kind of work. The aspiring data scientists are faced with the prospect of devoting considerable time and energy to learning a language that will ultimately serve them poorly, requiring line after line of complex code to implement any useful algorithm.

On the other side of the spectrum are the "plug-and-play" languages, where all the complexities of programming have been carefully encapsulated. The most tedious (and often most widely-utilized) algorithms have been pre-packaged and handed over to the user; there's very little to actually learn. The problem with these languages is that they tend to be slow, with severe limitations in memory and capability. The data scientist here faces the opposite dilemma: take advantage of a language without a steep learning curve, but be stuck with a fairly weak tool for the job.

Julia is one of the languages that lies somewhere between these two extremes, offering the best of both worlds. In essence, it is a programming language designed for technical computing, offering speed, ease of use, and a variety of tools for data processing. Even though it's still in its infancy (version 1.0 is still pending and is expected to be released summer 2017), those who have toyed with it enough to recognize its potential are already convinced of its utility in technical computing and data science applications.

Some of the features that make Julia stand out from other programming languages include:

- **Julia exhibits incredible performance** in a variety of data analyses and other programming ventures. Its performance is comparable to that of C, which is often used as a benchmark for speed.

- **Julia has a strong base library**, allowing for all kinds of linear algebra operations that are often essential components of data analytics modules–without the need to employ other platforms.

- **Julia utilizes a multiple dispatch style,** giving it the ability to link different processes to the same function. This makes it easy to extend existing functions and reuse them for different types of inputs.

- **Julia is easy to pick up**, especially if you are migrating to it from Python, R, or Matlab/Octave.

- **Julia has a variety of user-friendly interfaces–both locally and on the cloud**–that make it an enjoyable interactive tool for all kinds of processes. It features a handy help for all functions and types.

- **Julia seamlessly connects with other languages,** including (but not limited to) R, Python, and C. This makes it easy to use with your existing code-base, without the need for a full migration.

- **Julia and all of its documentation and tutorials** are open-source, easily accessible, detailed, and comprehensible.

- **Julia's creators are committed** to enhancing it and helping its users. They give a variety of talks, organize an annual conference, and provide consulting services.

- **Julia's custom functions** are as fast and compact as those built into the base Julia code.

- **Julia has excellent parallelization capabilities**, making it easy to deploy over various cores of your computer or a whole cluster of computers.

- **Julia is exceptionally flexible** for developing new programs, accommodating both novice and expert users with a wide range of coding levels. This feature is rare in other languages.

As you learn and practice with Julia, you'll certainly uncover many more advantages particular to the data science environment.

HOW JULIA IMPROVES DATA SCIENCE

"Data science" is a rather ambiguous term that has come to mean a lot of different things since its introduction as a scientific field. In this book we will define it as: *the field of science dealing with the transformation of data into useful information (or "insights") by means of a variety of statistical and machine learning techniques.*

Since reaching critical mass, data science has employed all kinds of tools to harness the power and overcome the challenges of big data. Since a big part of the data science process involves running scripts on large and complex datasets (usually referred to as "data streams"), a high performance programming language is not just a luxury but a necessity.

Consider a certain data-processing algorithm that takes several hours to run with a conventional language: even a moderate increase in performance will have a substantial impact on the overall speed of the process. As a language, Julia does exactly that. This makes it an ideal tool for data science applications, both for the experienced and the beginner data scientist.

DATA SCIENCE WORKFLOW

People view data science as a process comprising various parts, each intimately connected to the data at hand and the objective of the analysis involved. More often than not, this objective involves the development of a dashboard or some clever visual (oftentimes interactive), which is usually referred to as a "data product."

Data science involves acquiring data from the world (from data streams stored in HDFS, datasets in CSV files, or data organized in relational databases), processing it in a way that renders useful information, and returning this information to the world in a refined and actionable form. The final product usually takes the form of a data product, but this is not essential. For instance, you may be asked to perform data science functions on a company's internal data and keep the results limited to visuals that you share with your manager.

Take for example a small company that is opting for data-driven market research, through the use of questionnaires for the subscribers to their blog. Data science involves these five steps:

1. Acquisition of the data from the marketing team

2. Preparation of the data into a form that can be usable for predictive analytics

3. Exploratory analysis of the data to decipher whether certain people are more inclined to buy certain products

4. Formatting of work to make the whole process resource-efficient and error-free

5. Development of models that provide useful insights about what products the company's clients are most interested in, and how much they are expected to pay for them.

We will go into more detail about this process in Chapter 5.

Figure 1.1 introduces the "big picture" of data science processes and how the Julia language fits in. The three stacked circles have come to represent Julia in general; in the figure, this symbol indicates a practical place to utilize Julia. It is clear that apart from the development of the data product and the acquisition of the data, Julia can be used in almost every phase of the data science process.

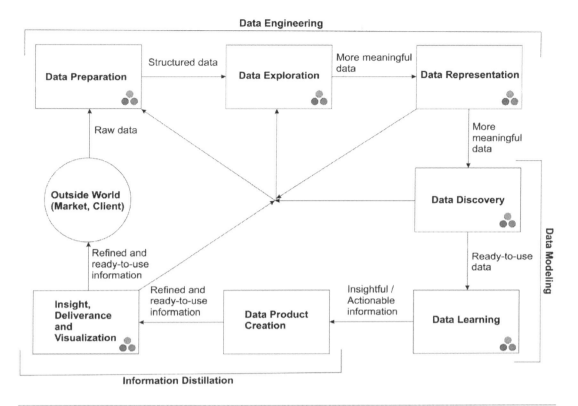

Figure 1.1 The data science process overview. The symbol with three stacked circles indicates steps where Julia fits in.

Consider how much this will simplify your workflow. No need to stitch code from other platforms into your pipeline, creating troublesome bottlenecks. Furthermore, once you have written and tested your code in Julia there is no need to translate it into a low-level language like C++ or Java, since there is no performance benefit from doing this. That's particularly important considering that this is an essential step when prototyping in languages like R and Matlab.

JULIA'S ADOPTION BY THE DATA SCIENCE COMMUNITY

You might be asking yourself: "If Julia is such a great language, why hasn't it yet been widely adopted by the data science community?" It would be expected that such a versatile language as Julia would have started to shine, like R and Python, claiming its place in the data scientist's toolbox.

Although Julia is an excellent choice for any kind of data processing project, it still lacks the variety of add-on packages that other, more established languages have to offer (even though the number of available packages is steadily growing, along with the number of Julia users). That's primarily because of its young age, and is bound to change as time goes by.

What's more, data science practitioners and learners are still not convinced that they can master it with the same ease as Python and R. These languages boast large user communities poised to make programming not only easy, but fun. Consider the Python Challenge: a series of programming tasks that make learning Python an adventure.

Although there is little doubt that Julia will one day experience comparable levels of fandom, it is not quite there yet—especially among data science practitioners. Despite its great potential, many people still find it challenging to write clean code and debug their first drafts in Julia. This may make the whole development process seem a bit daunting for newer users, leading to discontinuation.

Pre-made programs usually come in collections called libraries or packages. Although there are sufficient packages in Julia to perform all data science tasks, some algorithms may be missing, making some coding necessary. The early adopters of HTML and CSS faced similar difficulties during the first years of the web, but when their esoteric skill became more mainstream they found themselves in a good situation. It is likely that the same thing can happen to Julia practitioners as well. Even if you don't actively participate in the Julia coding community, you are bound to see great benefits from becoming familiar with the language. Besides, as the community grows, things are only going to get easier for its users— particularly the early adopters.

JULIA EXTENSIONS

Although Julia currently has a relatively small set of libraries (usually referred to as "packages") that expand its functionality, Julia's resources are continually expanding. Between early 2015 and mid-2016 the packages doubled in quantity; this doesn't seem to be slowing. As Julia is used primarily by people who deal with advanced computing applications, the packages being developed are designed to meet that need. They are also updated relatively frequently, making them robust additions to the language. Finally, since the Julia community is small and well-connected, there are rarely duplicate packages.

PACKAGE QUALITY

"What about the quality of the existing packages?" you may wonder. As the users developing these packages are generally experienced, they try to generate high-quality code, often reflected by the "stars" GitHub users award. It is worth noting that across the various packages, the number of stars these packages have received by the users has grown by about 50% between late 2015 and the time of this writing. Evidently there is a growing appreciation of the Julia code that is uploaded in this well-known repository.

An interesting attribute of many GitHub packages out there (across different languages) is that they are tested for build integrity, coverage, etc. so that you have a good idea of their reliability before you start using them. For the current version of Julia (0.4) the tests are impressive: out of 610 packages, 63% of the packages pass all the tests while only 11% of all packages fail the tests (the remaining packages have not been tested yet or are not testable).

FINDING NEW PACKAGES

For more up-to-date information on how the Julia packages fare, you can visit http://pkg.julialang.org/pulse.html. In addition, at the end of this book there is a reference list of the most useful packages for data science applications. It's also worth noting that even though Julia may not have the breadth of packages of other languages, it does have a great depth of packages relevant to data analytics. Throughout this book we will be exploring how these packages work and how they can help you tackle challenging data science problems.

ABOUT THE BOOK

If you are reading this book (and plan to follow the examples and exercises in it), you must be at least somewhat committed to the field of data science. We assume that you have basic programming experience, and have some understanding of data structures, GitHub repositories, and data analysis processes. If you have implemented an algorithm yourself, created any program from scratch, or adapted an existing program from GitHub to solve a problem—even a simple one—you are off to a great start.

Most importantly, we hope that you have a hands-on attitude and are comfortable using various technical documents and forums when you are stuck. Finally, you must have a genuine interest in learning this tool and making it a part of your workflow in data analytics projects.

If you're still reading at this point, you should be able to get the most out of this book, making considerable progress toward mastery of Julia for data science applications. You may not become an expert Julia developer, but you will be knowledgeable enough to understand a new script, and competent enough to get Julia to do some interesting data analytics for you. This includes some data engineering, which is generally an irksome process in most programming languages.

This book will present you with a series of hands-on problems representative of those commonly encountered throughout the data science pipeline, and guide you in the use of Julia to solve them. You won't have to reinvent the wheel, as the majority of these problems make use of existing packages and built-in functions. What's more, you will have the opportunity to practice on a couple of real datasets and let experience be your teacher, without having to go through the trial-and-error loops that arise in the absence of guidance.

The topics we are going to cover include:

1. The various options for IDEs that exist for Julia, as well as the use of a text editor for creating and editing Julia scripts.

2. Language specifics (main programming structures and functions), along with how they apply in a few relatively simple examples.

3. The different ways Julia can help you accomplish data engineering tasks, such as importing, cleaning, formatting and storing data, as well as performing data preprocessing.

4. Data visualization and some simple yet powerful statistics for data exploration purposes.

5. Dimensionality reduction through a variety of techniques designed to eliminate the unnecessary variables. In this section we'll also cover feature evaluation.

6. Machine learning methods, ranging from unsupervised (different types of clustering) to supervised (decision trees, random forests, basic neural networks, regression trees, and Extreme Learning Machines).

7. Graph analysis, from examining how the most popular algorithms can be applied to the data at hand, to pinpointing the connections among the various entities.

In addition to all this we will revisit some data science essentials, so that you have the data science pipeline fresh in your mind before delving into its various components. Furthermore, all of the material is accompanied by supplementary information that will be particularly useful to the novice users of Julia, including a number of resources for learning the particulars of the language as well as installing it on your machine.

Throughout the book, you will be exposed to examples and questions that will reinforce the material covered in each chapter. Once you are confident that you have internalized at least most of the information presented here, you will be able to write your own wrapper programs, and make good use of this extraordinary programming language.

You will be given directions on how you could extend all this to a parallelized setting (even on a single computer if you don't have access to a cluster). For those of you who are bold enough, in the last chapter of the book you will have an opportunity to create a data science application from scratch using Julia, making use of all the stuff you'll have learned in this book. Are you ready to begin?

CHAPTER 2
Setting Up the Data Science Lab

Just like every applied scientist worth his or her title, if you are to use Julia for data science, you will need to set up a lab where you can explore the data you have to your avail and distill its essence. Similar to most other programming languages, the interface that comes pre-equipped with Julia is minimalistic. Usually referred to as Read, Evaluate, Print, Loop (REPL), this basic interface is great for trying out the language and creating some fundamental scripts.

However, if you want to do some serious work with Julia, you will need an IDE tailored for Julia. And if you want to do something powerful enough to *wow* your organization, you will need to equip Julia with a few additional packages beyond the base set.

In this chapter we will examine the following topics:

- IDEs and packages for Julia

- Walkthrough of the IJulia IDE

- Datasets we'll be using in this book

- An example of a simple machine learning algorithm implemented in Julia

- Saving your workspace into a data file.

Before we start to set up the lab, though, you must install Julia on your machine. Appendix A will walk you through how to install Julia.

Julia IDEs

It is highly recommended that you install an IDE. If you are comfortable with text editors, you can get your editor of choice to recognize Julia code, enabling you to create and edit Julia scripts there with ease.

Moreover, now would be a good time to get acquainted with Julia's selection of packages and how you can install them on your machine. You can also start getting a bit of hands-on experience with Julia, using it on some relatively simple algorithms, while at the same time getting acquainted with its IO capabilities.

JUNO

Juno is a minimalistic yet powerful IDE, based on Light Table, that specializes in Julia scripts. Juno is equipped with autocomplete, which predicts the functions or variables that you will type, similar to the predictive text input features of most smartphones. Autocomplete increases the speed and accuracy with which you code.

Juno is intuitive and easy to master–definitely a worthy option for Julia. If you wish to learn more about its functionality, you can always refer to its abundant online documentation, which is accessible via the "Help" menu. You can see a screenshot of Juno in Figure 2.1.

Juno's console features a handy little animation that shows you when Julia is occupied with a script or with starting up; this makes it easy to understand what's currently going on (you can see it on Figure 2.1, right below the line numbers). Unfortunately, you cannot write directly in the console area, as you would in other IDEs (such as Canopy, for Python). That's not too inconvenient, though, since it is easy to run individual commands in a script window by pressing Ctrl-Enter (or Shift-Enter) after typing your command.

It's important to remember that whenever you want to execute something in Juno, you have to make sure that the script you are using has the `.jl` extension, as this is the only way for the IDE to recognize Julia code and therefore be able to run it.

Toolbar
(basic Juno commands)

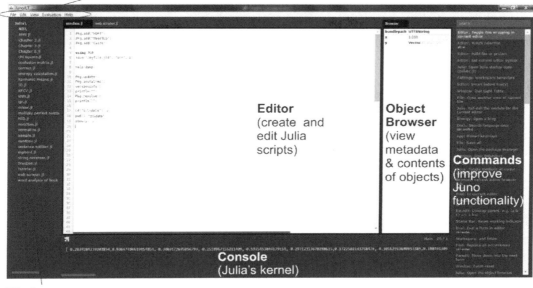

Editor
(create and edit Julia scripts)

Object Browser
(view metadata & contents of objects)

Commands
(improve Juno functionality)

Console
(Julia's kernel)

Workspace
(file management tool)

Figure 2.1 A screenshot of Juno with all its viewers open.

When scripts don't work as expected, Juno has a straightforward way of letting you know: through the use of red highlighted text in the console (see Figure 2.2).

Figure 2.2 A partial screenshot of Juno, focusing on the part of the IDE where an error message would appear. The text highlighted in red denotes encountered issues.

Although Juno is still in development, it has a lot of great features that are constantly being refined. A recent development on the Atom software (a generic IDE for all kinds of languages) allowed it to integrate the Julia kernel, enabling it to identify and run Julia scripts (see http://bit.ly/2akTBua for details).

What's more, Atom allows the user to switch back and forth between the text editor (where you normally develop all your scripts) and the REPL, making it ideal for testing out ideas before you put them in your programs. This makes the Julia plug-in for Atom a viable alternate IDE, which is gradually being incorporated into the Juno project. So keep a close eye on these developments, as they may prove to be the new norm for Julia IDEs. You can learn more about this in the corresponding article in the official Julia blog (http://bit.ly/29Nzsf1).

IJULIA

Until the Atom-based option matures (eventually making Juno the go-to IDE for Julia scripts) there are other options out there that are already developed enough to be completely reliable. One such option is IJulia, which is simply Julia on your web browser. If you come from a Python background and you are already used to IPython notebooks, you may want to get started working with IJulia. In fact, this is the IDE we'll be using throughout the book, partly because it's more established (the creators of Julia and other experts use it in most of their presentations), and partly because it is easy to showcase code using this IDE.

Curiously, IJulia is in a way older than any other Julia IDE, since it is essentially the notebook software that was developed for Python (currently known as Jupyter, and formerly known as IPython, available at https://jupyter.org), with the only difference being the Julia kernel in the backend. Consider Jupyter a car that can have different engines under its hood: although it usually runs on the Python engine, it works perfectly with the Julia engine as well.

IJulia is also handy when it comes to presentations and tutorial building, as well as data exploration. It's no coincidence that Jupyter is popular among data scientists who use Python.

All IJulia notebooks are rendered on your web browser, although their code files are stored natively. You can find the corresponding installation files on this site: http://bit.ly/1aA7oeg. Alternatively, you can run it from the cloud, through

JuliaBox (https://juliabox.com), although you will need a Google account for that. You can get an idea of IJulia's interface in Figure 2.3.

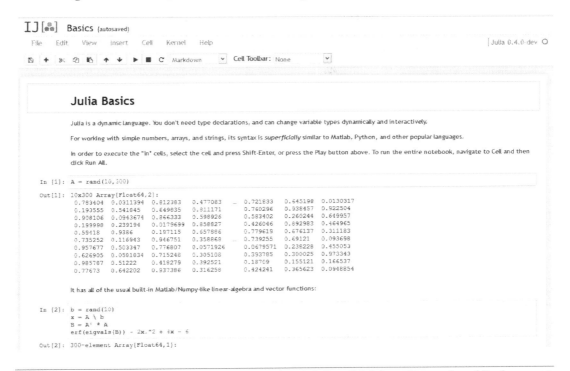

Figure 2.3 A screenshot of IJulia from its online version, JuliaBox. This interactive version of the language is ideal for sharing code in presentations, for building tutorials, and for high-level programming.

ADDITIONAL IDES

In addition to Juno and IJulia, another Julia IDE was recently released by the company that created Julia Studio. Julia Studio was an excellent IDE that made Julia as user-friendly as R and Matlab, and is probably what made people fall in love with Julia "back in the day." However, it has been discontinued for a while now, even though some Julia tutorials still refer to it as the go-to IDE for Julia.

This latest IDE is called Epicenter. Although it is a worthy alternative to the existing IDEs, the functionality of its free version is limited. If you wish to create more elaborate Julia applications, you may want to consider investing in one of Epicenter's paid editions. You can find more about it here: http://bit.ly/29Nzvrv.

Another IDE that so far has escaped publicity is the Julia IDE that was created by the well-known Tutorials Point website (http://bit.ly/29KlxWp). It is similar to JuliaBox in that it's cloud-based, but doesn't require you to log in and has an intuitive interface that rivals that of Juno. Furthermore, it offers you direct access to the console, so you can work on script development and script experimentation in the same window (instead of having to switch between the editor and the REPL, or between two different tabs of the Juno editor). However, it doesn't always have the latest version of Julia and may therefore not be able to run state-of-the-art packages properly, so we recommend you use it only for simple scripts.

You can always use a combination of all these IDEs. Maybe you can have Juno on your main workstation, use IJulia when sharing your code with your team and/or your clients, use JuliaBox when you are on a computer that doesn't have Julia installed (and you don't have the option to do so), and use Epicenter when working on more sophisticated projects that require advanced features, such as sophisticated GUIs.

Finally, if you are comfortable using the REPL coupled with a simple text editor for all your Julia development tasks, and you are a Windows user, you can use Notepad++, which now has a Julia language package available (http://bit.ly/29Y9SWL). Just be sure to save your script files with the extension (.jl) so that the text editor recognizes them as Julia scripts and applies the right highlighting to them. Alternatively, if you are using Linux or Mac OS, you could use Emacs for your Julia scripts by applying the corresponding language pack (http://bit.ly/29Y9CqH).

JULIA PACKAGES

FINDING AND SELECTING PACKAGES

As we learned in the previous chapter, packages are an important and sought-after aspect of any programming language. The reason is simple: packages empower you to efficiently do things that would normally take a lot of time to do yourself, by providing the essential auxiliary functions. The best part about packages is that the tasks they are designed to help with are the tasks that are most tedious and time-consuming. Until you reach a level of mastery of Julia, you may need to rely on packages to obtain the functions you need to work with your data.

Finding packages is a relatively straightforward task when it comes to the Julia platform. The safest place to do so is through the corresponding page on the official Julia site (http://pkg.julialang.org), which provides a list of all the packages that have been officially adopted by the Julia ecosystem. These packages can also be found on the GitHub: https://github.com/JuliaLang.

If you are more adventurous with your package use, you can always roam around GitHub to find other, more experimental Julia code repositories. Keep in mind, however, that these are provided on an as-is basis and you are welcome to use them at your own risk. Be sure to install all of the dependencies they may have to ensure a smoother experience.

Selecting the right package for the job is also a straightforward process, if a more subjective one. What we recommend is to carefully read the documentation provided in the package's README.md file. Once you decide that the package will meet your needs, check out the test statistics below the file listing. Figure 2.4 shows an example of such stats.

Figure 2.4 Test statistics for a relatively mature Julia package. Although the package seems to still need some work, it passes all the functionality tests for both the latest stable version (bottom left) and the nightly release (bottom right).

If the package passes most of the tests for the version of Julia that you plan to be using it on, then it should work well for you. Even if it's not quite ready yet, it doesn't hurt to keep that package in mind for the future, since Julia's packages evolve rapidly and it probably won't be long before that package meets expectations.

INSTALLING PACKAGES

Whether you are using Juno, IJulia, Epicenter, a text editor, or even the REPL, at one point or another you will come to the realization that the base package that Julia has is limited (though much more powerful than Python's base package–at least for data analysis work). To install a package in Julia, you need to execute the following code:

```
Pkg.add("mypackage")
```

where `mypackage` is the name of the package you want to install. This has to be in double quotes, as Julia views it as a string variable. Depending on the size of the package, it can take some time to download and install on your computer, at the location C:\Users\username\.julia\v0.4 for Windows, and ~/.julia/v0.4 for UNIX-based systems.

Packages that are not official (mainly because they are still under development) need to be added manually. Fortunately, the `Pkg.clone()` command makes the whole process easy. To install such a package you just need to run this command, passing the package's GitHub URL as an argument:

```
Pkg.clone("git://github.com/AuthorName/SomeCoolPackage.jl.git")
```

Some of these packages may not work properly (especially if they have not been updated for a while), or may even not work at all. Still, it is useful to be familiar with them, in case you want to explore the bleeding edge of Julia tech!

Although not required, it is good practice to update the package once you install it, since there are bound to be newer versions of it. You can do that by executing the snippet:

```
Pkg.update()
```

It may take some time for this command to complete, particularly the first time it is run. If you are installing many packages, run this command only after you have installed all packages, as there is no way to update just a single package. Also, it is a good idea to run the `Pkg.update()` command periodically, to ensure that you always have the latest version of your installed packages. While running this command on the REPL, any issues will appear in red, while everything else should be in blue.

USING PACKAGES

Once the package is installed, you can make use of the functions it contains by executing the following in every Julia session where you need to use the package's functions:

```
using mypackage
```

After a package is installed, it will be recognized by Julia as a keyword, so you won't need to put it in double quotes to load it into memory.

HACKING PACKAGES

Once you have become confident in your Julia programming skills, you can try your hand at improving an existing package without needing to know C. To do this, you can change the package's source code and then load it into memory again (using the aforementioned command). For example, the source code of a package called `CoolPackage` should be all the `.jl` files at the directory C:\Users\username\.julia\v0.4\CoolPackage\src in the case of Windows, and !/username/.julia/v0.4/CoolPackage for UNIX-based systems.

IJULIA BASICS

HANDLING FILES

Creating a notebook

Creating a new file in IJulia (referred to as an IJulia notebook) is a fairly straightforward process. An IJulia notebook is something that is usable only in IJulia, either natively or on the cloud. If you wish to create a script file to be shared with people who use a different IDE, you'll need to export your IJulia notebook as a `.jl` file (something we'll cover shortly).

Once you have opened the application, just click the "New" button at the top-right and then select the "Julia" option toward the bottom of the menu that appears. If you are already processing a notebook, you can create a new one using the "File" menu. Figure 2.5 shows both of these options.

Figure 2.5 Creating a new notebook in IJulia: whether on the main screen (top), or while processing another notebook (bottom).

Saving a notebook

You can save a Julia notebook in IJulia by clicking on the disk button to the top-left, or you can select the fifth command in the "File" menu (see Figure 2.6).

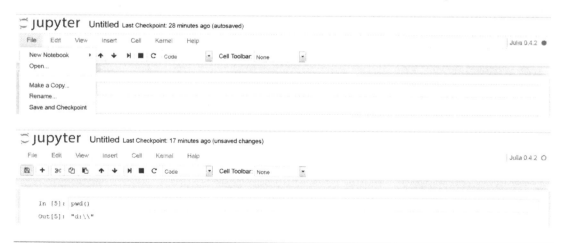

Figure 2.6 Saving a notebook in IJulia: through the "File" menu (top) and through the disk button (bottom).

When this happens, IJulia takes all your text and code and puts it in a text file having the `.ipynb` extension. This kind of file is readable by the Jupyter program (even if IJulia is not installed on the computer). We recommend you keep all your Julia scripts in the same folder for easier access and referencing.

Jupyter will periodically auto-save your notebook; even if you close the notebook, nothing will be lost as long as the IDE is running. An IJulia notebook contains a variety of information–not just code. So when you save such a file (with the extension `.ipynb`), you are saving all of the markup you have developed (e.g. the section headers and HTML text), the Julia code, and all the results this code has produced by the time you save the notebook (including both text and graphics).

Renaming a notebook

Renaming a Julia notebook in IJulia can be done in two ways (beyond renaming the actual file in the OS shell). The simplest method is to click on its name ("Untitled" by default) at the top of the screen, right next to the Jupyter logo, and type the new name in the text box that appears. You can do the same task by selecting the fourth option on the "File" menu. See Figure 2.7.

Figure 2.7 Renaming a notebook in IJulia.

Loading a notebook

There are several ways to load a Julia notebook in IJulia. From the main screen, just click on the notebook file (or any text file for that matter). Alternatively, if you are already processing a file, you can load another one using the "File" menu (this opens another browser tab showing the Jupyter main screen). See Figure 2.8.

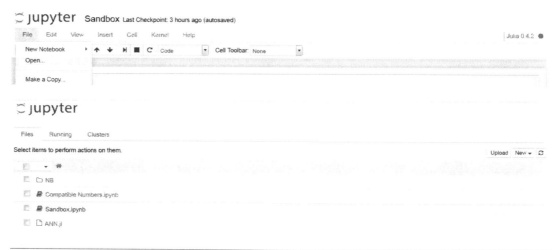

Figure 2.8 Loading a notebook in IJulia.

Exporting a notebook

A notebook can be exported in several ways, depending on what you plan to do with it afterwards. Here are your options:

- If you wish to move the actual notebook file onto another machine and process it using IJulia there, you can export it as a notebook (`.ipynb` file).

- If you wish to use the code in the notebook on the REPL, commenting out all its other content (headings, explanatory text, etc.), exporting it as a `.jl` file would be the best option.

- If you prefer to share the notebook with other people without needing to run code (e.g. via a website, or as part of a demonstration), you can export it either as an .html file or a LaTex-based digital printout (.pdf file).

All of these exporting options, as well as other ones, are available to you via the "File" menu, as shown on Figure 2.9.

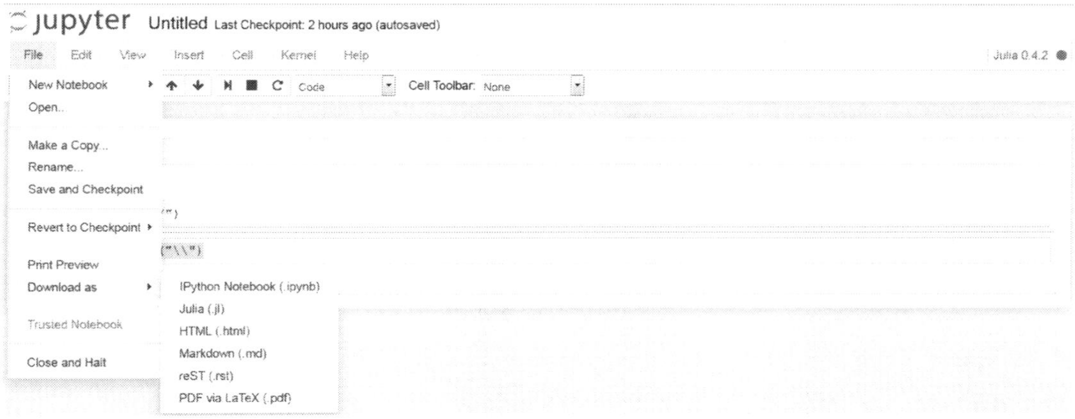

Figure 2.9 Exporting a notebook in IJulia.

ORGANIZING CODE IN .JL FILES

Since Julia takes a functional approach to programming, the scripts you find and create will commonly take the form of functions. Functions can coexist in the same .jl file without interfering with each other. Related functions should exist within the same file.

For instance, if you have a function called `fun(x::Int64)` and another one called `fun(x::Array{Int64, 1})`, you may want to put these together since they extend each other through multiple dispatch. Also, you may want to store the function `MyFun(x::Int64, y::Int64)` which relies on `fun()` in that same .jl file. We suggest that you put any testing code in a wrapper function, such as `main()`, to ensure that it won't be run unless you want to run it.

None of this is crucial if you are using IJulia, but if you want to share your code with other Julians, it is prudent to know how to do so. Because all .jl files can be run from an IJulia notebook (using the `include()` command) it is a good idea to have commonly-used programs saved as .jl files–especially if you plan to make changes to these programs at any point.

REFERENCING CODE

Implementing and executing simple algorithms is straightforward. However, at some point you'll want to build something more elaborate that makes use of other functions that may be already stored in other `.jl` files. Naturally, you could always copy and paste the corresponding code into your current `.jl` file, but that would create unnecessary redundancy. Instead, call the code you need by referencing the corresponding `.jl` file. This is possible through the following command:

```
include("my other script.jl")
```

If the referenced `.jl` file is in another directory, be sure to include the full path as well. Remember that the folder separator is not the conventional \ character, but either the double slash \\ or the backslash /. Julia views the double slash as a single character, even though it consists of two. Type `length("\\")` to verify.

Once you run the `include()` command, everything in that file will be executed:

```
include("D:\\Julia scripts\\my other script.jl")
```

It is important that you don't have any unnecessary code that is not within a function in the referenced file as this may create confusion when running your current program.

WORKING DIRECTORY

At some point in your Julia scripting you may want to identify the location where Julia thinks you are working, and perhaps change that location. All this is done using two simple commands: `pwd()` and `cd()`.

The `pwd()` command is short for "print working directory" and does just that:

```
In[1]: pwd()
Out[1]: "c:\\users\\Zacharias\\Documents\\Julia"
```

If you want to change the directory where you are, you can do this using `cd()`, just like in the command prompt:

```
In[2]: cd("d:\\")
In[3]: pwd()
Out[3]: "d:\\"
```

The default folder that Julia works with is listed in the `juliarc.jl` file, which is in the folder where Julia is installed, and then within this folder the path \resources\app\julia\etc\julia. If you plan to make changes to that file, we recommend that you create a backup copy first, as it may seriously disrupt the function of Julia.

DATASETS WE WILL USE

No lab is complete without some data to work with. Normally, this would come from a combination of data streams. For the purpose of this book, we'll assume that you have already queried your data sources and you have everything in a series of data files, primarily in the `.csv` format (comma separated values). For data that is not so formatted, we will illustrate how you can parse it, obtain its more information-rich elements, and then store it in a structured format like `.csv` or any other delimited file (see Chapter 5 for details).We will also cover a case of semi-structured data, in the form of raw `.txt` files.

DATASET DESCRIPTIONS

For most of the case studies we will be utilizing two `.csv` files: `magic04.csv` and `OnlineNewsPopularity.csv` (obtained from the UCI machine learning repository, http://archive.ics.uci.edu/ml). We will also make use of the `Spam Assassin` dataset, which more closely parallels a real-world problem than any of the benchmark datasets you can find in a repository.

Magic dataset

The `Magic` (aka `Magic04`) dataset refers to the data collected by the Magic telescope using the imaging technique. It consists of approximately 19,000 data points and 10 features. The attribute we are trying to predict (located in the last column in the dataset) represents the kind of radiation each data point corresponds to: either gamma or hadron (represented as g and h, respectively). As such, this is a classification problem. You can take a look at a couple of lines of the dataset below:

```
22.0913,10.8949,2.2945,0.5381,0.2919,15.2776,18.2296,7.3975,21.068,
    123.281,g
100.2775,21.8784,3.11,0.312,0.1446,-48.1834,57.6547,-
    9.6341,20.7848,346.433,h
```

OnlineNewsPopularity dataset

As its name suggests, the OnlineNewsPopularity dataset comprises data from a variety of news websites, including their popularity measured in number of shares the articles received (target variable). The dataset consists of about 40,000 data points and 59 features (not counting the URL attribute, which is more like an identifier for each data point). As the attribute we are trying to predict in this case is a continuous one, this is a classical regression problem. You can view a sample of this dataset below:

```
http://mashable.com/2013/01/07/beewi-smart-toys/, 731.0, 10.0,
    370.0, 0.559888577828, 0.999999995495, 0.698198195053, 2.0,
    2.0, 0.0, 0.0, 4.35945945946, 9.0, 0.0, 0.0, 0.0, 0.0, 1.0,
    0.0, 0.0, 0.0, 0.0, 0.0, 0.0, 0.0, 0.0, 0.0, 0.0, 8500.0,
    8500.0, 8500.0, 1.0, 0.0, 0.0, 0.0, 0.0, 0.0, 0.0, 0.0,
    0.0222452755449, 0.306717575824, 0.0222312775078,
    0.0222242903103, 0.626581580813, 0.437408648699,
    0.0711841921519, 0.0297297297297, 0.027027027027,
    0.52380952381, 0.47619047619, 0.350609996065, 0.136363636364,
    0.6, -0.195, -0.4, -0.1, 0.642857142857, 0.214285714286,
    0.142857142857, 0.214285714286, 855
http://mashable.com/2013/01/07/bodymedia-armbandgets-update/,
    731.0, 8.0, 960.0, 0.418162618355, 0.999999998339,
    0.54983388613, 21.0, 20.0, 20.0, 0.0, 4.65416666667, 10.0, 1.0,
    0.0, 0.0, 0.0, 0.0, 0.0, 0.0, 0.0, 0.0, 0.0, 0.0, 0.0, 0.0,
    0.0, 0.0, 545.0, 16000.0, 3151.15789474, 1.0, 0.0, 0.0, 0.0,
    0.0, 0.0, 0.0, 0.0, 0.0200816655822, 0.114705387413,
    0.0200243688545, 0.0200153281713, 0.825173249979,
    0.514480300844, 0.268302724212, 0.0802083333333,
    0.0166666666667, 0.827956989247, 0.172043010753,
    0.402038567493, 0.1, 1.0, -0.224479166667, -0.5, -0.05, 0.0,
    0.0, 0.5, 0.0, 556
```

Spam Assassin **dataset**

The final dataset in our collection is composed of `.txt` files, representing a collection of 3,298 emails, 501 of which are spam. The rest are normal emails (referred to as `ham`) and are divided into two categories: `easy ham` and `hard ham`, depending on the difficulty of detecting them accurately. As you would expect, this is a classical classification problem.

In this case, we will need to do some work since there are no features per se. We will have to create them from scratch, using the text data of the emails. Below is a sample of one such email. The subject of the email, which will be our focus when dealing with this email, is in bold.

```
Return-Path: <Online#3.19578.34-
    UgGTgZFN19NAr9RR.1.b@newsletter.online.com>
Received: from acmta4.cnet.com (abv-sfo1-acmta4.cnet.com
    [206.16.1.163])
by dogma.slashnull.org (8.11.6/8.11.6) with ESMTP id g69MseT08837
for <qqqqqqqqq-cnet-newsletters@example.com>; Tue, 9 Jul 2002
    23:54:40 +0100
Received: from abv-sfo1-ac-agent2 (206.16.0.224) by acmta4.cnet.com
    (PowerMTA(TM) v1.5); Tue, 9 Jul 2002 15:49:15 -0700 (envelope-
    from <Online#3.19578.34-
    UgGTgZFN19NAr9RR.1.b@newsletter.online.com>)
Message-ID: <1100198.1026255272511.JavaMail.root@abv-sfo1-ac-
    agent2>
Date: Tue, 9 Jul 2002 15:54:30 -0700 (PDT)
From: "CNET News.com Daily Dispatch" <Online#3.19578.34-
    UgGTgZFN19NAr9RR.1@newsletter.online.com>
To: qqqqqqqqq-cnet-newsletters@example.com
Subject: CNET NEWS.COM: Cable companies cracking down on Wi-Fi
Mime-Version: 1.0
Content-Type: text/html; charset=ISO-8859-1
Content-Transfer-Encoding: 7bit
X-Mailer: Accucast (http://www.accucast.com)
X-Mailer-Version: 2.8.4-2
```

DOWNLOADING DATASETS

The above datasets were selected because they are complex enough to be interesting, but not necessarily daunting. They are also universal enough to relate to many different data science applications. You can download them in either one of these ways:

- Directly from the UCI repository

- From the dedicated Dropbox folder the author has created: http://bit.ly/29mtzIY.

Once downloaded and unpacked, you can take a peek at the datasets in a spreadsheet software (such as MS Excel, Numbers, or Gnumeric, depending on the OS you are using), or even a text editor (the data is stored in the .csv files so they can be opened as normal text files even by your system's default editor). You can learn more about these datasets by reading the corresponding .names files.

LOADING DATASETS

CSV files

To make access to the aforementioned datasets easier, especially if you are new to Julia, it is recommended that you move the extracted .csv files to the working folder of the language. To reveal Julia's working folder, just run the pwd() command we saw previously:

```
In[1]: pwd()  #A
```

#A println(pwd()) is also an option, particularly for other IDEs and the REPL.

You can load a .csv file into Julia's workspace (the memory of your computer that is handled by Julia) using the following simple command:

```
In[2]: data = readcsv("magic04.csv");
```

The semicolon at the end is optional, but useful if you don't want the console window to fill up with data from the uploaded file. The data from the file is now stored in a two-dimensional array (matrix) called "data." You can also load the data into other formats (such as our all-time favorite: the data frame), but we'll get to that later on. Also, keep in mind that you can incorporate the file path in the filename. If your .csv file was stored in D:\data\, you would run the following code instead:

```
In[3]: data = readcsv("D:\\data\\magic04.csv");
```

Text files

You can load text data (say, one of the spam emails) in the Julia workspace just as easily, using the following commands:

```
In[1]: f = open(filename, "r")
lines = readlines(f);
close(f)
```

The above snippet will load a text file whose path and name are passed as filename as an IO object f. The parameter r tells Julia that when you create this object, you only want to read data from it.

To make use of the IO object f you need to apply a function such as readlines() that can receive such objects as an input. readlines() can parse the whole file, split its contents into one-line strings, and return an array of these strings as its output.

Here's a variant of the above method, where each line of the file is parsed in a sequential manner using a for-loop:

```
f = open(filename, "r")
for line in eachline(f)
    [some code]
end
close(f)
```

If you wish to have the whole contents of the text file stored in a single string, you can do that using the following snippet:

```
f = open(filename, "r")
text = readall(f);
close(f)
```

Although this approach may seem more elegant, it may be suboptimal in practice. The reason is twofold. First, the text files you encounter in the data science world are often large and storing them in a variable (or an array) takes up a great deal of memory (which usually comes at a cost). Second, we generally won't need the whole file, so we can process it line by line without having to store more than one line in memory.

CODING AND TESTING A SIMPLE MACHINE LEARNING ALGORITHM IN JULIA

To familiarize yourself with your new lab, let's start with a relatively simple example. If you are completely new to Julia, don't worry if you don't understand everything here; this is just to help you get acquainted with the look and feel of the language. We encourage you to revisit this example once you feel comfortable with Julia code.

In the meantime, you can either type the code yourself, or use the `kNN.jl` file, provided along with the rest of the Julia code that accompanies this book (just open the file on IJulia or a text editor, copy all its contents, and then paste it on a new IJulia notebook).

We selected one of the simplest algorithms that is still useful. We want you to learn to code something that you may actually use in your work as a data scientist, such as an algorithm that can help you with classification tasks. One such algorithm is the one applicable to the `magic` dataset, which involves classifying the observed radiation of the telescope as `gamma` or `hadron` (denoted as `g` and `h` respectively, in the last attribute of the dataset).

This is possible using the information in the remaining attributes, which we will use as-is for the purposes of this example. The end result will be a prediction of some unknown observations into one of these two classes, and the validation of this prediction based on the actual classes of these observations.

The focus of this section is not to make you an expert in classification algorithms (which we'll discuss in detail at a later chapter), so it's alright if you don't understand everything. For the time being, you can focus on the Julia aspect of it and try to understand how the programs involved work.

ALGORITHM DESCRIPTION

The algorithm we'll be examining is called "k Nearest Neighbor" (or kNN) and is a basic classification algorithm from the early days of machine learning. Despite its antiquity, it is still used in image analysis and recommender systems, among other fields. kNN is a distance-based classifier. Although it doesn't have a training phase, it is robust when speed is of the essence.

Its philosophy is straightforward: in order to classify a given (unknown) data point X, find the k data points that are most similar to it, and apply the majority vote. Similarity is usually based on the reverse of the distances involved, so the data points with the smallest distances to X are selected. The pseudo-code of the algorithm is shown in Listing 2.1.

```
Inputs: training data input values (X), training data labels (x),
    testing data input values (Y), number of neighbors (k)
Output: predicted labels for testing data (y)
for each element i in array Y
    calculate distances of Yi to all training points Xj          #A
    find indexes of k smallest distances
    break down these data points based on their classes
    find the class with the majority of these k data points      #B
    assign this class as the label of Yi
end for
#A    distance function
#B    classify function
```

Listing 2.1 Pseudo-code for the kNN algorithm.

This is shown in more detail in Figure 2.10.

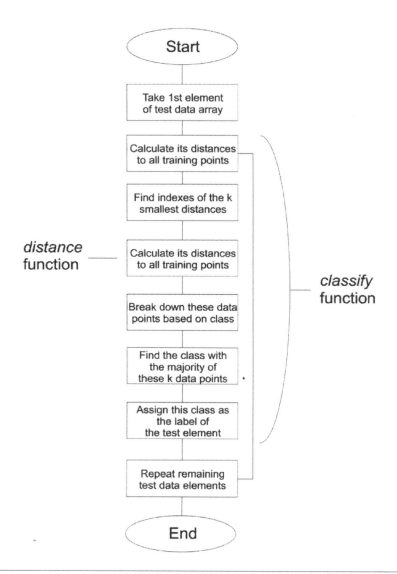

Figure 2.10 A flowchart of the kNN algorithm, a basic machine learning algorithm for classification.

ALGORITHM IMPLEMENTATION

To implement kNN in Julia we need two things: a distance calculation function and a classification function. These can be wrapped in the main function, which we'll call kNN(). For simplicity, in this implementation of kNN we will use the Euclidean distance (though in practice you can use any distance metric you prefer). It is generally best to start with the auxiliary functions–in this case, `distance()` and `classify()`. If you run the whole code as a single script, you need to have all the functions defined before you can use them, as we saw in the previous chapter.

First, we need to think about what each one of these functions will have as its input(s) and what it will yield as an output. In the case of `distance()`, it is rather obvious: it needs to take in two data points as vectors (one-dimensional arrays) and yield a single number (float). As for `classify()`, it needs to take the distances of all the data points as vectors, along with their labels as vectors, and the number of neighbors to examine (a single number), ultimately yielding a single element (which could be either a number or a string, depending on what populates the labels array of our dataset).

In Julia, although it is important to define all these elements, being too specific may cause frustrating errors. For example, if we need two numbers `x` and `y` as inputs, and it doesn't matter what kind of numbers these are, we can define `x` and `y` as just numbers instead of, say, floats or integers. This will also allow our functions to be more versatile. However, in cases where some types of numbers wouldn't make sense as inputs, we must be more specific.

In the case of `classify()`, for example, we don't want `k` to be a number with a decimal point, a fraction, or a complex number. It needs to be an integer. So in the corresponding functions (in this case our wrapper function `kNN()` as well as the `classify()` function), it is better off being defined as such. As for the dataset to be used in `kNN()`, this will be in the form of a matrix and will need to be defined accordingly.

Let's start with the auxiliary functions of the algorithm, so that you get familiar with how an algorithm is implemented in Julia. We'll first define how we want to calculate the distance between two data points, such as the code in Listing 2.2 (there are better ways to implement this, but this one is easier to understand).

We could include this code in the main method since it's fairly small, but what if we wanted to try out different distance metrics? It is much easier to make this kind of change when the code is broken down into several auxiliary functions which are self-sufficient and easier to understand and edit.

```
In[1]: function distance{T<:Number}(x::Array{T,1}, y::Array{T,1})
dist = 0                              #A
for i in 1:length(x)                  #B
    dist += (x[i] - y[i])^2
end
dist = sqrt(dist)
return dist
end
#A initialize distance variable
#B repeat for all dimensions of x and y
```

Listing 2.2 An auxiliary function for the implementation of the kNN algorithm. This one is responsible for calculating the distance between two points, x and y, represented as vectors.

Now let's get into the meat of the algorithm: the classification process for a single data point, based on the distances we've calculated. The distance function has been applied several times to create a single dimensional array called `distances`, which we'll use as one of the inputs in the `classify()` function. The code for this function is available in Listing 2.3.

```
In[2]: function classify{T<:Any}(distances::Array{Float, 1},
    labels::Array{T, 1, k::Int64)
    class = unique(labels)                        #A
    nc = length(class)                            #B
    indexes = Array(Int,0)                        #C
    M = maxtype(typeof(distances[1]))             #D
    class_count = Array(Int, nc)
    for i in 1:k
        indexes[i] = inmin(distances)
        distances[indexes[i]] = M                 #E
    end
    klabels = labels[indexes]

    for i in 1:nc
        for j in 1:k
            if klabels[j] == class[i]
                class_count[i] += 1
                break
```

```
            end
       end
end
index = inmax(class_count)
return class[index]
   end
#A find all the distinct classes
#B number of classes
#C initialize vector of indexes of the nearest neighbors
#D the largest possible number that this vector can have
#E make sure this element is not selected again
```

Listing 2.3 Another auxiliary function of the implementation of the kNN algorithm. This one performs classification of a point based on its distances from the known points of the dataset.

Now it's time to see how it all fits together by implementing the main function (often referred to as the wrapper function). This is the function we'll call whenever we want to use the kNN algorithm (although we can always call the other functions on their own, which is particularly useful for debugging). So, let's type the code in Listing 2.4 and conclude our project.

```
In[3]: function apply_kNN{T1<:Number, T2<:Any}(X::Array{T1,2},
    x::Array{T2,1}, Y::Array{T1,2}, k::Int)
N = size(X,1)                                    #A
n = size(Y,1)                                    #B
      D = Array(Float, N)                        #C
      z = Array(typeof(x[1]), n)                 #D
for i in 1:n
    for j in 1:N
          D[j] = distance(X[j,:], Y[i,:])
    end

z[i] = classify(D, x, k)
end
return z
      end
#A number of known data points
#B number of data points to classify
#C initialize distance vector
#D initialize labels vector (output)
```

Listing 2.4 The main function (wrapper) of the implementation of the kNN algorithm.

ALGORITHM TESTING

In order to use this function, we are going to need some data. So, let's load the `magic` dataset we saw in the previous section:

```
In[4]: data = readcsv("magic04.csv")
```

This puts all the data into a single matrix. To make it easier to work with, we can organize it first into inputs (features) and outputs (labels). You can do this with the following commands:

```
In[5]: I = map(Float64, data[:, 1:(end-1)])    #A
In[6]: O = data[:, end]                          #B
#A take all the columns of the data matrix, apart from the last one
    and convert everything into a Float. Result = 10-dim Array of
    Float numbers
#B take only the last column of the data matrix. Result = 1-dim
    Array
```

Now, if you were to use this data to test a classifier (in this case the kNN algorithm), both of these arrays would need to be divided into training and testing sets. This is a technique that is worth looking into detail, so we'll describe it in a later chapter. For now, we can do a basic random sampling.

First we'll get a random set of indexes for the training set (say, half of the total number of data points). Then we'll select the corresponding data points and their labels from `I` and `O` respectively, and store them in two arrays. Afterwards, we'll put the remaining data points and their labels in two other arrays. You can do all that with the code (which we encourage you to write on IJulia or some other Julia IDE) in Listing 2.5.

```
In[7]: N = length(O)              #A
In[8]: n = round(Int64, N/2)      #B
In[9]: R = randperm(N)            #C
In[10]: indX = R[1:n]             #D
In[11]: X = I[indX,:]             #E
In[12]: x = O[indX]               #F
In[13]: indY = R[(n+1):end]
In[14]: Y = I[indY,:]             #E
```

```
In[15]: y = O[indY]                                    #F
#A number of data points in the whole dataset (which is equivalent
    to the length of array O)
#B the half of the above number
#C a random permutation of all the indexes (essential for sampling)
#D get some random indexes for the training set
#E input values for training and testing set respectively
#F target values for training and testing set respectively
#G some random indexes for the testing set
```

Listing 2.5 Code for testing the implementation of the kNN algorithm, using the preloaded Magic dataset.

Now you are ready to see the kNN classifier you have built in action. Just run the following commands:

```
In[16]: z = apply_kNN(X, x, Y, 5)                      #A
In[17]: println( sum(y .== z[1]) / n )
println(z[1][1:5], z[2][1:5])                          #B
#A predicted values and the accompanying probabilities (output of
    the classifier)
#B accuracy rate of classification and small sample of the
    classifier's output
```

Upon running this code, you should see something like the following in your IJulia notebook (results may vary every time due to the random sampling involved):

```
Out[17]: 0.805888538380652
    Any["g","g","g","g","g"][0.6,0.8,0.6,0.8,0.6]
```

Congratulations! You have just run your first data science experiment using Julia! Be sure to save this code to an IJulia notebook (or some other format such as a .jl file) as you may want to go back to it later.

SAVING YOUR WORKSPACE INTO A DATA FILE

Now that you have some results, you may want to store them somewhere for future reference or even further processing. Unlike R, Julia does not store your workspace once you exit; if you want certain variables to be accessible next time you spin up the Julia kernel, you'd better save them somewhere yourself. Fortunately you can do that it two effective ways:

- Save the data in a delimited file (e.g. a .csv) for easy access of the data from other programs (e.g. a spreadsheet)

- Use the native Julia data file format (.jld), by employing the corresponding package.

Each one of these methods has its own advantages, which we will examine in more detail in the subsections that follow.

SAVING DATA INTO DELIMITED FILES

This is probably the simplest and most widely used option. It doesn't require any packages, it creates files that are easily accessible by other programs, and it uses formats that most people are already familiar with. You can save your data (say, an array A) in a delimited file with semi-colons (;) as the separators among the data fields, by employing the writedlm() function as seen here:

```
writedlm("/data/mydata.dat", A, ";")
```

As you can see, the first argument of the writedlm() function is the file name (including the path), the second is the array to be saved, and the third is the delimiter. The delimiter is usually a character, although it can be any string (e.g. :). The default value for this parameter is a tab (denoted \t), yielding .tsv files. Nevertheless, the extension of the delimited file you create is up to you; Julia will not assume anything, even if it seems obvious to you.

One special case of delimited files, which is particularly popular when it comes to numeric data, is .csv files. You can save your data in a .csv by selecting the comma as a delimiter, but there is a simpler way: the writecsv() function. You can use this as follows:

```
writecsv("/data/mydata.dat", A)
```

Delimited files are not the most resource-efficient methods of saving a dataset, yet it is often necessary to utilize them. When the volume of your data increases, or when you wish to preserve the metadata of the variables involved, it is best to make use of the second alternative to saving data files. As the examples in this book involve a quite manageable data size, we will be using delimited files for all our data exports.

SAVING DATA INTO NATIVE JULIA FORMAT

Often it is easier to use the native format of a language for storing the data used (e.g. SFrames, SArrays, and SGraphs in Graphlab; .RData in R; or .mat files in Matlab). That's not to say that other languages cannot access these formats–they are just each more practical for the language they were created for. The Julia Data Format (.jld files) is one such native format developed by Simon Kornblith and Tim Holy to address this need, using the more generic HDF5 data format. As this is no small feat, the Julia data format took a while to enter the scene.

To employ this data format you first need to add the JLD and HDF5 packages, and then use them to create a .jld file containing your data (say an array A composed of floats, and an integer b). You can do all this using the following code:

```
Pkg.add("HDF5")
Pkg.add("JLD")
using JLD
f = open("mydata.jld", "w")
@write f A
@write f b
close(f)
```

The @ character has a specific function in Julia, which when applied on a function changes its syntax, making it more versatile. We recommend you look into it only once you feel confident enough with the basics: perhaps after solving a number of problems using Julia, and getting well-acquainted with all the functions described in this book.

Alternatively, instead of the last four lines, you can write the following equivalent code:

```
save("mydata.jld", "var_A", A, "var_b", b)
```

where the arguments in quotes correspond to the filename and the stored names of the variables (here we have made them different than the original ones to avoid any confusion). If you wish to save all the variables in the workspace, you just need to type the following:

```
save("mydata.jld")
```

To retrieve the data stored in a .jld file, type:

```
D = load("mydata.jld")
```

Loading a .jld file creates a dictionary where all its contents can be found. The variable names are stored as keys in that dictionary. If you wish to access only a particular variable in a .jld file (e.g. the variable called "var_b"), you simply specify it using the following piece of code:

```
b = load("mydata.jld", "var_b")
```

Another way to access the variables stored in a .jld file is to use the following:

```
f = jldopen("mydata.jld","r")
dump(f, 20)
```

This will spit out the first 20 variables in the .jld file, the way they are stored in the corresponding dictionary (i.e. variable name: variable type and dimensionality). This approach is particularly useful if you are not sure which variable you want to access.

The JLD package is still new and the documentation is incomplete at the time of this writing. We encourage you to probe it in more depth on your own, as it is bound to evolve over time. It is a useful tool and can make your data storing and retrieving work much easier. You can read more in the corresponding documentation file in the GitHub location: http://bit.ly/29fVavH.

SAVING DATA INTO TEXT FILES

If your data is highly unstructured and none of the above options work, you can always save it in simple text files. Keep in mind, though, that retrieving the data afterwards may require some more work (something we will revisit in Chapter 6). To save data in a `.txt` file you just need to do the following:

```
f = open("/data/mydata.txt", "w")
write(f, SomeStringVariable)
write(f, AnotherStringVariable)
 .
 .
 .
close(f)
```

In order for your data file to have some spacing between each pair of consecutive variables, you need to add new line characters at the end of each string (represented as \n in Julia). So, if you want to save the string data "Julia rocks!" to your (already open) data file, you need to make the following adjustment:

```
data = string(data, "\n")
```

Naturally, you aren't limited to string variables, even though whatever you save into a text file will eventually be converted into a string type. So, if you have an array A, you can save it as follows:

```
A = [123, 34423.23, -322,
     45534523523452342523452345345261709106832734]
f = open(("/data/mydata.txt", "w")
for a in A
write(f, string(a, "\n"))
end
close(f)
```

This way the array will be saved into the mydata.`txt` file in the data folder, with one element per line. This will make it easier to read afterwards in a text editor, as well as access it using a script from any language.

HELP!

Regardless of your background, you'll eventually run into a situation where you need some assistance–usually with a function. When this happens, before you rush off to Stackoverflow, you may want to check out Julia documentation. To do that, just type:

```
help(somefunction)
```

Alternatively you can type the following:

```
? somefunction
```

Although the output of this function is not the easiest to understand, it is very useful. The more you use the function, the easier it will get. In this ever-changing environment that is Julia, it is essential to get acquainted with the Julia documentation. Embrace it as your best resource for learning various aspects of the language, particularly concerning the use of data types, operators, and functions.

If you have a more general question, you can search the Julia manual at http://bit.ly/29bWHU2 or the Julia wikibook at http://bit.ly/29cIges. The latter is usually preferable as it has more examples and it is much easier to read. For more subjective questions (like "How do I evaluate the performance of this code?") your best bet would be to consult the experts. Stackoverflow is a good place to start (use the tag "julia-lang"), though the Julia users group at Google is also a viable option. Whatever the case, don't fret! Just like every new technology, Julia has its quirks and may take a while to get used to. That's why through the rest of the book we will try to keep the coding to a minimum, so that you can focus on the more interesting (and valuable) parts of the language.

Summary

- Julia is easier to work with when you make use of an IDE, such as Juno, IJulia (Jupyter), or Epicenter.

- You can easily access Julia on the cloud using JuliaBox. This allows you to create and store IJulia notebooks on a server, using a Google account.

- Installing packages is essential for serious Julia programming. This can be done using the `Pkg.add()` command. To install package `abc` you just need to type: `Pkg.add("abc")`.

- You can load a `.csv` file in the Julia workspace using the `readcsv()` function. For example, the data file `mydata.csv` can be accessed as follows: `readcsv("mydata.csv")`.

- You can load data from a `.txt` file in various ways, the simplest one being: `f = open(filename, "r")`; lines = `readlines(f)`; `close(f)`.

- k Nearest Neighbor (kNN) is a simple yet efficient machine learning algorithm that can be used to perform classification on any labeled dataset (i.e. a dataset that has a target variable which is discreet).

- When implementing a non-trivial algorithm, it is useful to break it down into auxiliary functions. The auxiliary functions need to be loaded into memory before the main (wrapper) function is executed.

- You can save data into files using one of the following methods:

  o **For a delimited file:** `writedlm(filename, variable, delimiter)`. The delimiter can be any printable string, although it is usually a character. If it's omitted, the tab character is used as a default.

  o **For a Julia native data file:** `save(filename.jld, "name_for_1st_variable", var1, "name_for_2nd_variable",` var2, …). You need to load into memory the `JLD` and `HDF5` packages first.

- o **For a simple text file:** `f = open(filename, "w"); write(f, StringVariable1); write(f, StringVariable2); …; close(f)`.

- You can seek help for a function in Julia using the `help()` command: `help(FunctionName)`.

- You can find help for more complex matters in the Julia wikibook, the Julia documentation, Stackoverflow, and any Julia users group (online or physical).

CHAPTER CHALLENGE

1. Which IDE(s) would you use if you wanted to take advantage of the latest developments in the language?

2. Which IDE would you use if you couldn't have Julia installed on your machine due to lack of administrative privileges?

3. What are the advantages of using an IDE (e.g. Juno or the online IDE at tutorialspoint.com) over REPL? What are the advantages of IJulia over an IDE and REPL?

4. Why is it useful to have auxiliary functions in a program?

5. What's a wrapper function?

6. What do the functions `sqrt()`, `inmin()`, and `length()` do? What data types are their arguments? (Hint: use the `help()` function for each one of these.)

7. What range of values does the expression `sum(y == z) / length(y)` take?

8. Say that you have an array `A` that you wish to save in `.csv` format. How would you go about doing this?

9. You have a variety of arrays and single value variables in your workspace and you have to shut down your machine because your OS wants to install another batch of updates (again!). How would you go about saving your most important variables while preserving their types so you can resume your work after the OS updates are completed?

10. What's the difference between the functions `max()` and `maximum()`? Which one would you use for finding the maximum value of two numbers? (Hint: make use of `help()` again, and try out a couple of examples to see their difference in practice.)

11. How would you install the package called `NMF`, get it up to date, and load it into memory?

12. Can you use the kNN algorithm to analyze text using the data as-is? Explain.

13. The senior data scientist in your group says that in the dataset you are working on, it would be better to use Manhattan/city-block distance instead of Euclidean (you can learn more about this type of distance on this website: http://bit.ly/29J8D0Y). How would you go about doing that, without having to rewrite the whole kNN algorithm from scratch?

Note: You can view the answers to all of the above in Appendix F.

CHAPTER 3
Learning the Ropes of Julia

The goal of this chapter is to get you acquainted with the specifics of the language, in order to gain enough mastery to use it for the problems we'll be working through. Again, it is assumed that you are familiar with the basics of programming and have some experience in other programming languages. This way, we will be able to focus more on the data science applications of Julia.

This chapter will also be a useful reference for the language when you develop your own scripts. You will learn enough to be able to understand the language's logic and figure out things yourself when needed. This chapter covers the following topics:

- Data types

- Arrays

- Dictionaries

- Basic commands and functions

- Loops and conditionals.

Let us now dive into this exciting new technology and see how we can unveil its potential within the data science domain. If you are already familiar with the Julia language, feel free to skip to Chapter 5, or just focus on the exercises at the end of this chapter as well as those of the next one.

DATA TYPES

Let's delve into Julia programming by looking at the building blocks of data, usually referred to as types. Every variable in Julia belongs to a particular type, such as integer, string, array, etc. Still, certain types (like matrix or vector, for example) are not as straightforward as you may expect, and can be subtypes of other types (in this case the array type).

Although optional, defining the type of a variable lets Julia know that the variable's values will be converted to that type. This is particularly useful when creating complex programs, where ambiguity often translates into errors and unexpected results. If you don't define the type of a variable, Julia will assume the simplest type that can relate to the value of that variable (if there is no value, it will just use the generic type "any"). Let's clarify all this will a couple of examples:

```
In[1]: x = 123                         #A
Out[1]: 123                            #B
In[2]: y = "hello world!"              #C
Out[2]:"hello world!"                  #D
#A Assign the value 123 to variable x
#B Julia interprets this as an Integer and stores it into x
#C Assign the value "hello world!" to variable y
#D Julia interprets this as a String and stores it into y
```

You can discover the type of a variable using the typeof() command. So for the above examples' variables:

```
In[3]: typeof(x)
Out[3]: Int64                 #A
In[4]: typeof(y)
Out[4]: ASCIIString
#A This could be Int32 as well, depending on your computer
```

Int64 is a subcategory (or subtype) of the integer type, while ASCIIString is a specific case (or subtype) of the string type.

You can define the type of a variable using the double colons (x::Int64), as we will see shortly. For now, let's just shift from one variable type to another using the corresponding constructor functions, which have the same names as their types, but with all lowercase letters. For example, the function Int32() will transform whatever you give it into a 32-bit integer (Int32 type). So, building on the example above:

```
In[5]: z = Int32(x)
Out[5]: 123
In[6]: typeof(z)
In[6]: Int32
```

Naturally, not all types can convert from one to another:

```
In[7]: w = Int32("whatever")
Out[7]: ERROR: invalid base 10 digit 'w' in "whatever"
```

Below is a list of the main types found in Julia with corresponding examples.

Data Type	Sample Values
Int8	98, -123
Int32	2134112, -2199996
Int64	123123123123121, -1234123451234
Float32	12312312.3223, -12312312.3223
Float64	12332523452345.345233343, -123333312312.3223232
Bool	true, false (notice that the contents of this type of variable are always lowercase in Julia)
Char	'a', '?'
String	"some word or sentence", " "
BigInt	3454893223743457239848953894985240398349234435234532
BigFloat	3454893223743457239848953894985240398349234435234532.3432
Array	[1, 2322433423, 0.12312312, false, 'c', "whatever"]

To get a better understanding of types, we highly recommend that you spend some time playing with these data types in the REPL (which is short for "Read, Evaluate, Print, Loop" and refers to the interactive interface that is now common among most scripting languages). Pay close attention to the char and string types as their constructors are similar. Make use of single quotes (') for the former, while for the latter we use double quotes (").

The BigInt and BigFloat types have no limit on the value of their contained numbers, making them ideal for handling arbitrary large numbers. They do take a toll on memory usage use, though, so it's best not to be too liberal with the use of these types. If you do plan to use them, make sure that you initialize the corresponding variables accordingly. For instance:

```
In[8]: x = BigInt()
```

As BigInt and BigFloat are special types, they cannot be defined with the double colon notation (::), so you will have to use the BigInt() and BigFloat() constructors respectively. When dealing with small values (between -128 and 127), use Int8 as it's more frugal in terms of computer resources and is particularly useful for counter variables and many other cases dealing with small integer values (e.g. indexes).

ARRAYS

ARRAY BASICS

Arrays are fundamental in Julia. They allow you to handle collections of any type of data, as well as combinations of different types. Just like in other languages such as R and Python, indexing an array takes place using square brackets, which are also used for defining a set of variables as an array. So, for the array p = [1, 2322433423, 0.12312312, "false", 'c', "whatever"], you can access its third element (the float number, in this case) by typing p[3]:

```
In[9]: p = [1, 2322433423, 0.12312312, false, 'c', "whatever"];
    p[3]
Out[9]: 0.12312312
```

Unlike most other languages (e.g. C#), indexing in Julia starts with 1 instead of 0; if you try to access the first element of an array by typing p[0] you'll get a Bounds Error. You'll obtain the same error if you try to access something beyond the last element of an array. The index of an array always needs to be an integer (although you can use the Boolean value "true" as well, to access the first element of the array). To access the last element of an array, you can use the pseudo-index "end":

```
In[10]: p[end]
Out[10]: "whatever"
```

This is particularly useful if you don't know the exact dimension of an array, which is common when you add and remove elements in that array. Just like in other languages, arrays in Julia are mutable structures, making them relatively slower than immutable ones such as tuples or certain types of dictionaries. So if you are opting for versatility (e.g. in the case of a variable, or a list of coefficients), arrays are the way to go. Should you wish to initialize an array so that you can populate it at a later time, you merely need to provide Julia with the data type of its elements and its dimensions. Say that you want to have an array with three rows and four columns, for example, so that you can store Int64 values to it. Simply type:

```
In[11]: Z = Array(Int64, 3, 4)
Out[11]: 3x4 Array{Int64,2}:
 34359738376 0 1 3
 2147483649 4 1 4
       0  5  2  5
```

An array's contents upon initialization are whatever happens to dwell in that part of the memory that Julia allocates to it. It is uncommon that you find such an array full of zeros. If you wish to have a more generic array that you will use to store all kinds of variables (including other arrays), you need to use the "Any" type when you initialize it:

```
In[12]: Z = Array(Any, 3, 1)
Out[12]: 3x1 Array{Any,2}:
 #undef
 #undef
 #undef
```

Such an array is going to be full of undefined values (referred to as `#undef`). You cannot use these with any calculations, numeric or otherwise, so be sure to allocate some meaningful data to this array before using it (to avoid an error message).

ACCESSING MULTIPLE ELEMENTS IN AN ARRAY

You can access several elements of an array at once using a range or an array of integers as an index. So, if you need to get the first three elements of `p`, you just need to type `p[1:3]` (note that 1:3 is an inclusive range for all integers between and including 1 and 3):

```
In[13]: p[1:3]
Out[13]: 3-element Array{Any,1}:
     1
 2322433423
     0.123123
```

As sometimes the exact length of the array is unknown, it is handy to refer to the last element of the array as "end," as we saw earlier. So, if you want to get the last three elements of `p`, type `p[(end-2):end]`, with or without the parentheses (including them simply makes the code easier to understand).

Using an array of integers as an index is very similar. If you want to get only the first and the fourth element of `p`, you just need to type `p[[1,4]]`. The double brackets used here: the outermost are for referencing the `p` array, while the innermost are used to define the array of the indexes 1 and 4:

```
In[14]: p[[1,4]]
Out[14]: 2-element Array{Any,1}:
     1
 false
```

In practice, you would store the indexes of interest to you in an array–let's call it `ind`–and access the elements of interest using `p[ind]`. This makes for cleaner and more intuitive code.

MULTIDIMENSIONAL ARRAYS

For arrays that have more than one dimension, you must provide as many indexes as the number of dimensions. For example, say that `A` is a 3x4 matrix, which we can build and populate as follows:

```
In[15]: A = Array(Int64, 3,4); A[:] = 1:12; A
Out[15]: 3x4 Array{Int64,2}:
 1 4 7 10
 2 5 8 11
 3 6 9 12
```

To obtain the third element in the second row, you need to type `A[2,3]`. Now, if you wish to get all the elements of the third row, you can do this by typing `A[3,:]` (you can also achieve this with `A[3,1:end]` but it is more cumbersome). If you want to access all elements in the matrix you would type `A[:,:]`, though typing `A` would yield the same result, as we saw in the above example. By the way, if you wish to obtain the contents of `A` in a single file, just type `A[:]`. The result will be a one-dimensional array.

DICTIONARIES

As the name suggests, a dictionary is a simple look-up table used for organizing different types of data. Just like an array, it can contain all kinds of data types, though usually there are two types in any given dictionary. Unlike an array, a dictionary doesn't have to have numeric indexes. Instead, it has an index of any type (usually referred to as a key). The data corresponding to that key is referred to as its value. Julia implements this data structure with an object called `dict`, which provides a mapping between its keys and its values: `{key1 => value1, key2 => value2, ..., keyN => valueN}`. The `=>` operator is used specifically in this structure only, and is an abbreviation of the `pair()` function. It is completely different than the `>=` operator, which is an abbreviation of the "greater or equal to" algebraic function. You can easily create a dictionary as follows:

```
In[16]: a = Dict()                                        #A
Out[16]: Dict{Any,Any} with 0 entries
In[17]: b = Dict("one" => 1, "two" => 2, "three" => 3,
    "four" => 4)                                          #B
Out[17]: Dict{ASCIIString,Int64} with 4 entries:
 "two" => 2
 "four" => 4
 "one" => 1
 "three" => 3
#A This creates an empty dictionary
#B This creates a dictionary with predefined entries (it is still
    mutable). Note that this format works only from version 0.4
    onwards
```

To look up a value in a dictionary, just type its name and the key as an index, like you would for an array (using an integer instead of a key):

```
In[18]: b["three"]
Out[18]: 3
```

Naturally, if the key doesn't exist in the dictionary, Julia throws an error:

```
In[19]: b["five"]
Out[19]: ERROR: key not found: "five"
in getindex at dict.jl:617
```

Dictionaries are useful for certain cases where you need to access data in a more intuitive manner, but don't need to access ranges of data, such as in a database table containing book titles and their ISBNs.

BASIC COMMANDS AND FUNCTIONS

We'll continue our journey into Julia with a few basic commands and functions, which can make types more meaningful and useful. Get comfortable with each of these so you can create your own use cases. Every command will produce some kind of response, to show you that Julia has acknowledged it. To avoid this acknowledgment, you can use a semicolon right after the command, leading instead to another prompt.

PRINT(), PRINTLN()

Syntax: `print(var1, var2, …, varN)`**, where all of the arguments are optional and can be variables of any type.** `println()` **has exactly the same syntax.**

Although the REPL makes it easy to view the values of variables when you enter their names, this perk is rarely available in real-world scenarios. Instead, simply enter `print()` and `println()`. These functions barely need an introduction as they are essentially identical across various high-level languages.

Print() simply prints a variable at the terminal, right after the previously printed data; this allows you to save space and customize how you view your data. Println() prints a variable along with a carriage return, ensuring that whatever is printed afterwards will be in a new line. You can use print() and println() with a number of variables (e.g. print(x,y,z), print(x, " ", y)) as follows:

```
In[20]: x = 123; y = 345; print(x, " ",y)
Out[20]: 123 345
In[21]: print(x,y); print("!")
Out[21]: 123345!
In[22]: println(x); println(y); print("!")
In[22]:123
345
!
```

All variables used with print() and println() are turned into strings, which are then concatenated and treated as a single string. These functions are particularly useful for debugging and for presenting the results of a program.

TYPEMAX(), TYPEMIN()

Syntax: typemax(DataType), typemin(DataType)

These commands provide you with some useful information about the limits of certain numeric types (e.g. Int32, Float64, etc.). For example:

```
In[23]: typemax(Int64)
Out[23]: 9223372036854775807
In[24]: typemin(Int32)
Out[24]: -2147483648
In[25]: typemax(Float64)
Out[25]: Inf
```

Finding the min and max values of a data type is particularly handy when you are dealing with numbers of high absolute value and you want to conserve memory. Although a single Float64 doesn't utilize much memory on its own, imagine the impact if you were using a large array comprised of such variables.

COLLECT()

Syntax: `collect(ElementType, X)`, **where** `X` **is any data type that corresponds to a kind of range (usually referred to as a "collection"), and** `ElementType` **is the type of elements of** `X` **that you wish to obtain (this parameter is usually omitted).**

A handy function that allows you to obtain all the elements in a given object, in an array form. This is particularly useful if you are dealing with a variety of objects that were developed to improve Julia's performance (e.g. ranges) but are counter-intuitive to high-level users (since it is unlikely for them to encounter these objects in the real world). For example:

```
In[26]: 1:5
Out[26]: 1:5
In[27]: collect(1:5)
Out[27]: 5-element Array{Int64,1}:
 1
 2
 3
 4
 5
```

SHOW()

Syntax: `show(X)`, **where** `X` **is any data type (usually an array or dictionary).**

This useful function allows you to view the contents of an array without all the metadata that accompanies it, saving you space on the terminal. The contents of the array are shown horizontally, making it particularly handy for large arrays, which tend to be abbreviated when you try to view them otherwise. For example:

```
In[28]: show([x y])
Out[28]: [123 345]
In[29]: a = collect(1:50); show(a)
Out[29]:
    [1,2,3,4,5,6,7,8,9,10,11,12,13,14,15,16,17,18,19,20,21,22,23,24
    ,25,26,27,28,29,30,31,32,33,34,35,36,37,38,39,40,41,42,43,44,45
    ,46,47,48,49,50]
```

LINSPACE()

Syntax: `linspace(StartPoint, EndPoint, NumberOfPoints)`, **where the** `NumberOfPoints` **argument is optional and defaults to 50. All arguments are floats or integers.**

When you want to plot a mathematical function, you often need an array of equidistant values for your independent variable. These can be provided by the `linspace()` function. When run with two arguments, `a` and `b`, it yields a list of 50 values (including `a` and `b`) with each consecutive value having the same distance to the next. This output takes the form of a special object called linspace, but you can view its elements using the `collect()` function. For example, `show(collect(linspace(0,10)))` will yield the following:

```
[0.0,0.20408163265306123,0.40816326530612246,0.6122448979591837,
    ..., 10.0]
```

If you want to specify the number of points in this array, you can add a third argument `c` (always an integer), denoting just that. For example, `show(collect(linspace(0,10,6)))` will yield:

```
[0.0,2.0,4.0,6.0,8.0,10.0]
```

MATHEMATICAL FUNCTIONS

ROUND()

Syntax: `round(var, DecimalPlaces)`, **where** `var` **is the numeric variable you want to round to the nearest integer, and** `DecimalPlaces` **is the number of decimal places to take into account (this parameter is optional and has a default value of 0, rounding to the nearest integer).**

As the name suggests, this function rounds off a given number (usually of the float type) to the nearest integer. The output of the function is of the same type as the input:

```
In[30]: round(123.45)
Out[30]: 123.0
In[31]: round(100.69)
Out[31]: 101.0
```

Although int() does the same kind of rounding (for zero decimal points), it is not supported any more (although the current version recognizes it). Most likely, it will throw an error in future releases of the language. You can also customize round() to give you the number of decimal places you want:

```
In[32]: round(100.69, 1)
Out[32]: 100.7
In[33]: round(123.45, -1)
Out[33]: 120.0
```

Since round() is used on float variables, it returns a float too. If you want an int instead, you need to specify that as an argument:

```
In[34]: round(Int64, 19.39)
Out[34]: 19
```

This is particularly useful if you plan to use the output of this function as part of a range or an index to a matrix or multi-dimensional array.

RAND(), RANDN()

Syntax: rand(type, dimension1, dimension2, …, dimensionN), **where** type **is the data type you wish to have the output in (default is float) and** dimensionX **is the number of random values in the** X **dimension of the output. There needs to be at least one dimension (i.e. the output is a vector). The** type **argument is optional.** randn() **shares the same syntax, with the only difference being that it doesn't have the** type **argument.** Rand() **yields numbers that follow the uniform distribution [0, 1], while** randn() **numbers that follow the normal distribution N(0,1).**

These are a couple of particularly useful functions, especially if you plan to do simulations in your analyses. What they do is provide you with a random float. In the case of rand() it is between 0 and 1 and follows the uniform distribution; in randn() it is a number in the normal distribution with mean = 1 and standard deviation = 1. If you want a series of random numbers, you can add an integer argument to the function. For example:

```
In[35]: show(rand(10))
Out[35]:
    [0.7730573763699315,0.5244000402202329,0.7087464615493806,0.306
    94152302474875,0.052097051188102705,0.7553963677335493,0.277540
    39163886635,0.365138971248734,0.2772384170629354,0.96071525140
    21782]
```

If you want a matrix of random numbers, just add an extra integer in the arguments, to denote the length of the second dimension. For example:

```
In[36]: show(rand(5,3))
Out[36]: [0.9819193447719754 0.32051953795789445
    0.16868830612754793
 0.5650335899407546 0.6752962982347646 0.6440294745246324
 0.3682684190774339 0.06726933651330436 0.5005871456892146
 0.5592698510697376 0.8277375991607441 0.6975769949167918
 0.7225171655795466 0.7698193892868241 0.4455584310168279]
```

Yet, we don't always need floats between 0 and 1. We often require integers or Booleans. When you require random integers, just add a type argument before the integer ones:

```
In[37]: show(rand(Int8, 10))
Out[37]: Int8[-111,6,0,-91,105,123,-76,-62,127,25]
```

If you require random Boolean values, you can use the rand() function with the Bool type as its first parameter. For example:

```
In[38]: show(rand(Bool, 10))
Out[38]: Bool[false,true,true,true,true,false,true,true,false,true]
```

It is often useful to have an array of integers between two given values. This can be accomplished by using a range as the first argument of the rand() function. For example, rand(1:6,10) will provide an array of 10 integers between 1 and 6:

```
In[39]: show(rand(1:6,10))
Out[39]: [5,2,3,2,3,1,4,5,1,2]
```

This style of `rand()` makes use of multiple dispatch, as it's a slightly different method than is used in the backend. This use of `rand()` is particularly helpful for simulating stochastic processes. Also, `rand()` always provides results based on the uniform distribution. Should you need something that follows the Bell curve, `randn()` is the function you would use:

```
In[40]: show(randn(10))
Out[40]: [-0.0900864435078182,1.0365011168586151,
    -1.0610943900829333, 1.8400571395469378,
    -1.2169491862799908,1.318463768859766,
    -0.14255638153224454,0.6416070324451357,
    0.28893583730900324,1.2388310266681493]
```

If you require a few random numbers that that follow N(40, 5), you can type the following:

```
In[41]: show(40 + 5*randn(10))
Out[41]:
    [43.52248877988562,29.776468140230627,40.83084217842971,39.8832
    5340176333,38.296440507642934,43.05294839551039,50.350131288717
    01,45.07288143568174,50.14614332268907,38.70116850375828]
```

Naturally, these results will be different every time you run either one of these functions. To ensure that the same sequence of random numbers is always going to be used, you can set the seed of the random number generator that Julia uses (the seed needs to be a number between 0 and 2147483647):

```
In[42]: srand(12345)
In[43]: show(randn(6))
Out[43]:
    [1.1723579360378058,0.852707459143324,0.4155652148774136,0.5164
    248452398443,0.6857588179217985,0.2822721070914419]
In[44]: srand(12345)
In[45]: show(randn(6))
Out[45]:
    [1.1723579360378058,0.852707459143324,0.4155652148774136,0.5164
    248452398443,0.6857588179217985,0.2822721070914419]
```

To create random numbers that follow any form of the normal distribution, apply a linear transformation to the outputs of the `randn()` function. Say, for example, that we require ten random numbers stemming from a distribution having an average μ = 40 and standard deviation σ = 10. In this case we need to type the following:

```
In[46]: show(10*randn(10) - 40)
Out[46]: [-32.55431668595578,-39.940916092640805,
    -33.735585473277375,-31.701071486620336,-44.81211848719756,
    -42.488100875252336,-39.70764823986392,-41.9736830812393,
    -52.122465106839456,-56.74087248032391]
```

SUM()

Syntax: sum(A, dimension), **where** A **is the array containing the values to be summed up, and dimension is the dimension upon which the summing up takes place (this argument is optional and has a default value of 1).**

This function barely needs any explanation as it is pretty much the same across most programming languages (including spreadsheet software, like Excel). Still, it's worth describing, as it's commonly used. The key thing to remember is that it takes arrays as its main input. For example:

```
In[47]: sum([1,2,3,4])
Out[47]: 10
```

For larger collections of data, such as matrices, you can use this function with an additional parameter: an extra argument (integer) to denote which dimension you want to calculate the sum on. For example, say you have a 3x4 2-D matrix A, containing the integers between 1 and 12:

```
In[48]: A = Array(Int64, 3,4); A[:] = 1:12; show(A)
Out[48]: [1 4 7 10
 2 5 8 11
 3 6 9 12]
```

If you type sum(A) you'll get the sum of all the elements of A. To get the sum of all the rows (i.e. sum across dimension 1), you would need to type sum(A,1), while for the sum across all the columns, sum(A,2) would do the trick:

```
In[49]: sum(A,1)
Out[49]: 1x4 Array{Int64,2}:
 6 15 24 33
In[50]: sum(A,2)
Out[50]: 3x1 Array{Int64,2}:
 22
 26
 30
```

The arrays you put into the sum() function don't have to be composed of integers or floats only. You can also add up Boolean arrays, as "true" is equivalent to 1 in Julia. For example:

```
In[51]: sum([true, false, true, true, false])
Out[51]: 3
```

This is the only case where sum() will yield a result of a different type than its inputs.

MEAN()

Syntax: mean(A, dimension), **where** A **is the array containing the values to be averaged, and** dimension **is the dimension upon which the summing up takes place (this argument is optional and has a default value of 1).**

This is another well-known function that remains consistent across various programming platforms. As you may have guessed, it just provides the arithmetic mean of an array. The values in that array need to be of the number type (e.g. floats, integers, real, or complex numbers) or Booleans. If these values are of the number type, the output is either a float, a real, or a complex number (depending on the exact type of the inputs), while in the case of Booleans, the result is always a float. Here a few examples of this function in action:

```
In[52]: mean([1,2,3])
Out[52]: 2.0
In[53]: mean([1.34, pi])
Out[53]: 2.2407963267948965
In[54]: mean([true, false])
Out[54]: 0.5
```

The same additional arguments of `sum()` apply to this function too: `mean(A,1)` will yield the average of all the rows of matrix A.

ARRAY AND DICTIONARY FUNCTIONS

IN

Syntax: `V in A`, **where** `V` **is a value that may or may not exist in the Array** `A`.

This is a handy command for searching an array for a particular value. Say, for instance, that you have the Array `x = [23, 1583, 0, 953, 10, -3232, -123]` and you are interested to see whether 1234 and 10 exist within it. You can perform these checks using the in command:

```
In[55]: 1234 in x
Out[55]: false
In[56]: 10 in x
Out[56]: true
```

This command works with all kinds of arrays and always provides a Boolean as its output. Although you can use this to search for a particular character in a string, there are better ways to accomplish that, as we'll see in Chapter 4.

APPEND!()

Syntax: `append!(Array1, Array2)`, **where** `Array1` **and** `Array2` **are arrays of the same dimensionality.** `Array2` **can be a single cell (1x1 array).**

This is a useful function for merging existing arrays. These arrays can have values of any type. For example:

```
In[57]: a = ["some phrase", 1234]; b = [43.321, 'z', false];
In[58]: append!(a,b); show(a)
Out[58]: Any["some phrase",1234,43.321,'z',false]
```

Note the exclamation mark right before the parentheses. Functions with this feature make changes to their first variable, so keep that in mind when using them. It logically follows that there is no need to use another variable for their output (although you can if you want to).

POP!()

Syntax: `pop!(D, K, default)`, **where** `D` **is a dictionary,** `K` **is the key we are searching for, and** `default` **is the value to return if the key is not present in the dictionary. The final argument is optional.** `pop!(A)`, **where** `A` **is an array (or any other type of collection, apart from dictionary since these require the special syntax described previously). Although** `pop!()` **works with arrays, there will be performance issues when working with large arrays.**

When dealing with dictionaries you often need to fetch an element while simultaneously removing it. This can be accomplished with the `pop!()` function. This function is agnostic of the values of that dictionary, so it is versatile. Take for example the following scenario:

```
In[59]: z = Dict("w" => 25, "q" => 0, "a" => true, "b" => 10, "x"
    => -3.34);
In[60]: pop!(z, "a")
Out[60]: true
In[61]: z
Out[61]: Dict{ASCIIString,Any} with 4 entries:
  "w" => 25
  "q" => 0
  "b" => 10
  "x" => -3.34
In[62]: pop!(z,"whatever", -1)
Out[62]: -1
```

Note that -1 appears because the element "whatever" doesn't exist in the dictionary `z`. We could put anything else in its place, such as a whole string like "can't find this element!" if we prefer.

PUSH!()

Syntax: push!(A, V), **where** A **is a one-dimensional array, and** V **is a value. Just like in the case of** pop!, **we recommend that you don't use this function, particularly for larger arrays.**

The push!() function is something of an opposite to pop!(), as it augments an existing array with a new element. So, if we wanted to add the element 12345 to an array z, we'd run the following:

```
In[63]: z = [235, "something", true, -3232.34, 'd'];
In[64]: push!(z,12345)
Out[64]: 6-element Array{Any,1}:
  235
   "something"
 true
 -3232.34
  'd'
 12345
```

SPLICE!()

Syntax: splice!(A, ind, a), **where** A **is an array (or collection in general),** ind **is the index you are interested in retrieving, and** a **is the replacement value (optional).**

Splice!() is a generalization of the pop!() function: instead of retrieving the last element of the collection, it fetches any element you wish. The desired element is defined by the ind variable (an integer). Once the function is applied on the collection A (usually an array, though it can be a dictionary, or any other type of collection), it automatically removes that element from the collection.

If you wish to preserve the size of A, you can put something in the place of the index you remove (usually something you can easily identify, like a special character, or the value -1 for numeric collections). This is possible by using the third parameter, a, which is entirely optional. So, in the z array from earlier, you can take away its fifth value (the d character) by typing the following:

```
In[65]: splice!(z, 5)
Out[65]: 'd'
In[66]: show(z)
Out[66]: Any[235,"something",true,-3232.34,12345]
```

You can also replace the value "true" with something else, say "~", since that's a character not often encountered; you can use it in your application to mean "the value in this index has been used already." All this is possible through the following command:

```
In[67]: splice!(z, 3, '~')
Out[67]: true
In[68]: show(z)
Out[68]: Any[235,"something",'~',-3232.34,12345]
```

INSERT!()

Syntax: insert!(A, ind, a)**, where** A **is an array (or collection in general),** ind **is the index you are interested in retrieving, and** a **is the replacement value.**

This function is similar to splice!(), sharing exactly the same syntax. The difference is that it doesn't remove anything from the collection it is applied to, nor does it have any optional arguments. As its name suggests, it inserts a value a into a given collection A, at the index ind. So, if we wish to put the value "Julia rocks!" as the fourth element of our previous Array z, we just need to type the following:

```
In[69]: insert!(z, 4, "Julia rocks!")
Out[69]: 6-element Array{Any,1}:
   235
    "something"
    '~'
    "Julia rocks!"
  -3232.34
  12345
```

Naturally, all the elements from the fourth position on will be shifted forward, increasing the array's length by one.

SORT(), SORT!()

Syntax: `sort(A, dim, rev, ...)`, **where** `A` **is an array,** `dim` **is the dimension upon which the sorting will take place (in the case of a multi-dimensional array), and** `rev` **is a Boolean parameter for getting the results in reverse order (default = "false", i.e. smallest to largest).**

This is a handy function, particularly when you are dealing with alphanumeric data. As the name suggests and as you may already know from other languages, `sort()` takes an array of data and orders it using one of the many sorting algorithms (the default is QuickSort for all numeric arrays and MergeSort for all other arrays). If you don't intend to keep the original version of the array, you can use the `sort!()` function, which does the same thing but replaces the original array as well. Let's try to sort the array `x = [23, 1583, 0, 953, 10, -3232, -123]` using these functions:

```
In[70]: x = [23, 1583, 0, 953, 10, -3232, -123];
In[71]: show(sort(x))
Out[71]: [-3232, -123, 0, 10, 23, 953, 1583]
In[72]: show(x)
Out[72]: [23, 1583, 0, 953, 10, -3232, -123]
In[73]: sort!(x); show(x)
Out[73]: [-3232, -123, 0, 10, 23, 953, 1583]
```

If you prefer to sort your array from largest to smallest, you'll need to use the `rev` parameter of the function: `sort(x, rev=true)`. Naturally, `sort()` works well with strings too:

```
In[74]: show(sort(["Smith", "Brown", "Black", "Anderson",
    "Johnson", "Howe", "Holmes", "Patel", "Jones"]))
Out[74]: ASCIIString["Anderson", "Black", "Brown", "Holmes",
    "Howe", "Johnson", "Jones", "Patel", "Smith"]
```

GET()

Syntax: `get(D, K, default)`, **where** `D` **is the name of the dictionary you wish to access,** `K` **is the key you are querying, and** `default` **is the default value to return if the**

key is not found in the dictionary (to avoid getting an error message). The last parameter is optional.

Sometimes the key you are looking for doesn't exist in a particular dictionary. To avoid error messages, you can set a default value for Julia to return whenever that happens. You can do that as follows:

```
In[75]: b = Dict("one" => 1, "two" => 2, "three" => 3, "four" =>
    4);
In[76]: get(b, "two", "String not found!")
Out[76]: 2
In[77]: get(b, "whatever", "String not found!")
Out[77]: "String not found!"
```

KEYS(), VALUES()

Syntax: `keys(D)` **and** `values(D)`, **where** `D` **is the name of the dictionary you wish to access.**

You can access all the keys and all the values of a dictionary using `keys()` and `values()` respectively:

```
In[77]: b = Dict("one" => 1, "two" => 2, "three" => 3, "four" =>
    4);
In[78]: keys(b)
Out[78]: Base.KeyIterator for a Dict{ASCIIString,Int64} with 4
    entries. Keys:
 "one"
 "two"
 "three"
 "four"
In[79]: values(b)
Out[79]: ValueIterator for a Dict{ASCIIString,Any} with 4 entries.
    Values:
 1
 2
 3
 4
```

LENGTH(), SIZE()

Syntax: length(X), **where** X **is an array, dictionary, or string (this also works on the number and Boolean types, but always yields "1" in those cases).**

This is by far the most commonly used function when handling arrays, as it provides the number of elements in a given array (in the form of an integer). Let's take Array x used previously, as well as a 4x5 matrix of random numbers:

```
In[80]: x = [23, 1583, 0, 953, 10, -3232, -123];
In[81]: length(x)
Out[81]: 7
In[82]: length(rand(4,5))
Out[82]: 20
```

This function can also be used for finding the size of a given string, in terms of characters. So, if you want to see how long the string "Julia rocks!" is, for example:

```
In[83]: y = "Julia rocks!"
In[84]: length(y)
Out[84]: 12
```

MISCELLANEOUS FUNCTIONS

TIME()

Syntax: time()

If you ever wonder how many seconds have passed since the Unix epoch began (i.e. midnight of January 1, 1970), time() is there to help you answer this question. The actual number probably won't make much of a difference in your life (unless you were born that day, in which case it would be great!), but having an accurate time stamp (with microsecond precision) can be useful at times. This function doesn't need any arguments and always yields a float:

```
In[85]: t = time()
Out[85]: 1.443729720687e9
```

Unfortunately, it is not user-friendly. Nevertheless, it is useful for the applications it is designed for (mainly bench-marking code performance). In fact, one of the most widely used programming commands in Julia, @time, is based on this function. Without this command it would be downright impossible to measure the performance of a Julia program from within the language.

CONDITIONALS

if-else statements

This type of statement, often referred to as conditional evaluation, is essential for the majority of algorithms (data science and otherwise). In essence, an if-else statement allows you to execute certain pieces of code when a given condition holds true, and other pieces of code otherwise. This gives you a lot of flexibility and allows for more elaborate programming structures, particularly if you use a combination of such statements together (nested if-statements). Here are a couple of examples to illustrate the use of if-else statements:

```
In[99]: x = 2; y = 1; c = 0; d = 0;
In[100]: if x >= 1
           c += 1
         else
           d += 1
         end;
In[101]: show([c, d])
Out[101]: [1,0]
In[102]: if x == 2
           c += 1
           if y < 0
       d += 1
           else
       d -= 1
           end
         end;
In[103]: show([c, d])
Out[103]: [2,-1]
```

The `else` clause is optional. Also, the semicolons are not necessary, but they help avoid any confusion from the outputs of the conditionals, since there are two variables involved. You can always merge the `else` clause with additional if-statements, allowing for more powerful filters using the `elseif` command:

```
In[104]: x = 0; c = 0; d = 0;
In[105]: if x > 0
            c += 1
         elseif x == 0
            d += 1
         else
            println("x is negative")
         end
In[106]: show([c, d])
Out[106]: [0,1]
```

You can abbreviate this whole if-else structure using what is called the ternary operator, which is useful when the end result of the statement is the assignment of a value to a variable. The ternary operator takes the form `variable = condition ? (value if condition is "true") : (value if condition is "false")`. The parentheses are included for clarification and are entirely optional. For example, these two snippets of code are identical in function:

```
Snippet 1
In[107]: x = 123;
In[108]: if x > 0
            "x is positive"
         else
            "x is not positive"
         end
Out[108]: "x is positive"

Snippet 2
In[109]: x = 123; result = x > 0 ? "x is positive" : "x is not
         positive"
Out[109]: "x is positive"
```

If x is negative, the same conditional will yield a different result:

```
In[110]: x = -123; result = x > 0 ? "x is positive" : "x is not
    positive"
Out[110]: "x is not positive"
```
Note that the ternary operator can be nested as well:
```
In[111]: result = x > 0 ? "x is positive" : x < 0 ? "x is negative"
    : "x is zero"
```

STRING()

Syntax: `string(var1, var2, …, varN)`, **where** `varX` **is a variable of any type. All arguments are optional, though the function is meaningful if there is at least one present.**

Transforming a data type into a string can be accomplished using the `string()` function:

```
In[86]: string(2134)
Out[86]: "2134"
```

Furthermore, `string()` can also concatenate several variables together, after converting each one of them into a string:

```
In[87]: string(1234, true, "Smith", ' ', 53.3)
Out[87]: 1234trueSmith 53.3
```

This function is particularly useful when preparing data for IO processing. It also makes formatting easier and allows you to handle special characters effectively. We'll look more into string-related functions in the following chapter.

MAP()

Syntax: `map(fun, arr)`, **where** `fun` **is a function that you want to apply on every element of array** `arr`. **This makes for more elegant code and is crucial for more advanced programming structures (e.g. parallelization).**

Since you'll frequently need to apply transformations to your data, the creators of Julia came up with a function that does just that. This is equivalent to the `apply()` function in Python (mainly used for older versions of the language, as well as in the Graphlab Create Python API) and the `lapply()` and `sapply()` functions in R. Here is an example:

```
In[88]: show(map(length, ["this", "is", "a", "map()", "test"]))
Out[88]: [4, 2, 1, 5, 4]
```

In essence, this application of the `map()` function calculates the length of each string in the given array. The result is going to be an array, too.

Since Julia is inherently fast, this function provides little performance benefit. However, it can be handy if you are used to this kind of programming structure from pre-Julia languages.

VERSION()

Syntax: `VERSION()`.

As the name of this command suggests, this is the simplest way to view the version number of the Julia kernel you are running (whether you are accessing Julia through the REPL, or via an IDE). This information is usually not crucial, but if you are using older packages (that may be outdated) or very new ones, it is useful to ensure that they can run properly.

OPERATORS, LOOPS AND CONDITIONALS

In this section we'll take a look at how for-loops, while-loops, and if-else statements are implemented in Julia. Before we begin, however, it will be useful to see how Julia uses operators. Without these, both iteration and conditional structures would not be possible.

OPERATORS

Operators are logical functions that take two arguments (of the same type) and provide a Boolean as an output. Some of these operators can be chained together, yielding more complex logical structures. Operators are fundamental for all kinds of meaningful programs, and are essential for creating non-trivial algorithms that provide useful results. There are generally two types of operators: the alphanumeric ones and the logical ones. The former are used to compare a pair of numeric, string, or character variables; the latter apply only to Booleans. All operators, however, yield a Boolean as a result.

Alphanumeric operators (<, >, ==, <=, >=, !=)

Syntax: `A < B`, **where** `A` **and** `B` **are variables of the same data type. This applies to all of these operators.**

Alphanumeric operators are used to perform many types of comparisons. For example, `a < 5`, `a == 2.3`, `b > -12312413211121`, `a <= "something"`, `b >= 'c'`, and `a != b + 4` are all cases of alphanumeric operations. The only catch is that the variables involved must be comparable to each other. For instance, in the first case (`a<5`), `a` must be convertible to an integer (even if it is not an integer per se), otherwise the application of the operator would yield an error. When applying these operators to string or character types, the comparisons are based on the alphabetical order:

```
In[89]: "alice" < "bob"
Out[89]: true
In[90]: "eve" < "bob"
Out[90]: false
```

The case of a letter plays a role in these comparisons as well, since uppercase letters are considered "smaller" in value compared to lowercase ones. This is due to the fact that if you convert a character to an integer (based on the ASCII system), it yields a specific value. All uppercase letters appear first on the corresponding table, giving them smaller values.

Logical operators (&&, ||)

Syntax: `A && B`, **where** `A` **and** `B` **are Boolean variables.** `||` **has the same syntax too. Although** `&&` **and** `&` **are somewhat different under the hood, in practice they can be used interchangeably for this kind of application. Same goes for the** `||` **and** `|` **operators.**

The `&&` and `||` operators correspond to the AND and OR logical functions, which are complementary and particularly useful when performing different tests on the variables. These tests must yield Boolean variables, since they only work on this type. The `&&` operator yields the value `true` only if both of its arguments are true, yielding `false` in all other cases. For example, if `x` is an integer variable, you can find out if it is between 1 and 100 by employing the following operation: `(x > 1) && (x < 100)` or `(x > 1) & (x < 100)`:

```
In[91]: x = 50; y = -120; z = 323;
In[92]: (x > 1) && (x < 100)
Out[92]: true
In[93]: (y > 1) && (y < 100)
Out[93]: false
In[94]: (z > 1) && (z < 100)
Out[94]: false
```

The parentheses are not essential, but they make the whole expression more comprehensible. This is particularly useful when you use several of these operators in a sequence, e.g. `(x > 1) && (y > 1) && (z != 0)`.

The `||` operator works similarly to `&&`, but it marks the value "true" if either one of its arguments (or both of them) is true, while it yields "false" if both of its arguments are false. For example, `(x <= -1) || (x >= 1)` will cover all cases where `x` is greater than 1 in absolute value:

```
In[95]: x = 0.1; y = 12.1;
In[96]: (x <= -1) || (x >= 1)
Out[96]: false
In[97]: (y <= -1) || (y >= 1)
Out[97]: true
```

Operators can also be nested to create even more sophisticated structures, through the use of additional parentheses: `((x > 1) && (z > 1)) || ((x == 0) && (y != 1))`.

LOOPS

Loops, in general, allow you to perform repetitions of the commands you choose, change the values of variables, and dig into your data, without having to write too many lines of code. Although they are seldom used in high-level languages like

Matlab, where they are inefficient, in Julia they are lightning-fast and effective. This is because all the code is compiled in a low-level form that the computer understands, instead of just being interpreted, like in the case of Matlab.

for-loops

This is the most common type of loop, and probably the simplest. In essence, a for-loop involves iterating a variable over a given range and repeating everything in that loop for every value of this iteration. Julia implements this type of loop as follows:

```
for v = x:s:y
    [some code]
end
```

where v is the name of the variable, x and y are the first and the last values it takes, and s is the step (usually this is omitted, having a default value of 1). All of these parameters have to be of the integer type. With all that in mind, take a look at the following for-loop and try to figure out what it does to Int64 variable s which is initialized to be equal to 0.

```
In[97]: s = 0
    for i = 1:2:10      #1
        s += i          #2
        println("s = ", s)
    end
#1 Repeat for values of i ranging from 1 to 10, with a step of 2
    (i.e. only odd numbers in that range)
#2 Just like pretty much every other programming language, Julia
    uses a += b, a -= b, a *= b, etc. as shortcuts for a = a + b, a
    = a - b, a = a * b, etc. respectively.
```

As there are five odd numbers in the range 1:10, the code in the for-loop repeats five times. With each iteration the corresponding number is printed in a separate line, while s increases in value by that number. So at the end of the loop s has taken the value 20. You can track the value of variable s as this script is executed.

while-loops

This while-loop is similar to the for-loop but more open-ended, as the terminating condition of the loop is a logical expression. The while-loop comprises one or more of the aforementioned operators, and as long as it holds "true," the loop continues. The general structure is as follows:

```
while condition
    [some code]
end
```

The condition usually includes a variable that is intricately connected to the code in the loop. It is important to ensure that the condition changes its value at some point (i.e. it becomes "false"), otherwise the code in the loop will be running relentlessly (infinite loop). Below is an example of a valid while-loop, building on the variable c which is initialized to 1:

```
In[98]: c = 1
    while c < 100
      println(c)
      c *= 2
    end
```

This brief program basically doubles the value of c until it surpasses 100, printing it along the way. If c had been initialized differently (say to -1) this loop would never end. Also, you may encounter while-loops that start with `while true`, which could make them infinite if we are not careful. Even in these cases there are workarounds making them a viable programming strategy, as we'll see later on in this chapter.

BREAK COMMAND

There are times when we don't need to go through all the iterations in a loop (particularly if we want to optimize the performance of an algorithm). In such cases, we can escape the loop using the break command. This is usually done using an `if` statement, as in the example that follows. Here, Julia parses a one-dimensional array x until it finds an element equal to -1, in which case it prints the corresponding index (i) and escapes the loop, because of the break command:

```
In[113]: X = [1, 4, -3, 0, -1, 12]
    for i = 1:length(X)
      if X[i] == -1
        println(i)
        break
      end
    end
```

SUMMARY

- Data types are important in Julia, as they allow for better performance and less ambiguity in the functions and programs developed.
- You can convert data from one type to another using the target data type's name in lowercase as a function (e.g. Int64() for converting something into the Int64 type).
- Unlike Python and most other programming languages, Julia's indexing starts with 1, instead of 0.

CHAPTER CHALLENGE

1. Have you checked out the useful tutorials and reference material on Julia in Appendix B?

2. Is it better to use a function implemented in Julia (optimized for code performance) or to call the corresponding function from another language?

3. Say you want to create a list of the various (unique) words encountered in a text, along with their corresponding counts. What kind of data structure would you use to store this, to make the data most easily accessible afterwards?

4. Does it make sense to define the exact type of each input parameter in a function? Could this backfire?

CHAPTER 4
Going Beyond the Basics in Julia

This chapter will help you get comfortable with advanced aspects of the Julia language, and allow you to use it for more customized tasks. We cover:

- String manipulation basics

- Custom functions

- Implementation of a simple algorithm

- Creating a complete solution.

STRING MANIPULATION

As numbers are generally easy to handle, the biggest challenge of data engineering often boils down to manipulating strings. Strings also constitute the vast majority of data nowadays, making them practically ubiquitous. In addition, the fact that any data type can be converted to a string in one way or another makes strings the most versatile of data types. As such, strings require special attention.

Although the string manipulation field is a fairly large one, we'll delve into the most fundamental functions, and then direct you toward resources for further exploration of the topic. One thing to always keep in mind when handling strings in Julia is that each byte of a string is of type character (and not string) and cannot be directly compared to a string.

To access any part of a string, just index the characters you are interested in as if parsing an array, using an int or an array containing numbers of type int. For example:

```
In[1]: q = "Learning the ropes of Julia"
In[2]: q[14:18]
Out[2]: "ropes"
In[3]: q[23]
Out[3]: 'J'
In[4]: q[[1,6,10,12]] #1
Out[4]: "Lite"
#1 Note that the outer set of brackets are for referencing the q
    variable, while the inner ones are for defining the array of
    indexes (characters) to be accessed in that variable. If this
    seems confusing, try breaking it up into two parts: indexes =
    [1, 6, 10, 12] and q[indexes].
```

In the first case we obtain a string output, while in the second we receive a character. Now, let's look into some more powerful ways of manipulating strings.

SPLIT()

Syntax: split(S1, S2), **where** S1 **is the string variable to be split, and** S2 **is the character or string to be used as the separator.** S2 **can be an empty string ("").**

This is a useful command that allows you to turn a string variable into an array of strings, which you can process later in a more systematic way. For example, say you have a sentence (string s) and you want to obtain a list of its words. You can do this easily by typing split(s) or split(s, " "):

```
In[5]: s = "Winter is coming!";
In[6]: show(split(s))
Out[6]: SubString{ASCIIString}["Winter","is","coming!"]
```

If you want a list of characters in that sentence, just use "" as a separator string:

```
In[7]: s = "Julia";
In[8]: show(split(s, ""))
Out[8]: SubString{ASCIIString}["J","u","l","i","a"]
```

In general, this function is applied with two arguments: the string you want to analyze and the separator string (which will be omitted at the output, naturally). If the second argument is not provided, blank spaces will be used by default. This function is particularly useful for analyzing different pieces of text and organizing text data.

JOIN()

Syntax: `join(A, S)`, **where** `A` **is an array (of any type of variable), and** `S` **is the connector string.** `S` **could be an empty string ("").**

This function is in essence the opposite of `split()`, and is handy for concatenating the elements of an array together. All elements of the array will be converted to the string type first, so if there are any Boolean variables in the array they will remain as they appear (instead of turning into 1s and 0s first).

Such a concatenation is rarely useful, though, because the end result is a rather long, incomprehensible string. This is why it is helpful to add a separator string as well. Enter the second argument of the function. So, if you want to join all the elements of an array `z` by putting a space in between each pair of them, you just need to type `join(z, " ")`. Using the array `z` from a previous example we get:

```
In[9]: z = [235, "something", true, -3232.34, 'd', 12345];
In[10]: join(z, " ")
Out[10]: "235 something true -3232.34 d 12345"
```

REGEX FUNCTIONS

Syntax: `r"re"`, **where** `re` **is some regular expression code.**

Unlike other languages, Julia doesn't have a particularly rich package for string manipulation. That's partly because Julia has a built-in regular expressions package that can handle all kinds of tasks involving string search, which is undoubtedly the most important part of string manipulation.

We have already seen how it is possible to find various parts of a string if we know the indexes of the characters involved. However, most of the time this information is not available; we need to parse the string intelligently to find what we are looking for. Regular expressions make this possible through their unique way of handling patterns in these strings.

We will not go into much depth on how regex objects are created, as this involves a whole new language. It would behoove you to look into that on your own, though, by spending some time learning the intricacies of regex structures on websites like http://www.rexegg.com and http://bit.ly/1mXMXbr. Once you get the basics down, you can practice the pure regex code in interactive regex editors like http://www.regexr.com and http://www.myregexp.com.

Unlike other aspects of programming, it is not essential to have a mastery of regexes to make good use of them. Many useful pieces of regex code are already available on the web, so you do not have to build them from scratch. And since they are universal in the programming world, you can use them as-is in Julia.

Once you have a basic familiarity with regexes, you can see how Julia integrates them gracefully in the corresponding (built-in) regex functions, the most important of which will be described in this section. Before you do anything with a regex function, though, you need to define the regex as a corresponding object. For instance: `pattern = r"([A-Z])\w+"` would be a regex for identifying all words starting with a capital letter (in a Latin-based language). Notice the `r` part right before the regex string (in double quotes); this denotes that the string that follows is actually a regular expression and that Julia should therefore interpret it as such.

Although most of the tasks involving regex can be accomplished by some combination of conventional string searching code, those methods may not be the most advisable. Using conventional string searching code for such a task would entail immense overhead, carry great risk of making a mistake, generate incomprehensible code, and ultimately compromise performance. Therefore, it is worth investing some time in learning regex. Remember, you don't need to master them before you can find them useful. We recommend you start with simpler regexes and develop them further as you get more experienced in this topic. Also, you can always get some pre-made regexes from the web and alter them to meet your needs.

ismatch()

Syntax: `ismatch(R, S)`, **where** `R` **is the regex you wish to use, and** `S` **is the string variable you wish to apply it on.** `R` **has to be prefixed with the letter** `r` **(e.g.** `r"[0-9]"` **).**

This is a useful regex function that performs a check on a given string for the presence or absence of a regex pattern. So, if we had the string `s = "The days of the week are Monday, Tuesday, Wednesday, Thursday, Friday, Saturday, and Sunday."` and the regex `p = r"([A-Z])\w+"` from before, we could use `ismatch()` as follows:

```
In[11]: ismatch(p, s)
Out[11]: true
In[12]: ismatch(p, "some random string without any capitalized
    words in it")
Out[12]: false
```

As you probably have guessed, `ismatch()` returns a Boolean value, i.e. "true" or "false." This you can store in a corresponding variable, or use as-is in a conditional, to save some time.

match()

Syntax: `match(R, S, ind)`, **where** `R` **is the regex that you wish to use,** `S` **is the string variable you wish to apply it on, and** `ind` **is the starting point of your search. The final argument is optional and has the default value of** `1` **(i.e. the beginning of the string).**

Once you have confirmed that a certain character pattern exists within a string using the `ismatch()` function, you may want to dig deeper and find out which substring corresponds to this pattern and where exactly this substring dwells. In this case, `match()` is the function you need. So, for the aforementioned example with the days of the week, you can apply `match()` in the following way:

```
In[13]: m = match(p, s)
Out[13]: RegexMatch("The", 1="T")
In[14]: m.match
Out[14]: "The"
In[15]: m.offset
Out[15]: 1
```

As you can see from this example, the output of `match()` is an object that contains information about the first match of the regex pattern in the given string. The most important parts of it are the actual matching substring (`.match` part of the object) and its position in the original string (`.offset` part of the object). You can access these attributes of the object by referring to them in the following format: `ObjectName.AttributeName`.

matchall()

Syntax: `matchall(R, S)`, **where** R **is the regex that you wish to use, and** S **is the string variable you wish to apply it on.**

You'll often need more than just the first match of a pattern. In the example used previously, it is clear that there are several words in the original string (s) that fit the given regex pattern (p). What if we need all of them? That's where the `matchall()` function comes in handy. By applying it to the original string containing the days of the week, you can obtain all of the matching substrings, in the form of an array:

```
In[16]: matchall(p, s)
Out[16]: 8-element Array{SubString{UTF8String},1}:
 "The"
 "Monday"
 "Tuesday"
 "Wednesday"
 "Thursday"
 "Friday"
 "Saturday"
 "Sunday"
```

Although this may seem like a trivial example, it can be useful when trying to find names or other special words (e.g. product codes) within a text, in a simple and efficient way.

eachmatch()

Syntax: `eachmatch(R, S)`, **where** R **is the regex that you wish to use, and** S **is the string variable you wish to apply it on.**

This function allows you to parse all the match objects of the string, as if you were to call `match()` on each one of them. This makes the whole process of searching and outputting results efficient and allows for cleaner and faster code. To make the most of this function, you need to incorporate it into a for-loop, so that you can access all of the found elements. So, if we were to employ the previous example with the days of the week string s, and the capitalized words regex p, we would type:

```
In[17]: for m in eachmatch(p, s)
          println(m.match, " - ", m.offset)
        end
Out[17]: The - 1
Monday - 26
Tuesday - 34
Wednesday - 43
Thursday - 54
Friday - 64
Saturday - 72
Sunday - 86
```

This simple program provides you with all the matching strings and their corresponding locations. With minor adjustments you can store this information in arrays and use it in various ways.

CUSTOM FUNCTIONS

FUNCTION STRUCTURE

Although Julia offers a large variety of built-in functions, the day will come when you need to create your own. When performing custom tasks, you can save yourself some time by tailoring existing functions to your needs. The good thing about Julia is that even these custom functions are super-fast. In order to create your own function you need to use the following structure:

```
function name_of_function(variable1::type1, variable2::type2, ...)
    [some code]
    return output_variable_1, output_variable_2, ...        #A
```

```
end
#A return(output) is also fine
```

You can have as many (input) variables as you want, including none at all, and the type of each argument is optional. It is good practice, however, to include the type of each input variable; it makes the operation of the function much smoother, allowing multiple dispatch.

If you are using arrays as inputs, you can also include the type of the elements of these arrays in curly brackets after the array term (this can also be applied to other variables too):

```
function name_of_function{T <: Type}(var1::Array{T,
    NumberOfDimensions}, var2::T, ...)
    [some code]
    return output
end
```

The output of the function (which is also optional) is provided using the `return()` command (which can be used with or without the brackets).

For simpler functions, you can just use the one-liner version instead:

```
res(x::Array) = x - mean(x)
```

ANONYMOUS FUNCTIONS

If you want to create a function that you are going to use only once (or you are just paranoid that someone else might use that same function without your permission!), you can use what are known as "anonymous functions." Simply put, these are functions that are applied as soon as they are created and are not stored in memory as objects, rendering them inaccessible after they are applied. Here is an example to clarify this concept:

```
In[18]: mx = mean(X)
  x -> x - mx
```

This simple function from before is now broken into two parts: calculating the mean of variable X and subtracting it from each element x. This function doesn't have a name, hence its category (anonymous function). The idea is that it's not going to be around for long, so we needn't bother naming it.

The use case of anonymous functions is somewhat common, at least for more experienced programmers. It's often used for applying a transformation to a bunch of values in an array, as we previously discussed (see `map()` function). Specifically:

```
In[19]: X = [1,2,3,4,5,6,7,8,9,10,11];
        mx = mean(X);
        show(map(x -> x - mx, X))
Out[19]: [-5.0,-4.0,-3.0,-2.0,-1.0,0.0,1.0,2.0,3.0,4.0,5.0]
```

MULTIPLE DISPATCH

Multiple dispatch refers to using the same function for different data types through completely different methods. In other words, a function `fun(a::Int)` can incorporate a completely different process than `fun(a::String)`, even though both functions have the same name. This is particularly useful if you want to make your function versatile and not have to remember a dozen names of its variants. Multiple dispatch allows for more intuitive code and is widely used in both the base and the auxiliary packages in Julia. So, for the example of the residuals function in the previous sections, we can also define it for single numbers:

```
In[20]: res(x::Number) = x
res (generic function with 2 methods)
```

Julia recognizes that this function already exists for array inputs, and sees this new definition as a new method for its use. Now, the next time you call it, Julia will try to match your inputs to the right method:

```
In[21]: show(res(5))
Out[21]: 5
In[22]: show(res([1,2,3,4,5,6,7,8,9,10,11))
Out[22]: [-5.0,-4.0,-3.0,-2.0,-1.0,0.0,1.0,2.0,3.0,4.0,5.0]
```

Multiple dispatch can be useful when creating (or extending) generic functions that can have any kind of inputs (e.g. `length()`). However, it requires some careful attention; you can easily get lost in the variety of functions with the same name, as you are building something and running it again and again while refining it. If you are creating a new function and change its inputs ever so slightly, Julia will recognize it as a totally different function. This can be an issue when debugging a script, which is why we recommend you restart the kernel whenever you get into this situation.

Here's an example of a typical case where multiple dispatch could be handy: you have created a function that you've made too specific (e.g. `fun(Array{Float64, 1})`) and you try to run it on inputs that don't fit its expectations (e.g. [1,2,3], an array of integers). In this case you could simply create another function, `fun(Array{Int64, 1})`, that is equipped to handle that particular input, making your function more versatile.

FUNCTION EXAMPLE

Let's look now at a simple example of a custom function, putting together some of the things we've examined. This function, which is described below, calculates the Hamming distance between two strings `X` and `Y`. The objective of the function is described in a brief comment right after the declaration of the function, using the "#" character. In general, you can put this character wherever you want in the program and be assured that whatever comes after it is not going to be checked by Julia.

```
In[23]:function hdist(X::AbstractString, Y::AbstractString)
   # Hamming Distance between two strings
      lx = length(X)
      ly = length(Y)
      if lx != ly                        #A
        return -1
      else                               #B
        lettersX = split(X, "")          #C
        lettersY = split(Y, "")          #C
        dif = (lettersX .== lettersY)    #D
        return sum(dif)
      end
   end
```

```
#A strings are of different length
#B strings are of the same length
#C get the individual letters of each string
#D create a (binary) array with all the different letters
```

Remember that if you want to use more generic or abstract types in your arrays (e.g. `Real` for real numbers, `Number` for all kinds of numeric variables) you must define them before or during the declaration of the function. For example, if you want the above function to work on any kind of string, define it as follows:

```
function hdist{T <: AbstractString}(X::T, Y::T)
```

Pay close attention to this rule, as it will save you a lot of frustration when you start building your own functions. Otherwise, you'll be forced to rely heavily on multiple dispatch to cover all possibilities, making the development of a versatile function a somewhat time-consuming process.

To call a function you must use the form `function_name(inputs)`. If you just type `function_name`, Julia will interpret it as a wish to obtain a high-level view of the given function (which is typically not very useful). You can view more details about the function, including all of its versions (or "methods") and which inputs they require, by using `methods(function_name)`. For example:

```
In[24]: methods(median)
Out[24]: # 2 methods for generic function "median":
median{T}(v::AbstractArray{T,N}) at statistics.jl:475
median{T}(v::AbstractArray{T,N},region) at statistics.jl:477
```

IMPLEMENTING A SIMPLE ALGORITHM

Now, let's look into how skewness can be implemented elegantly and efficiently in Julia. As you may already know from statistics, skewness is a useful measure for providing insights about the nature of a distribution. Here we'll discuss the type of the skewness: whether it's negative, positive, or zero.

Finding the type of skewness boils down to comparing the mean and the median of the distribution. As these metrics can apply to all kinds of numbers, the input will have to be an array, having a single dimension. So, the skewness type program will be something like the function in listing 4.1.

```
In[25]: function skewness_type(X::Array)      #A
        m = mean(X)                           #B
        M = median(X)                         #C
        if m > M                              #D
            output = "positive"
        elseif m < M
            output = "negative"
        else
            output = "balanced"
        end
        return output                         #E
    end
#A Function definition. This method applies to all kinds of arrays.
#B Calculate the arithmetic mean of the data and store it in
    variable m
#C Calculate the median of the data and store it in variable M
#D Compare mean to median
#E Output the result (variable "output")
```

Listing 4.1 An example of a simple algorithm implemented in Julia: skewness type.

Although the above program will work with all of the single-dimensional arrays we give it, multi-dimensional arrays will confuse it. To resolve this issue, we can be more specific about what inputs it will accept by changing the first line to:

```
function skewness_type{T<:Number}(X::Array{T, 1})
```

We can test this function using various distributions, to ensure that it works as expected:

```
In[26]: skewness_type([1,2,3,4,5])
Out[26]: "balanced"
In[27]: skewness_type([1,2,3,4,100])
Out[27]: "positive"
In[28]: skewness_type([-100,2,3,4,5])
Out[28]: "negative"
```

```
In[29]: skewness_type(["this", "that", "other"])
Out[29]: ERROR: 'skewness_type' has no method matching
    skewness_type(::Array{Any,1})
In[30]: A = rand(Int64, 5, 4); skewness_type(A)
Out[30]: ERROR: `skewness_type` has no method matching
    skewness_type(::Array{Int64,2})
```

CREATING A COMPLETE SOLUTION

Now, let's say that we need to create a more sophisticated program, involving more than a single function, in order to handle the missing values in a dataset. This is the time to demonstrate how various functions can be integrated into a whole (referred to as "a solution"), how we can design the solution effectively, and how we can develop the corresponding functions. To achieve this, we will need to split the problem into smaller ones and solve each one as a separate routine. For example, say that we need to fill in the missing values of a dataset using either the mode or the median, for discreet and continuous variables, respectively. One way of structuring the solution would be to build the workflow shown in Figure 4.1.

In this solution we employ the following functions, all of which are custom-built and aim to fulfill a particular purpose:

`has_missing_values()` – a function to check whether a feature has missing values. The input will need to be a one-dimensional array containing elements of type "any," while the output will be a Boolean ("true" if the feature has missing values and "false" otherwise). This will be used to assess whether a feature contains one or more missing values.

`feature_type()` – a function to assess whether a feature is discreet or continuous. The input here will need to be the same as in the previous function, while the output will be a string variable taking the values "discreet" and "continuous." This function is essential in figuring out the approach to take when filling in missing values for a feature.

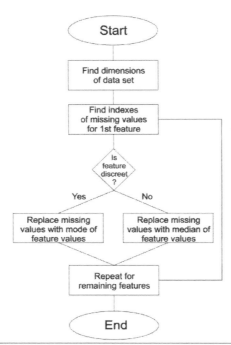

Figure 4.1 The workflow of one solution for handling missing values in a dataset.

`mode()` – a function for finding the mode of a discreet variable. Although the function for calculating the mode already exists in the `Distributions` package, here we'll build it from scratch for additional practice. The input of this function will need to be the same as in the previous two functions, while the output will be a number denoting the mode of that variable. This simple function will provide us with the most common element in a given discreet feature.

`main()` – the wrapper program that will integrate all the auxiliary programs together. The input will be a two-dimensional array with elements of type "any," while the output will be a similar array with all the missing values filled in, based on the types of the features involved. This is the function that the end-user will use in order to process a dataset containing missing values.

In this solution, the assumption made about missing values is that they are blank values in the data matrix. With that in mind, one solution is provided in Listings 4.2 - 4.5. All the empty lines and the indentation are not essential but make the code easier to read.

```
In[31]: function mode{T<:Any}(X::Array{T})
          ux = unique(X)              #1
          n = length(ux)             #2
          z = zeros(n)               #3
          for x in X                 #4
            ind = findin(ux, x)     #5
            z[ind] += 1             #6
          end
          m_ind = findmax(z)[2]     #7
          return ux[m_ind]          #8
        End
```

#1 find the unique values of the given Array X
#2 find the number of elements in Array X
#3 create a blank 1-dim array of size n
#4 iterate over all elements in Array x
#5 find which unique value x corresponds to
#6 increase the counter for that unique value
#7 get the largest counter in Array z
#8 output the mode of X

Listing 4.2 Code for an auxiliary function of the missing values solution: mode().

```
In[32]: function missing_values_indexes{T<:Any}(X::Array{T})
          ind = Int[]                  #1
          n = length(X)               #2
          for i = 1:n                 #3
            if isempty(X[i])         #4
              push!(ind, i)          #5
            end
          end
          return ind                  #6
        end
```

#1 create empty Int array named "ind" for "index"
#2 find the number of elements in Array x
#3 repeat n times (i = index variable)
#4 check if there is a missing value in this location of the X
   array
#5 missing value found. Add its index to "ind" array
#6 output index array "ind"

Listing 4.3 Code for an auxiliary function of the missing values solution: missing_values_indexes().

```
In[33]: function feature_type{T<:Any}(X::Array{T})
            n = length(X)                                    #1
            ft = "discreet"                                  #2
            for i = 1:n                                      #3
              if length(X[i]) > 0                            #4
                tx = string(typeof(X[i]))                    #5

                if tx in ["ASCIIString", "Char", "Bool"]    #6
                    ft = "discreet"                          #7
                    break                                    #8
                elseif contains(tx, "Float")                 #9
                    ft = "continuous"                        #10
                end
              end
            end
            return ft                                        #11
        end
```

```
#1 find the number of elements in array X
#2 set feature type variable to one of the possible values
#3 do n iterations of the index variable i
#4 check if the i-th element of X isn't empty
#5 get the type of that element
#6 is its type one of these types?
#7 feature X is discreet
#8 exit the loop
#9 is the type some kind of Float?
#10 feature X is continuous (for the time being)
#11 output feature type variable
```

Listing 4.4 Code for an auxiliary function of the missing values solution: feature_type().

```
In[34]: function main{T<:Any}(X::Array{T})
            N, n = size(X)                              #1
            y = Array(T,N,n)                            #2
            for i = 1:n                                 #3
              F = X[:,i]                                #4
              ind = missing_values_indexes(F)           #5
              if length(ind) > 0                        #6
                ind2 = setdiff(1:N, ind)                #7
                if feature_type(F) == "discreet"        #8
                    y = mode(F[ind2])                   #9
              else
```

```
        y = median(F[ind2])        #10
      end
      F[ind] = y                   #11
    end
    Y[:,i] = F                     #12
  end
  return Y                         #13
end
```

#1 get the dimensions of array X
#2 create an empty array of the same dimensions and of the same
   type
#3 do n iterations
#4 get the i-th feature of X and store it in F
#5 find the indexes of the missing values of that feature
#6 feature F has at least one missing value
#7 indexes having actual values
#8 is that feature a discreet variable?
#9 calculate the mode of F and store it in y
#10 calculate the median of F store it in y
#11 replace all missing values of F with y
#12 store F in Y as the i-th column
#13 output array Y

Listing 4.5 Code for the main function of the missing values: solution, main().

As you would expect, there are several ways to implement this solution–some more elegant than others. This one could have been made with fewer lines of code, but sometimes it is worthwhile to sacrifice brevity for the sake of having more comprehensible code. We encourage you to come back to this chapter and try out this solution on various datasets to see how it works, and try to figure out the details of the newly introduced functions.

You can always apply each one of the components of this solution independently, although in order to run the main() function you must have loaded the auxiliary functions into Julia first (by inputting the corresponding pieces of code). To test these functions, make up a simple dataset of your own (ideally a variety of arrays, each of a different type) and run the main() function on it:

```
data = readdlm("my dataset.csv", ',')
main(data)
```

If you have time, we recommend you test each one of the functions separately, to make sure you understand its functionality. Once you become more experienced with Julia, you can come back to this solution and see if you can find ways to improve it or refactor it in a way that makes more sense to you.

SUMMARY

- String manipulation in Julia takes place mainly through the use of regex functions, such as `match()`, `matchall()`, and `eachmatch()`.

- Regexes in Julia are prefixed by "r". For example: `r"([A-Z])\w+"` is a regex for identifying words starting with a capital letter.

- When defining a function that makes use of a generic or abstract type, you must define it beforehand (usually right before the input arguments of the function). This is done as follows: `function F{T <: TypeName}(Array{T})`, where `TypeName` is the name of the type (with first letter capitalized, as always).

- When developing a complete solution, it is a good idea to create a workflow of the algorithm that you are planning to implement, making a list of all necessary functions. The auxiliary functions need to be loaded into memory before the wrapper (main) function is executed.

CHAPTER CHALLENGE

1. Can you use the same function for processing completely different types of data? If so, which feature of the language would you make use of?

2. Consider the function `counters()` from previously. Why doesn't it work with the inputs 'a', 'b'? Shouldn't these have a distance of 1?

3. Is it possible to extend the function `mode()` from before so that it can handle an input like 234 (a single number instead of an array) and return that input as an output? What characteristic of Julia would such a modification make use of?

4. Write a simple function that counts the number of words in a given text (assume that there are no line breaks in this text). Once you are done, test it with a couple of cases (you can take a random paragraph from a blog post or an ebook) and evaluate its performance.

5. Write a simple function that counts the number of characters in a given text and calculates the proportion of the ones that are not spaces.

6. Write a complete solution that takes an array of numbers (you can assume they are all floats) and provides you with a distribution of all the digits present in that text (i.e. how may 0s there are, how many 1s, and so on). What's the most common digit out there? The simplest way to implement this is through a function that counts how many characters x exist in a given string, and a wrapper method that accumulates and outputs all the stats. You may use additional auxiliary functions if you find them helpful.

CHAPTER 5
Julia Goes All Data Science-y

Before we dig into using Julia to help with our data science endeavors, let's take a look at the data science pipeline, in order to get a sense of perspective. The high level pipeline will be covered in this chapter, and subsequent chapters will get into the details.

DATA SCIENCE PIPELINE

Unlike other types of data analysis (e.g. statistics), data science involves a whole pipeline of processes, each stage intricately connected to each other and to the end result, which is what you ultimately share with the user or customer. As we demonstrated in Chapter 1, Julia fits in well in almost all of these processes, making it an ideal tool for data science projects. We'll start with an enhanced version of our data science chart from earlier, seen here in Figure 5.1.

In general, data science involves one of two things: the creation of a data-driven application (usually referred to as a data product), or the generation of actionable insights. Both of these end results are equally worth examining, though certain data streams lend themselves more to one than the other. To achieve these end results, a data scientist needs to follow the steps presented in this figure, in roughly this order, paying particular attention to the end result.

The first three processes are often referred to collectively as data engineering. Julia is helpful in completing all the tasks within this part of the pipeline, even without any additional packages. Data engineering is something we'll focus our attention on, as it typically takes up around 80% of a data scientist's work, and is often considered the most challenging part of the pipeline.

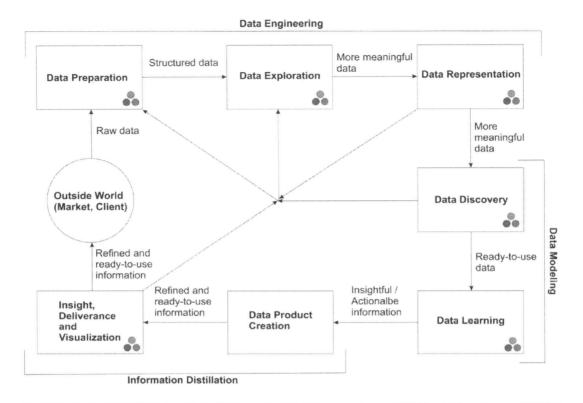

Figure 5.1 A map showing the interconnectivity of the data science process. The direction of the lines connecting the nodes is not set in stone; there are often back-and-forth relationships between consecutive phases of the process. Also, we have proposed a grouping of these stages that may help you better organize them in your mind.

The two stages following data engineering can be considered the data modeling part of the process–where all the fun stuff happens. Julia also shines in these stages, as its efficiency is a huge plus when it comes to all the resource-heavy work that is required. However, Julia's base functions aren't as adequate in this phase of the pipeline, and it relies heavily on the packages developed for the relevant tasks.

The results of all your hard work are revealed to the world in the final two stages, which we can call information distillation. Actually, this part of the process doesn't have an official name and hasn't been formally researched, but it is equally important and is inherently different than the other two groups of stages. It's worth considering on its own.

In this chapter we'll explore each one of the processes of the pipeline at a high level, examining how it integrates with the other processes, as well as with the end result. Parallel to that, we'll see how all this translates into specific actions, through a case study using a realistic dataset. In this case study, we'll be working with a fictitious startup that plans to promote Star Wars®-related products from various sellers, catering to an audience of fans that populate its Star Wars-themed blog. The firm started by collecting some survey data from a random sample of its users, questioning their experience with the Star Wars franchise. Now they're trying to answer questions like "what product should we market to particular individuals?" and "what is the expected revenue from a particular customer?"

Jaden is the startup's data scientist, and he recently starting working with Julia. Jaden's first observation is that these questions relate to the variables FavoriteProduct and MoneySpent, which will be our target variables. Let's see how he goes about applying the data science process on this project, which is known inside the company as "Caffeine for the Force".

The Caffeine for the Force project is fleshed out in the IJulia notebook that accompanies this chapter. We encourage you to take a look at it as you go through this chapter. This notebook will give you a better grasp of the bigger picture and how all the concepts presented in this chapter are translated into Julia code. Finally, there is some room for improvement of this project–the code is not optimal. This is because in practice you rarely have the resources to create the best possible code, since data science is not an exact science (particularly in the business world). A great way to learn is to play, so definitely play with this notebook to optimize it as you see fit.

DATA ENGINEERING

DATA PREPARATION

This is a fundamental process, even though it is not as creative or interesting as the ones that follow. Paying close attention to this stage enables you to proceed to the following stages smoothly, as you will have laid a solid foundation for a robust data analysis. Think of it as tidying up your desk at work, organizing your documents and your notes, and making sure that all your equipment is working. Not a lot of fun, but essential if you want to have a productive day!

Data preparation first involves cleansing the data and encoding it in matrices (or arrays in general), and often in data frames. A data frame is a popular data container that was originally developed in R. It's a strictly rectangular formation of data, which offers easy access to its variables by name instead of indexes; this enables the user to handle its contents in a more versatile manner than conventional arrays.

For the data attributes that are numeric (ratio variables), this process also entails normalizing them to a fixed range (usually [0, 1], or (0, 1), or around 0 with a fixed dispersion level). The latter is the most commonly used normalization method and it involves subtracting the mean (μ) of the variable at hand and dividing the result by the standard deviation (σ). When it comes to string data, normalization entails changing all the text into the same case (usually lowercase). For natural language processing (NLP) applications in particular, it involves the following techniques:

- Retaining only the stem of each word instead of the word itself, a process known as stemming (for example running, ran, and run would also be changed into "run" as they all stem from that root word).

- Removing "stop words", which add little or no information to the data (e.g. "a", "the", "to", etc.). You can find various lists of stop words at http://bit.ly/29dvlrA).

- Removing extra spaces, tabs (\t), carriage returns (\r) and line breaks (\n).

- Removing punctuation and special characters (e.g. "~").

Data cleansing is largely about handling missing values. For string-based data, it entails removing certain characters (e.g. brackets and dashes in phone number data, currency symbols from monetary data). This is particularly important as it allows for better handling of the data in the data representation and other parts of the pipeline.

Handling outliers is another important aspect of data preparation, as these peculiar data points can easily skew your model—even though they may contain useful information. They often need special attention, as discerning between useless and important outliers is not trivial. Although this process is easily done using statistical methods, some data scientists prefer to identify outliers in the data exploration stage. The sooner you deal with them, the smoother the rest of the process will be.

More often than not, the type of work required in data preparation is not readily apparent. It always depends on the information that is ultimately going to be derived from the data. That's one of the reasons why it is difficult to automate this entire process, although certain parts of it can be handled in an automated way (e.g. text cleansing, variable normalization).

You can always revisit this stage and perform more rigorous engineering on the data, ensuring that it is even fitter for the applications required. Since this process can get messy, always document in detail everything you do throughout this process (ideally within the code you use for it, through comments). This will be particularly useful towards the end of your analysis when someone may inquire about your process, or for when you need to repeat this work for other similar data streams. We'll go into the details of this part of the pipeline, along with other data engineering related processes, in Chapter 6.

In our case study, data preparation would involve filling out the missing values of each one of the variables, as well as normalizing the numeric variables (namely, MoviesWatched, Age and MoneySpent).

The output of the data preparation stage is not necessarily refined data that can be fed into a stats model or a machine learning algorithm. Often, the data will require additional work. This will become apparent only after the following stage, when we get to know the data more intimately. You can *attempt* to use the output on a model as-is, but it's unlikely you'll have any noteworthy results or performance. To ensure that you make the most of your refined data, you'll need to get to know it better; this brings us to data exploration.

DATA EXPLORATION

For most people, this open-ended stage of the pipeline is the most enjoyable part of any data science project. It involves calculating some descriptive statistics on the structured part of the data, looking into the unstructured data and trying to find patterns there, and creating visuals that can assist you in the comprehension of the data at hand. The patterns you find in the unstructured data are then translated into features, which can add quantifiable value to the dataset being built for your project.

Data exploration also enables you to come up with novel questions to ask about your data, which are often referred to as hypotheses. Hypotheses allow you to scientifically test the hunches you get from looking at the data, unveiling the information that is hidden in the data stream. Testing involves some statistics work as well as some reasoning, as you need to connect your findings with the bigger picture of your project. That's why many people consider data exploration a creative process. As such, it is often a bit messy, and the visuals involved are more like "rough drafts" than polished products.

This part of the pipeline also includes carefully selecting which data to use for the analysis tasks at hand. In a way, data exploration is a manual search for the variables that are relevant to your questions.

When this process is automated, particularly in structured datasets, it is referred to as "association rules extraction," which is a popular field of data analysis. However, automating your data exploration may lead to oversights, as it lacks the data scientist's discerning eye and creative mind. Some manual work is inevitable if you are to produce truly valuable data science work. There is simply no substitute for the intuition that you, the data scientist, bring to the data exploration approach. We'll cover data exploration in depth in Chapter 7.

Back at our startup, Jaden looks for any potentially insightful relationships among the variables, particularly between a feature and each one of the target variables (e.g. the correlation of average values of Age with MoneySpent, as depicted in the plot in Figure 5.2). He also creates histograms for each relationship he explores, like the one for FavoriteProduct (Figure 5.3), which reveals a noticeable class imbalance.

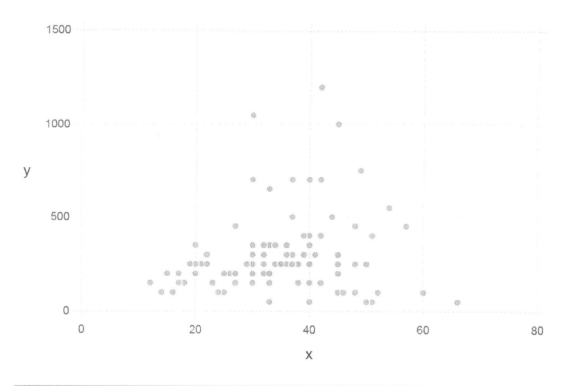

Figure 5.2 A visual for the data exploration stage of the "Caffeine for the Force" project. Although not so refined (since Jaden is the only one needing to use them), it depicts an interesting pattern that sheds some light on the problem at hand.

All this information, though not actionable, will help Jaden understand the dataset in greater depth and better choose the right models and validation metrics to use. Plus, if one of the graphics he creates at this stage looks particularly interesting, he can refine it and use it in the visualization stage.

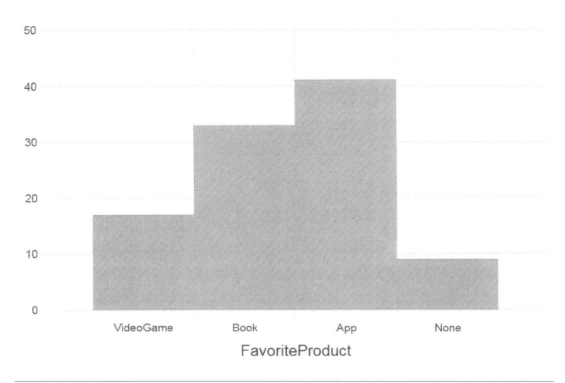

Figure 5.3 Another visual for the data exploration stage of the "Caffeine for the Force" project. This one reveals that the classes of the dataset are not balanced at all; this will prove useful later on.

DATA REPRESENTATION

Data representation addresses the way data is coded in the variables used in your dataset. This is particularly useful for larger datasets (which are the bread and butter of a data scientist) as good data representation allows for more efficient use of the available resources, particularly memory. This is important, as even when there is an abundance of resources (e.g. in the cloud) they are not all necessarily free, so good resource management is always a big plus. In addition, representing data properly will make your models more lightweight and allow for higher speed and sustainability. You'll be able to reuse them when more data becomes available, without having to make major changes.

Picking the right type of variable can indeed make a difference, which is why declaring the variable types is essential when importing data from external sources or developing new features. For example, if you are using a feature to capture the number of certain keywords in a text, you are better off using an unsigned 8- or 16-bit integer, instead of the Int64 type, which takes four to eight times the memory and uses half of it on negative values which you'd never use in this particular feature.

This is also helpful when it comes to understanding the data available and dealing with it in the best way possible (e.g. employing the appropriate statistical tests or using the right type of plots). For example, say you have a numeric attribute that takes only discreet values that are relatively small. In this case it would make more sense to encode this data into an integer variable—probably a 16-bit one. Also, if you were to plot that feature, you would want to avoid line or scatter plots, because there would be lots of data points having the same value.

Data representation also involves the creation of features from the available data. This is an essential aspect of dealing with text data, as it is difficult to draw any conclusions directly from the text. Even some basic characteristics (e.g. its length in characters, the number of words it contains) can reveal useful information, though you may need to dig deeper in order to find more information-rich features. This is why text analytics techniques (especially Natural Language Processing, or NLP) rely heavily on robust data engineering, particularly data representation.

Feature creation is also important when it comes to signal processing, including processing data from medical instruments and various kinds of sensors (such as accelerometers). Even though such signals can be used as-is in certain analytics methods, usually it is much more efficient to capture their key aspects through certain features, after some pre-processing takes place (e.g. moving the signal into the frequency domain or applying a Fourrier transformation).

In our example, Jaden will need to do some work on the representation of the nominal variables. Specifically, we can see that FavoriteMovie and BlogRole are variables with more than two distinct values and could be broken down into binary groups (e.g. BlogRole could be translated into IsNormalUser, IsActiveUser, and IsModerator). Gender, on the other hand, could be changed into a single binary.

Unfortunately there is no clear-cut stopping point for the data representation stage of the data science process. You could spend days optimizing the representation of your dataset and developing new features. Once you decide that enough is enough (something that your manager is bound to be kind enough to remind you of!), you can proceed to other more interesting data science tasks, such as data modeling.

DATA MODELING

DATA DISCOVERY

Once your dataset is in a manageable form and you have explored its variables to your heart's content, you can continue with the data modeling segment of the pipeline, starting with data discovery. Patterns are often hiding within data in the feature space's structure, or in the way the data points of particular classes populate that space. Data discovery aims to uncover these hidden patterns.

Data discovery is closely linked with data exploration; it is usually during data explorations that the patterns in the data begin to reveal themselves. For example, you may run a correlation analysis and find out that certain features have a high correlation with your target variable. That in itself is a discovery that you can use in the predictive model you'll be building. Also, you may find that certain variables correlate closely with each other, so you may want to weed them out (remember, less is more).

Hypothesis formulation and testing is also essential in this part of the pipeline. That's where a good grasp of statistics will serve you well, as it will enable you to pinpoint the cases where there is a significant difference between groups of variables, and to find meaningful distinctions between them. All this will ultimately help you build your model, where you will try to merge all these signals into a predictive tool.

Sometimes, even our best efforts with all these techniques don't provide all the insights we expected from our data. In such cases, we may need to perform some more advanced methods, involving dimensionality reduction (which we'll cover in Chapter 8), visualization (Chapter 7), and even group identification (Chapter 9). Also, certain patterns may become apparent only by combining existing features (something we'll examine more in Chapter 6). An example of a technique often used in this stage is factor analysis, which aims to depict which features influence the end result (the target variable) the most, and by how much.

Skilled data discovery is something that comes with experience and practice. It requires delving thoughtfully into your data–more than just applying off-the-shelf techniques. It is one of the most creative parts of the whole data science process and a critical part of building a useful model. Yet, we'll often have to revisit it in order to continuously improve the model, since this stage's workload is practically limitless.

Upon examining our case study's dataset more closely, we realize that none of the variables appear to be good predictors of the FavoriteProduct overall, although some of them do correlate with certain values of it. Also, none of the variables seem to correlate well with the MoneySpent apart from Age, although the connection is non-linear.

DATA LEARNING

Data learning is a process that involves the intelligent analysis of the patterns you have discovered in the previous stages, with the help of various statistical and machine learning techniques. The goal is to create a model that you can use to draw some insightful conclusions from your data, by employing the process of generalization. In this context, generalization refers to the ability to discern high-level patterns in a dataset (e.g. the form of rules), empowering you to make accurate predictions with unknown data having the same attributes (features).

Generalization is not an easy task; it involves multiple rounds of training and testing of your model. More often than not, in order to achieve a worthwhile generalization you will need to create several models, and sometimes even combine various models in an ensemble. The ultimate goal is to be able to derive the underlying pattern behind the data and then use it to perform accurate predictions on other data, different from that which you used to train your model.

Naturally, the better your generalization, the more applicable (and valuable) your model will be. That's why this process requires a great deal of attention, as there is a strong impetus to go beyond the obvious patterns and probe the data in depth (hence the term "deep learning," which involves sophisticated neural network models that aim to do just that).

A computer can learn from data in two different ways: using known targets (which can be either continuous or discreet) or on its own (without any target variable). The former is usually referred to as supervised learning, as it involves some human supervision throughout the learning process. The latter approach is known as unsupervised learning, and it is generally what you will want to try out first (sometimes during the data exploration stage).

An important part of this whole process (especially for the unsupervised learning case) is validation. This involves measuring how well the model we have created performs when applied to data that it's not trained on. In other words, we put its generalization ability to the test and quantify how accurate it is, either by measuring how many times it hits the right target (classification) or by calculating the error of the estimated target variable (regression). In any case, this validation process often leads to plots that provide interesting insights to the model's performance.

Data learning is an essential part of the data science pipeline, as it is the backbone of the whole analysis. Without proper data learning, you would be hard-pressed to create a worthwhile data product or generate conclusions that go beyond the traditional slicing and dicing methods of basic data analytics. Although this stage is usually the most challenging, it is also the most enjoyable and requires some creativity, especially when dealing with noisy data. We'll further discuss this part of the data science process in Chapters 10 and 11, where we'll be looking at methods like Decision Trees, Support Vector Machines, k means, and more.

As for our case study, the way data learning can be applied is twofold: first as a classification problem (predicting the FavoriteProduct nominal variable using the first five variables), and then a regression problem (predicting the value of the MoneySpent numeric variable using the same feature set). You can view the performance of one of the models created (for the classification problem), depicted through the Receiver Operating Characteristic (ROC) curve in Figure 5.4.

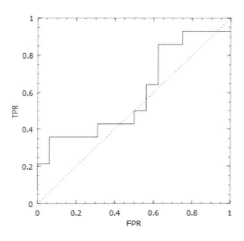

Figure 5.4 An ROC curve illustrating the performance of the best one of the classification models (random forest) developed for the "Caffeine for the Force" project.

INFORMATION DISTILLATION

DATA PRODUCT CREATION

This stage of the pipeline encompasses several tasks that ultimately lead to the creation of an application, applet, dashboard, or other data product. This makes all the results gleaned throughout the previous parts of the pipeline accessible to everyone in an intuitive way. Moreover, it is usually something that can be repeatedly used by the organization funding your work, providing real value to the users of this product. As you would expect, it may need to be updated from time to time, or expanded in functionality; you will still be needed once the data product is deployed!

To create a data product you need to automate the data science pipeline and productionalize the model you have developed. You also must design and implement a graphical interface (usually on the web, via the cloud). The key factor of a data product is its ease of use, so when building one you should optimize for performance and accessibility of its features.

Examples of data products are the recommender systems you find on various websites (e.g. Amazon, LinkedIn), personalized interfaces on several retail sites (e.g. Home Depot), several apps for mobile devices (e.g. Uber), and many more. Basically, anything that can run on a computer of sorts, employing some kind of data model, qualifies as a data product.

Although the development of a data product comprises a lot of different processes that aren't all dependent on use of a programming language, Julia can still be used for that particular purpose. However, this involves some of the more specialized and complex aspects of the language, which go beyond the scope of this book.

The data product created by our Star Wars Startup could take the form of an application that the marketing team will use to bring the right product to the right customers. The application could also indicate the expected amount of money that customers are willing to spend. Based on products like these, targeted and effective marketing strategies can be created.

INSIGHT, DELIVERANCE, AND VISUALIZATION

This final stage of the data science pipeline is particularly important as it has the highest visibility and provides the end result of the entire process. It involves creating visuals for your results, delivering presentations, creating reports, and demonstrating the data product you have developed.

The insights derived from data science work tend to be actionable: they don't just provide interesting information, but are used practically to justify decisions that can improve the organization's performance, ultimately delivering value to both the organization and its clients. Insights are always intuitively supported by a model's performance results, graphics, and any other findings you glean from your analysis.

Delivering your data product involves making it accessible to its targeted audience, acquiring feedback from your audience, making improvements based on the feedback, and when necessary tweaking your process and expanding its capabilities.

Although visualization takes place throughout the pipeline (particularly in the data exploration stage), creating comprehensive and engaging visuals in this final stage is the most effective way to convey your findings to people who aren't data scientists. These visuals should be much more polished and complete than those generated in previous steps; they should have all the labels, captions, and explanations necessary to be completely self-explanatory and accessible to people with a wide range of knowledge of and experience with data analysis and the topic in question.

Insight, delivery, and visualization may be the final stage of the data science pipeline, but they may also launch the beginning of a new cycle. Your findings will often fuel additional hypotheses and new questions that you'll then attempt to answer with additional data analysis work. The new cycle may also require you to apply your previous model to different types of data, leading you to revise your model.

Jaden is finally ready to wrap up his data analysis. Figure 5.5 demonstrates one of the many ways Jaden can share the insights derived from his analysis. Furthermore, the data product from the previous stage can enter a beta-testing phase, and some visuals like the one in Figure 5.5 can be shared with the stakeholders of the project.

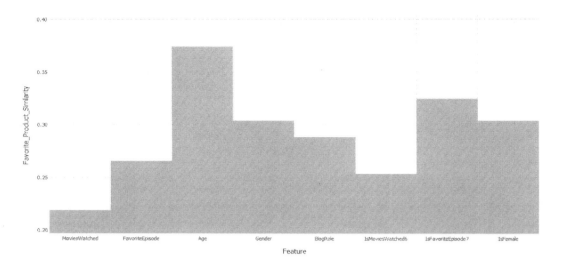

Figure 5.5 A visual data product for the final stage of the "Caffeine for the Force" project. What's shown here is the relative importance of each feature used in the classification model.

KEEP AN OPEN MIND

Although there has been considerable effort to introduce packages that enhance the data science process, you don't need to rely on them exclusively. This is because unlike Python, R, and other high-level languages, Julia doesn't rely on C to make things happen. So, if you find that you need a tool that is not yet available in the aforementioned packages, don't hesitate to build something from scratch.

The data science process is often messy. It's not uncommon to glue together pieces of code from various platforms in order to develop your product or insight. Julia helps solve this patchwork problem by being more than capable of handling all your data science requirements. Still, if you wish to use it only for one particular part of the process, you can always call your Julia script from other platforms, such as Python and R. Naturally, the reverse applies too; should you wish to call your Python, R, or even C scripts from Julia, you can do that easily (see Appendix D for details on how to do both of these tasks).

Finally, it's important to keep in mind that the data science process is not set in stone. As the field evolves, some steps may be merged together, and we may even see new steps being added. So, it's good to keep an open mind when applying the process.

APPLYING THE DATA SCIENCE PIPELINE TO A REAL-WORLD PROBLEM

Let's consider the `spam` dataset we discussed in the previous chapters, as it's a concept familiar to anyone who has used email. This dataset consists of several hundred emails in text format, all of which are split into two groups: normal (or "ham") and spam. The latter class is much smaller, as you would hope. Now let's see how each part of the pipeline would apply in this case study.

DATA PREPARATION

First of all, we'll need to structure the data. To do that, we have to decide what parts of the email we plan to use in our data product, which might be a spam filter that a user can use on their computer or smartphone. If we want to make this process relatively fast, we should opt for simplicity, using as few features as possible.

One way to accomplish structuring the data is to focus on one aspect of the email which usually contains enough information to make the call of "spam or ham": the subject line. We have all received emails with subjects like "free Viagra trial" or "sexyJenny's date invite is pending," and it doesn't take much to figure out that they are not legitimate. So, our spam detection data product could actually work if it learns to recognize enough email subjects like these ones.

To prepare our data for this task, we'll need to extract just the relevant parts of the emails. Upon looking closer at the various email files, you can see that the subject is always prefaced by the character string "Subject:" making it easy to identify. So, in this stage of the pipeline we'll need to extract whatever follows this string, on that line. To make things simpler, we can remove all special characters and set everything to lowercase.

Also, the location of the email (i.e. the folder it is stored in) denotes whether it is spam or not, so we can store this information in a variable (e.g. "IsSpam"). We could attempt a finer distinction of the email type by marking the normal emails "easy_ham" or "hard_ham," and naming the class variable "EmailType," though this would complicate the model later on (you are welcome to try this out, once you master the simpler approach we'll work with here).

DATA EXPLORATION

Now that we have gotten our data neatly trimmed, we can start probing it more thoroughly. To do that, we'll try out different features (e.g. number of words, length of words, the presence of particular words) and see whether they return different values across the classes (in the simplest case, between the spam and ham cases). We'll also create a variety of plots, and try to understand what the feature space looks like. In this stage we'll also look at some statistics (e.g. mean, mode, and median values) and run some tests to see if the differences we have observed are significant.

For example, if we noticed that the average length of the subject line is much greater in the spam class, we may be inclined to use that as a feature, and possibly investigate other similar features (e.g. the maximum length of the words). In this stage we may also try out various words' frequencies and remove the ones that seem to be present too often to make any difference (e.g. "a", "the"). These are often referred to as "stop words" and are an important part of text analytics.

DATA REPRESENTATION

In this part of the pipeline we'll be looking at how we can encode the information in the features in an efficient and comprehensible way. It makes sense to model all features related to countable objects as integers (e.g. the number of words in the subject), while all the features that take two values as Boolean (e.g. the presence or absence of the "RE" word), and features that may have decimal values are better off as float variables (e.g. the average number of letters in the words of the subject).

Since the counts may not yield all the gradients of the information present in a particular buzz word, we may go a step further and apply statistical methods more specific to this particular problem. For instance, we could try a Relative Risk or Odds Ratio, a couple of continuous metrics that can be derived from a contingency table. Alternatively, we can just leave the counts as they are and just normalize the features afterwards. At this stage, don't be shy about creating lots of features, since everything and anything may add value to the model. If something ends up without much use, we'll find out in the statistical tests we run.

DATA DISCOVERY

Now things will get more interesting as we delve into the information-rich aspects of the dataset. It's here that we'll be experimenting with more features, stemming from our better understanding of the dataset. It's not uncommon to use some machine learning techniques (like clustering) at this stage of the pipeline, as well as dimensionality reduction (since it's practically impossible to visualize a multidimensional dataset as it is). Using a machine learning technique may reveal that certain words tend to appear often together; this is something we could summarize in a single feature.

During the data discovery phase we'll also assess the value of the features and try to optimize our feature set, making sure that the ensuing model will be able to spot as many of the spam emails as possible. By evaluating each one of these potential features using the target variable (IsSpam) as a reference, we can decide which features are the most promising and which ones can be omitted (since they'll just add noise to the model, as in the case of the "stop words"). Once we are satisfied with what we've discovered and how we've shaped the feature set, we can move on to figuring out how all this can be summed up into a process that we can teach the computer.

DATA LEARNING

In this stage we'll put all our findings to the test and see if we can create a (usually mathematical or logical) model out of them. The idea is to teach the computer to discern spam emails from normal ones, even if such a skill is entirely mechanical and often without much interpretability.

The ability to interpret results is critical, since the project manager of the data science project has to be able to understand and convey the key elements of the model (such as the importance of specific features). Whatever the case, the model will be much more sophisticated and flexible than the strictly rule-based systems (often called "expert systems") that were the state-of-the-art a few years ago.

In the data learning stage we'll build a model (or a series of models, depending on how much time we can devote) that takes the features we created in the previous stages and use them to predict whether an email is spam, often also providing a confidence score. We'll train this model using the email data we have, helping it achieve a high level of generalization so that it can accurately apply what it has learned to other emails. This point is important because it dictates how we'll evaluate the model and use it to justify all our work. Predicting the known data perfectly is of no use, since it's unlikely that the same identical emails will reach our mailboxes again. The "true" value of the model comes when it's able to accurately identify an unfamiliar email as spam or "ham."

DATA PRODUCT CREATION

Once we're convinced that we have a viable model, we are now ready to make something truly valuable out of all this hard work. In this stage we would normally translate the model into a low-level language (usually C++ or Java), though if we implement the whole thing in Julia, that would be entirely unnecessary. This proves that Julia can provide start-to-finish solutions, saving you time and effort.

We may want to add a nice graphical interface, which can be created in any language and then linked to our Julia script. We can also create the interface in a rapid application development (RAD) platform. These platforms are high-level software development systems that make it easy to design fully functional programs, with limited or no coding. Such systems are not as sophisticated as a regular production-level programming languages, but do a very good job at creating an interface, which can then be linked to another program that will do all the heavy lifting on the back end. A couple of popular RAD platforms are Opus Pro and Neobook.

We are bound to make use of additional resources for the data product, which will usually be in a cloud environment such as AWS / S3, Azure, or even a private cloud. To do this, we will need to parallelize our code and make sure that we use all the available resources. That may not be necessary if we just need a small-scale spam-detection system. But if we are to make our product more valuable and useful to more users, we'll need to scale up sooner or later.

INSIGHT, DELIVERANCE, AND VISUALIZATION

Finally, we can now report what we've done and see if we have a convincing argument for spam detection based on our work. We'll also create some interesting visuals summarizing our model's performance and what the dataset looks like (after the data discovery stage). Naturally, we'll need to make a presentation or two, perhaps write a report about the whole project, and gracefully accept any criticism our users offer us.

Based on all of that, and on how valuable our work is to the organization that funds this project, we may need to go back to the drawing board and see how we can make the product even better. This could entail adding new features (in the business sense of the word) such as automatic reports or streaming analytics, and will most likely target improved accuracy and better performance.

Finally, at this stage we'll reflect upon the lessons learned throughout the project, trying to gain more domain knowledge from our experience. We'll also examine how all this spam-detection work has helped us detect potential weaknesses we have in the application of the whole pipeline, so that we can ultimately become better data scientists.

SUMMARY

- The end result of a data science project is either a data product (e.g. a data-driven application, a dashboard), or a set of actionable insights that provide value to the organization whose data is analyzed.

- The data science pipeline comprises seven distinct stages, grouped together into three meta-stages:

- Data Engineering:
  - o Data preparation – making sure the data is normalized, is void of missing values, and in the case of string data, doesn't contain any unnecessary characters.
  - o Data exploration – creatively playing around with the data, so that we can understand its geometry and the utility of its variables. This involves a lot of visualization.
  - o Data representation – encoding the data in the right type of variable and developing features that effectively capture the information in that data.

- Data Modeling:
  - o Data discovery – pinpointing patterns in the data, often hidden in the geometry of the feature space, through the use of statistical tests and other methods.

- Data learning – the intelligent analysis and assimilation of everything you have discovered in the previous stages, and the teaching of the computer to replicate these findings on new, unfamiliar data. Information distillation includes:
  - o Data product creation – the development of an easily accessible program (usually an API, app, or dashboard) that makes use of the model you have created.

    o   Insight-deliverance-visualization – the stage with the highest visibility, involving the communication of all the information related to the data science project, through visuals, reports, presentations, etc.

- Although the components of the data science process usually take place in sequence, you'll often need to go back and repeat certain stages in order to improve your end result.

- The completion of one data science cycle is often the beginning of a new cycle, based on the insights you have gained and the new questions that arise.

- Julia has packages for all the stages of the data science process, but if you cannot find the right tool among them, you can always develop it from scratch without compromising your system's performance.

- Although Julia can deliver every part of the data science pipeline, you can always bridge it with other programming tools, such as Python and R, if need be (see Appendix D).

- The data science process is an ever-evolving one. The steps presented here are not etched in stone. Instead, focus on the essence of data science: transforming raw data into a form that you can use to create something valuable to the end-user.

CHAPTER CHALLENGE

1. What is data engineering? Is it essential?

2. What is the importance of the data preparation stage?

3. What's the main difference between data science and other data analysis pipelines?

4. How would you perform data preparation on the following data: "The customer appeared to be dissatisfied with product 1A2345 (released last May)."

5. What does data exploration entail?

6. What are the processes involved in data representation?

7. What is included in data discovery?

8. What do we mean by data learning?

9. What is the data product creation process?

10. What takes place during the insight, deliverance, and visualization phase? How is it different from the creation of a data product?

11. Is the data science pipeline a linear flow of actions? Explain.

12. What is a data product and why is it important?

13. Give a couple of examples of data products.

14. How are the visualizations created in the final stage of the pipeline different from the ones created in the data exploration stage?

15. Are all the aspects of the pipeline essential? Why?

CHAPTER 6
Julia the Data Engineer

As we discussed in the previous chapter, data engineering encompasses the first parts of the data science pipeline, focusing on preprocessing (preparing) your data and generating features. Data engineering brings out the most information-rich aspects of your data and prepares them for further analysis. This maximizes your chances of getting some useful insights out of your process. Data engineering is extremely useful for complex or noisy data, since such data cannot be used as-is in the data analysis processes that ensue.

When engineering data, we explore datasets and develop visuals from its variables. We also statistically assess the relationships among those variables, as well as their connections with the target variable. This is a topic we'll cover in the next chapter, as it requires the use of particular packages. For now we'll focus on data preparation and data representation, which we can perform using the base package of Julia. This will also enable you to practice what you know about Julia programming and understand your data on a deeper level.

This chapter covers the following topics:

- Accessing data in additional files types, such as `.json` custom functions

- Cleaning up your data by removing invalid values and filling in missing values

- Applying advanced aspects of the Julia language, useful for more customized tasks

- Exploring various ways of data transformation

- Storing data in different file types, so that it is readily available for the stages that follow as well as for other applications.

DATA FRAMES

Data frames are popular data structures, originally introduced by the R analytics platform. Their main advantages over conventional data structures (such as matrices) are that they can handle missing values, and that they can accommodate multiple data types. An additional bonus of data frames is that the variables can be named and accessed through their names instead of numbers. This advantage applies to both variables stored in columns and to rows. Data frames are also easier to load directly from delimited files, such as .csv files, and saving them to such files is a straightforward process.

In order to work with data frames you need to add and load the corresponding package, called DataFrames, while also doing a package update, just in case:

```
In[1]: Pkg.add("DataFrames")
Pkg.update()
In[2]: using DataFrames
```

You can learn more about this useful package at its website: http://bit.ly/29dSqKP.

CREATING AND POPULATING A DATA FRAME

You can create a data frame in Julia as follows:

```
In[3]: df = DataFrame()
```

Alternatively, if you already have your data in an array format, you can put it into a data frame by doing the following:

```
df = DataFrame(A)
```

where A is the array containing the data you want to insert into the data frame.

Another way to populate a data frame is by adding DataArrays to it. A DataArray is another structure found in the DataFrames package, consisting of a one-dimensional array that has a name. Just like data frames, data arrays can include missing values. A DataArray can be constructed in a similar manner:

```
da = DataArray()
```

Or, to make it more useful, you can populate it and fill it at the same time:

```
In[4]: da = DataArray([1,2,3,4,5,6,7,8,9,10])
```

So, if you have a couple of data arrays, e.g. `da1` and `da2`, you can put them into a data frame `df` under the names `var1` and `var2` as follows:

```
In[5]: df[:var1] = da1
       df[:var2] = da2
```

The colon right before the name of each data array is an operator that tells Julia that what follows is a symbol. Whenever it sees `:var1` it will understand that you are referring to a column named `var1`. This may seem unusual at first, but it's a much more efficient way of referring to a column, than the quotes approach in the `pandas` package of Python and in Graphlab (e.g. `df["var1"]`).

DATA FRAMES BASICS

Now, let's look into how we can handle data frames effectively in order to leverage them for efficient data engineering.

Variable names in a data frame

Since having easily understood names for variables is a big selling point for data frames, let's examine this aspect first. To find out what names the variables have, you just need to apply the `names()` command:

```
In[6]: names(df)
Out[6]: 2-element Array{Symbol,1}:
     :var1
     :var2
```

After seeing the result, we realize that the names we chose for the variables are not intuitive. To change them into something more meaningful, we employ the `rename!()` command:

```
In[7]: rename!(df, [:var1, :var2], [:length, :width])
```

There is also a version of this command without the '!' part: `rename()`. This works the same way, but doesn't make any changes to the data frame it is applied on. Since it doesn't have any advantages over the command we mentioned previously, it is best to refrain from using it when working with a single data frame. Unless you want to make a copy of that data frame for some reason, it is best to use the `rename!()` command instead of `rename()`.

Upon renaming the variables of our data frame, we realize that the second variable was actually supposed to be "height," not "width." To change the name we use the `rename!()` command again, this time without the array inputs, something made possible with multiple dispatch:

```
In[8]: rename!(df, :width, :height)
```

Although this command changes the data frame in a way, it doesn't alter any of its data. We'll look at commands that change the actual content of the data frame later in this chapter.

ACCESSING PARTICULAR VARIABLES IN A DATA FRAME

To access a particular variable in our data frame `df` we simply need to reference it, just like we would reference a variable in an array. Be sure to use its name as a symbol variable, though:

```
In[9]: df[:length]
```

If the name of the variable is itself a variable, you need to convert it first using the `symbol()` function:

```
In[10]: var_name = "height"
    df[symbol(var_name)]
```

You can also refer to a given variable by number, just like in arrays. This is less practical since the column numbers are not clearly evident (you'll first need to view the data frame or run an exploratory command). However, if you have no idea how the variables are named and you just want to see whether the data frame has been populated correctly, you can use this option (e.g. `df[1]` will show you the first column and variable of data frame `df`).

EXPLORING A DATA FRAME

Once you have figured out what variables are in a data frame and have changed them into something that makes more sense to you than `X1` or `var1`, it is time to explore the actual contents of that data frame. You can do that in various ways; there is no right or wrong strategy. However, there are some commands that will come in handy regardless of your approach. First, as a data scientist, you must pay attention to the data types, which you can easily find through the following command:

```
In[11]: showcols(df)
3x2 DataFrames.DataFrame
| Col # | Name    | Eltype  | Missing |
|-------|---------|---------|---------|
| 1 | length | Int64  | 0       |
| 2 | height | Int64  | 0       |
```

This is particularly useful in large datasets with many different variables. As a bonus, you also get some metadata about the number of missing values in each variable.

In order to get a better feel for the variables, it helps to see a small sample of them, usually the first few rows. Just like in R and Python, we can view the first six rows using the `head()` command:

```
In[12]: head(df)
```

If that proves insufficient, we can take a peek at the last six rows using `tail()`, another familiar command to many R and Python users:

```
In[13]: tail(df)
```

Since that small glimpse of data may not be enough to help us understand the variables involved, we can also ask Julia for a summary of them, through the `describe()` command:

```
In[14]: describe(df)
```

What returns are a number of descriptive statistics. You could also retrieve these descriptions by examining each variable on your own, using the same command we saw in a previous chapter. But it's helpful to be able to gather this information by applying it to the data frame directly, thanks to multiple dispatch.

FILTERING SECTIONS OF A DATA FRAME

More often than not, we are more interested in a particular segment of the data frame than the entire data frame. So, just like with arrays, we must know how to select parts of a data frame. This is achieved using the same method as with arrays. The only difference is that with data frames, you can refer to the variables by name:

```
In[15]: df[1:5, [:length]]
```

The output of this will be another data frame containing the data of rows 1 and 2 for variable "length." If you omit the brackets around the variable name, e.g. df[1:2, :length], what you'll get is a data array instead. That's interesting, but the real value of filtering a data frame arises when you select rows that you don't know beforehand. Just like when filtering parts of an array, filtering a data frame is possible through the inclusion of conditionals. So, if we want to find all the cases where length is higher than 2 we type:

```
In[16]: df[df[:length] .> 2, :]
```

The colon after the comma tells Julia that you want the data from all the variables. Long expressions like this one can be somewhat challenging if you are not used to them, and may even cause errors due to typos. One good practice to simplify expressions is to introduce an index variable, say ind, that replaces the conditional. Naturally, this is going to be a binary variable, so it shouldn't take up too much memory:

```
In[17]: ind = df[:length] .> 2
        df[ind, :]
```

APPLYING FUNCTIONS TO A DATA FRAME'S VARIABLES

If you want to apply a certain function to a single variable, just apply it to the corresponding data array, exactly how you would if you were dealing with a regular array. If your target is a series of variables or the whole data frame, then the `colwise()` command is what you need:

```
In[18]: colwise(maximum, df)
```

If `df` had a bunch of variables and you wanted to apply a function, say `var()`, to only length and height, then you would proceed as follows:

```
In[19]: colwise(mean, df[[:length, :height]])
```

Applying a function to a data frame does not change the data frame itself. If you want the changes to be permanent you'll need to take an additional step and assign the result of the `colwise()` function to the variables involved.

WORKING WITH DATA FRAMES

Now that we've learned the basics of data frames, let's see how we can use them to better understand our data. To start, let's try using data frames to handle more challenging cases where there is some data missing from the dataset at hand.

Finding that your data has missing values is a major pain, but it's a common phenomenon that needs to be addressed. Fortunately, data frames are well-equipped to help. As such, the `DataFrames` package has a data type dedicated to them: `NA` (standing for Not Applicable or Not Available). These `NA`s, even if they are few, can cause some serious issues, since no operations you apply to the corresponding variables will work:

```
In[20]: df[:weight] = DataArray([10,20,-1,15,25,5,10,20,-1,5])
        df[df[:weight] .== -1,:weight] = NA
        mean(df[:weight])
Out[20]: NA
```

This code returns an `NA` because `mean()` cannot handle data arrays with missing values, leading them to taint the whole array. To get rid of missing values, you must either replace them with something meaningful (in the context of the data type of the variable where they are present), or delete the rows where they are present. You could also delete the whole variable, if the missing values are the majority of its elements, but not without loss of some signal in the dataset.

The most effective strategy is to replace the missing values with something that makes sense, such as the median, mean, or mode of that variable. In order to do this, we first need to spot the missing values (marked as NAs) in the data frame, which is made possible using the isna() function:

```
In[21]: isna(df[:weight])
Out[21]: 10-element BitArray{1}:
    false
    false
    true
    false
    false
    false
    false
    false
    true
    false
```

To make the result more intuitive, we can use isna() in combination with the find() function:

```
In[22]: find(isna(df[:weight]))
Out[22]: 2-element Array{Int64,1}:
    3
    9
```

So, we discover that we have missing values in rows 3 and 9. Now we're ready to replace them with something else. The best choice is usually the mean of the variable (for classification problems, we would take into account the class each one of these values belongs to). To ensure that the type of the variable is maintained, we will need to round it off, and convert it into an Int64:

```
In[23]: m = round(Int64,mean(df[!isna(df[:weight]), :weight]))
In[24]: df[isna(df[:weight]), :weight] = m
```

```
     show(df[:weight])
[10,20,14,15,25,5,10,20,14,5]
```

ALTERING DATA FRAMES

As we said earlier, there's an alternative method for dealing with missing values: deleting the entire row or column. This strategy is less desirable than simply filling in missing values, because the columns or rows in question may still contain valuable data. However, if you do need to make alterations to data frames (for this or any other reason), it can be done easily using the `delete!()` command:

```
In[25]: delete!(df, :length)
```

If you want to meddle with the rows, use the `push!()` and `@data()` commands:

```
In[26]: push!(df, @data([6, 15]))
```

With this command we've just added another data point having `length` = 6 and `weight` = 15. Although arrays can't handle `NAs` (a type that only works with `DataFrame` and `DataArray` objects), you can still use them with `@data()`.

If you wish to delete certain rows, you can do that using the `deleterows!()` command:

```
In[27]: deleterows!(df, 9:11)
```

Alternatively, you can use an array of indexes instead of a range, which has its own advantages:

```
In[28]: deleterows!(df, [1, 2, 4])
```

SORTING THE CONTENTS OF A DATA FRAME

One way to look at data frames is like tables in a database. As such, it is usually handy to apply some ordering operations to them, making their data more readily available. A couple of functions that are particularly useful for this task are `by()` and `sort!()`. The former groups the unique values of a given variable, putting them in ascending order and counting how many instances of each value exist in the data frame. It is often used in combination with the function `nrow()`, which creates a new row in a data frame. For example:

```
In[29]: by(df, :weight, nrow)
Out[29]:
     weight x1
 1    5      1
 2    10     1
 3    14     1
 4    20     1
 5    25     1
```

If you wish to order all the elements of a data frame based on a variable (or a combination of variables), the `sort!()` command is what you are looking for:

```
In[30]: sort!(df, cols = [order(:height), order(:weight)])
```

This code takes data frame `df` and sorts all its elements based on their height values and then on their weight. As there are no duplicates in the height variable, the second part of the ordering is redundant in this case, though it may be useful for a larger sample of this dataset.

DATA FRAME TIPS

Another interesting kind of data frame is the `SFrame`, a scalable tabular and graph data structure developed by Turi Inc. (formerly known as Dato) and used in the Graphlab big data platform. `SFrames` are designed to handle very large datasets outside the computer's memory. Using a native hard disk, they allow for scalable data analytics on both conventional table-based and graphical data. Although still experimental in Julia, `SFrames` are worth keeping in mind, as they are very versatile and can allow for seamless data transfer among various platforms. Should you wish to try them out in Julia, you can do so by using the `SFrames` package found at http://bit.ly/29dV7fy.

Although data frames have proven popular since their initial release (particularly among statisticians), they don't always offer a significant advantage over analytics work. So if you are working with a new data processing algorithm, you may still need to use conventional arrays. Also, arrays tend to be faster than data frames. If you need to do a lot of looping, you may want to steer away from data frames or use them in combination with arrays, so that you get the best of both worlds.

Data frames are particularly useful when loading or saving data, especially when dealing with missing values. We will look into how you can incorporate data frames in your IO processes in the next section.

IMPORTING AND EXPORTING DATA

ACCESSING .JSON DATA FILES

In Chapter 2 we saw how we could load data from `.csv`, `.txt`, and `.jld` files. However, we often need to access semi-structured data that is in other data formats. One such data format is `.json` and it's widely used for storing all kinds of data across different applications. You can load the data from a `.json` file into a variable X using the JSON package:

```
In[31]: Pkg.add("JSON")
In[32]: import JSON
In[33]: f = open("file.json")
        X = JSON.parse(f)
        close(f)
```

Note that we could have typed "`using JSON`" instead of "`import JSON`", something that would also work, but it's best to avoid that option as there is conflict among some of its functions with functions of the Base package. Also, the variable containing the parsed `.json` file is a dictionary, something that makes sense since `.json` is a dictionary structure too. Moreover, the `parse()` function of the JSON package also can be applied to a string containing the `.json` contents.

STORING DATA IN .JSON FILES

Because your data will usually be in tables, saving it to a `.json` file isn't something you will regularly want to do. But if the need should ever arise, Julia has this option for you. Apply the following code to export the dictionary variable X as a .json file:

```
In[34]: f = open("test.json", "w")
        JSON.print(f, X)
        close(f)
```

The test.json file that is created is bound to look different than the file.json file we used earlier. The reason is that the JSON package exports data in a compact format, omitting all extra spaces and new line characters that you would normally see in a data file. You can read about this package at http://bit.ly/29mk8Ye.

LOADING DATA FILES INTO DATA FRAMES

Data frames and data files are intimately related, so converting one to the other is a straightforward process. If you want to load data from a file into a data frame, your best bet is the readtable() command:

```
In[35]: df = readtable("CaffeineForTheForce.csv")
```

If you know how the missing values are denoted in the data file and you want to save some time, you can take care of them while loading the dataset into a data frame, using the following:

```
df = readtable("CaffeineForTheForce.csv", nastrings = ["N/A", "-",
    ""])
```

This command will load the Caffeine for the Force dataset, taking into account that missing values are represented as one or more of the following strings: "N/A", "-", "" (empty string).

You can load all kinds of delimited files into a data frame using the command readtable().

SAVING DATA FRAMES INTO DATA FILES

If you want to save data from a data frame into a file, the command you are looking for is writetable():

```
In[36]: writetable("dataset.csv", df)
```

This command saves our data frame `df` into a delimited file called `dataset.csv`. We can use the same command to save it in another format, without any additional parameters:

```
In[37]: writetable("dataset.tsv", df)
```

You can see that the new file has tab-separated values. Unfortunately, the `DataFrames` package has a limited range of delimited files, so if you try to save your data frame as something it doesn't recognize, it will export it as a `.csv`.

CLEANING UP DATA

To clean up data, you must address certain parts that don't fit or create gaps in your data structures (usually arrays or data frames). The first thing to do is take care of the missing values as we saw earlier in the chapter. Beyond that, depending on the data type, you can clean up your data in different ways.

CLEANING UP NUMERIC DATA

Cleaning up numeric data involves examining outliers: those nasty data points that usually have an extreme value in one or more of the variables, and an extreme capacity to mess up your models. Exterminating extreme values in a variable can be very helpful, especially when employing distance-based models. Even though sophisticated techniques like Deep Networks and Extreme Learning Machines are practically immune to outliers, it is good practice to handle them at this stage since a well-engineered dataset allows for a more versatile data modeling phase.

Outliers are an elusive kind of abnormality, not as clear-cut as missing values. Even after years of evolution of data analytics methods, there is still no foolproof approach to identifying them and no consensus as to whether we should eliminate them at all. That's because certain outliers may actually contain important information and should therefore not be ignored (it was the unconscious elimination of outliers, after all, that caused the hole in the ozone layer to remain undetected for a while).

Let's look at how we can find these outliers and then decide whether we ought to eliminate them (or replace them with some other value that makes more sense, as it is often the case). The process is relatively simple; all variables follow a certain distribution (which may or may not coincide with the familiars from statistics theory). So, certain values are more likely to be found than others, depending on the form of that distribution. If a particular value is extremely unlikely to be found (say less than 1% likely), then it qualifies as an outlier.

If we have a series of numeric variables, it makes sense to take into account all of the normalized variables together, when looking for outliers. We'll examine this process in the next section. For now, let's just pinpoint the extreme values for an individual variable. Check out the corresponding section in the "Caffeine for the Force" case study, where several outliers are pinpointed.

Once an outlier is identified, it is often replaced with something else, such as the maximum or minimum value of that variable. If it appears that none of these are meaningful (e.g. we decide that the outlier is probably due to some typo), we can also treat it as a missing value and replace it with the mean or median of that variable. In the case of a classification problem, it is useful to take into account the class of that data point before replacing its value. If we have a lot of data, it is not uncommon to get rid of that data point altogether. See the "Caffeine for the Force" case study for examples of how outliers are handled in the corresponding dataset.

CLEANING UP TEXT DATA

Cleaning up text data is fairly straightforward, but rather time-consuming. The idea is to remove "irrelevant" characters from the text, including but not limited to the following:

- Punctuation marks

- Numbers

- Symbols ("+", "*", "<", etc.)

- Extra white spaces

- Special characters ("@", "~", etc.).

Depending on the application, you may also want to remove words that don't appear in the dictionary, names, stop words, or anything else that isn't relevant to the problem you are trying to solve.

One efficient way of stripping a given text (stored in variable S) of most of the irrelevant characters is the following:

```
In[38]: Z = ""
    for c in S
     if lowercase(c) in "qwertyuiopasdfghjklzxcvbnm "
       Z = string(Z,c)
     end
    end
```

The result of the above snippet, variable Z, is a string variable stripped of all characters that are not in the alphabet and are not spaces. This may not be perfect (duplicate spaces may still be present, along with other undesirable character patterns), but it's a good start. In the next section we'll see how we can make the text data even more useful by applying normalization.

FORMATTING AND TRANSFORMING DATA

A clean dataset is much more usable, but it's still not entirely ready (although you could use it as-is in a model). To further polish it we must format it, which can save a lot of valuable resources. To format your dataset you must examine each one of its variables and determine the appropriate strategy depending on what kind of data it contains. Once the formatting is done, you'll often need to make some transformations (e.g. normalize the data) to ensure a cleaner signal. Let's look at each one of these steps, for the different types of data, in more detail.

FORMATTING NUMERIC DATA

Formatting numeric data is simple. Basically, you need to decide which data type best encapsulates the nature of the variables involved, and apply this type to each one of them. Doing so is a matter of intuition and domain knowledge. A good statistics book can get you started. Once you decide on the type of a numeric variable you need to format it accordingly. The Julia command `convert()` will do just that:

```
In[39]: x = [1.0, 5.0, 3.0, 78.0, -2.0, -54.0]
    x = convert(Array{Int8}, x)
      show(x)
      Int8[1,5,3,78,-2,-54]
```

In this example, Julia takes an array of floats and formats it as an array of 8-bit integers. You could always use other kinds of integers too, depending on your particular data. For instance, if you think this variable may take values larger than 128, you may want to use Int16 or higher. Whatever the case, float may not be the best type since none of the elements of that variable seem to have a value that cannot be expressed as an integer. If, however, you plan to perform distance calculations with this data, you may want to keep the float type and just reduce the bandwidth used:

```
In[40]: x = convert(Array{Float16}, x)
```

FORMATTING TEXT DATA

The main method of formatting text data is to convert it to the appropriate string subtype. Specifically, you'll need to decide whether your text data is going to be encoded. Using the default string type, `AbstractString`, usually works well with all your text manipulation applications.

In the rare occasions when you must analyze individual characters, you need to convert your data into the `Char` type. Keep in mind, though, that a `Char` variable can only contain a single character. More often than not you'll use `Char` as part of an array (i.e. `Array{Char}`). It's important to remember that even if the contents of a string variable of length 1 match exactly with a particular `Char` variable, Julia will never see them as the same thing:

```
In[41]: 'c' == "c"
Out[41]: false
```

So, if you wish to avoid confusions and errors, you may want to employ the `convert()` function accordingly:

```
convert(Char, SomeSingleCharacterString)
```

Or, in the opposite case:

```
convert(AbstractString, SomeCharacterVariable)
```

Fortunately, `string()` has been designed more carefully; when you need to aggregate string variables, you can use any combination of `AbstractString` variables (or any of its subtypes) and `Char` variables.

IMPORTANCE OF DATA TYPES

Although we talked about this in Chapter 2, it cannot be stressed enough that data types need to be chosen carefully, particularly when dealing with large data sets. An incorrect data type may waste valuable resources (especially RAM). That's the best case scenario, since an incorrect data type may yield some strange errors or exceptions, resulting in a waste of another valuable resource: time. So, be mindful when choosing types for your dataset's variables. A set of well-defined variables can go a long way.

APPLYING DATA TRANSFORMATIONS TO NUMERIC DATA

One arena where Julia excels is numeric computations, which form the core of data transformations (keep in mind that string variables can be seen as numbers coded in a particular way). Data transformations are a core part of data engineering as well, which is why Julia often doubles as a data engineer.

This is important to keep in mind because it weakens the argument that Julia isn't useful in data science because it doesn't have enough mature packages. Those who make this argument ignore the fact that a large part of data science involves tasks that don't need packages. Julia proves them wrong by being adept at numeric computations, and by gradually growing its package spectrum. Data transformation is at the core of all this.

There are several data transformation tasks that are applicable to numeric variables. Here we'll focus on the most important ones: normalization, discretization or binarization, and making a binary variable continuous.

NORMALIZATION

This process involves taking a variable and transforming it in such a way that its elements are not too large or too small compared to other variables' elements. Statisticians love this data transformation because it often makes use of statistical techniques. However, it is much deeper than it is often portrayed in statistics books.

A good normalization will allow for the development of several new features (e.g. `log(x)`, `1/x`) that can significantly enhance the performance of basic classifiers or regressors. These features may or may not be possible using the conventional normalization techniques, depending on the data at hand. Regardless, these normalization techniques can improve your dataset, especially if you are planning to use distance-based methods or polynomial models.

There are three main normalization techniques used in data science, each of which has its advantages and drawbacks:

1. Max-min normalization. This approach is fairly straightforward and it's computationally cheap. It involves transforming a variable to [0, 1], using its maximum and minimum values as boundaries. The main issue with this method is that if there are outliers in the variables, all of the values of the normalized variable are clustered together. A typical implementation in Julia is:

```
norm_x = (x - minimum(x)) / (maximum(x) - minimum(x))
```

2. Mean-standard deviation normalization. This is the most common approach, and it's also relatively computationally cheap. It makes use of the mean and the standard deviation as its parameters and yields values that are centered around 0 and not too far from it (usually they are in the area -3 to 3, though there are no fixed extreme values in the normalized variable). The main drawback of this method is that it yields negative values, making the normalized variable incompatible with certain transformations like `log(x)`. There are also no fixed boundaries for the normalized variable. Here is how you can implement it in Julia:

```
norm_x = (x - mean(x)) / std(x)
```

3. Sigmoidal normalization. This is an interesting approach that is more computationally expensive than the others. It is immune to outliers and yields values in (0, 1). However, depending on the data, it may yield a clustered normalized variable. With the proper parameters it can yield a virtually perfect normalized variable that is both meaningful and applicable for other transformations (e.g. `log(x)`). Finding these parameters, however, involves advanced data analytics that are way beyond the scope of this book. Its more basic implementation is straightforward in Julia:

```
norm_x = 1 ./ (1 + exp(-x))
```

Whichever normalization method you choose, it is good practice to make a note of it, along with the parameters used whenever applicable (e.g. in the mean-standard deviation normalization, note the mean and standard values you used in the transformation). This way, you can apply the same transformation to new data as it becomes available and merge it smoothly with your normalized dataset.

DISCRETIZATION (BINNING) AND BINARIZATION

Continuous variables are great, but sometimes it makes sense to turn them into ordinal ones, or even a set of binary variables. Imagine for example a variable that is brimming with missing values or a variable whose values are polarized (this is often the case with variables stemming from certain questionnaires). In such cases the additional detail that the continuous variable provides is not helpful. If a variable age has values that are clustered around 20, 45, and 60, you might as well treat it as a trinary variable age_new having the values young, middle_aged, and mature.

Turning a continuous variable into an ordinal one is a process called discretization, or binning (since all the values of the variable are put into several bins). One place where this process is utilized is the creation of a histogram, which will be covered in the next chapter.

To perform discretization you merely need to define the boundaries of each new value. So, in the previous example with the age variable, you can say that anyone with age <= 30 is young, anyone with age > 55 is mature, and anyone else is middle_aged. The exact values of the boundaries are something you can figure out from your data. In general, for N bins, you'll need N-1 boundary values, which don't have to follow any particular pattern.

Turning a discreet variable into a set of binary ones is an equally straightforward process. You just need to create one binary variable for each value of the discreet one (though you can actually omit the last binary variable if you want, since it doesn't yield any additional information). For example, in the previous case of the age_new variable, you can turn it into a set of 3 binary ones, is_young, is_middle_aged, and is_mature:

```
In[42]: age_new = ["young", "young", "mature", "middle-aged",
    "mature"]
    is_young = (age_new .== "young")
    is_middle_aged = (age_new .== "middle-aged")
    is_mature = (age_new .== "mature")
    show(is_young)

    Bool[true,true,false,false,false]
```

You could also handle missing values this way:

```
In[43]: age_new = ["young", "young", "", "mature", "middle-aged",
    "", "NA",
```

```
          "mature", ""]
          is_missing = (age_new .== "") | (age_new .== "NA")
          show(is_missing)

          Bool[false,false,true,false,false,false,true]
```

If there are several ways that a missing value is denoted, you can put them all in an array `NA_denotations` and use the following code for the missing values variable instead:

```
  is_missing = [age_value in NA_denotations for age_value in age_new]
```

BINARY TO CONTINUOUS (BINARY CLASSIFICATION ONLY)

Sometimes we need more granularity but all we have is a bunch of binary variables (these are usually variables that came from the original data, not from another continuous variable). Fortunately, there are ways to turn a binary variable into a continuous one—at least for a certain kind of problem where we need to predict a binary variable. These are often referred to as "binary classification problems".

The most popular method to turn a binary variable into a continuous one is the relative risk transformation (for more information, see http://bit.ly/29tudWw). Another approach that's somewhat popular is the odd-ratio (for details, see http://bit.ly/29voj4m). We'll leave the implementation part of these methods as an exercise for you. (Hint: create a table containing all four possible combinations of the binary variable you want to transform and the class variable.)

APPLYING DATA TRANSFORMATIONS TO TEXT DATA

When it comes to text data, Julia proves itself to be equally adept at performing transformations. In particular, you can change the case of the text (lower or upper case), and also turn the whole thing into a vector. Let's look into each one of these processes in more detail.

CASE NORMALIZATION

In common text, character case fluctuates often, making it difficult to work with. The most popular way to tackle this is through case normalization, i.e. changing all the characters of the text into the same case. Usually we choose to normalize everything to lower case, since it's been proven to be easier to read. Happily, Julia has a built-in function for that–we've seen it a couple of times already:

```
In[44]: S_new = lowercase(S)
Out[44]: "mr. smith is particularly fond of product #2235; what a
        surprise!"
```

Should you want to normalize everything to upper case instead, you can use the `uppercase()` function. Non-alphabetic characters are left untouched, making `lowercase()` and `uppercase()` a couple of versatile functions.

VECTORIZATION

Vectorization has nothing to do with the performance-improving vectorization performed in R, Matlab, and the like. In fact, in Julia it's best to avoid this practice since it doesn't help at all (it's much faster to use a for-loop instead). The vectorization we deal with here involves transforming a series of elements in a text string (or a "bag of words") into a relatively sparse vector of 1s and 0s (as well as a Boolean or a BitArray vector). Although this practice may take its toll on memory resources, it is essential for any kind of text analytics work.

Let's take a simple dataset comprising four sentences and see how it can be vectorized:

```
In[45]: X = ["Julia is a relatively new programming language",
        "Julia can be used in data science", "Data science is used to
        derive insights from data", "Data is often noisy"]
```

The first step is to construct the vocabulary of this dataset:

```
In[46]: temp = [split(lowercase(x), " ") for x in X]
    vocabulary = unique(temp[1])
    for T in temp[2:end]
     vocabulary = union(vocabulary, T)
```

```
end
vocabulary = sort(vocabulary)
N = length(vocabulary)
show(vocabulary)

SubString{ASCIIString}["a","be","can","data","derive","from","i
n",
"insights","is","julia","language","new","noisy","often",
"programming","relatively","science","to","used"]
```

Next we need to create a matrix for the vectorized results and populate it, using this vocabulary:

```
In[47]: n = length(X)
    VX = zeros(Int8, n, N) # Vectorized X
    for i = 1:n
     temp = split(lowercase(X[i]))
     for T in temp
       ind = find(T .== vocabulary)
       VX[i,ind] = 1
     end
    end
    println(VX)
    Int8[1 0 0 0 0 0 0 0 1 1 1 1 0 0 1 1 0 0 0
      0 1 1 1 0 0 1 0 0 1 0 0 0 0 0 0 1 0 1
      0 0 0 1 1 1 0 1 1 0 0 0 0 0 0 0 1 1 1
      0 0 0 1 0 0 0 0 1 0 0 0 1 1 0 0 0 0 0]
```

Here we chose 8-bit Integers as the type for the output, but we could have gone with Bool or BitArray if we preferred. Also, we could have removed some stop-words from the vocabulary, in order to make the whole process and the end result a bit lighter (and potentially more useful).

The vectorized representation of our text array x is a relatively compact (dense) matrix VX. That's because the vocabulary size is small (just 19 words). In most real-world problems, though, the number of words in a vocabulary is significantly larger; this will generate a huge matrix VX which will be sparse (i.e. the majority of its elements will be zeros). To remedy this, we often employ some kind of factorization or feature selection.

PRELIMINARY EVALUATION OF FEATURES

Feature evaluation is a fascinating part of data analytics, as it provides you with priceless insight regarding the value of individual features. In essence, feature evaluation serves as a valuable proxy for their predictive potential, by providing you with an intuitive measure of how useful they are going to be in predictive models. This is something useful to know, especially if you plan to use computationally expensive methods in the stages that follow. The method we use to evaluate features greatly depends on the problem at hand–particularly on the nature of the target variable. So, we'll tackle feature evaluation in the case of both a continuous target variable (as in regression problems) and a discreet one (as in classification problems).

REGRESSION

For regression problems there are two main ways to evaluate a feature:

- Examine the absolute value of the coefficient of a regression model, such as linear regression, support vector machine (SVM), or a decision tree

- Calculate the absolute value of the correlation of that feature with the target variable (particularly the rank-based correlation).

The higher each one of these two values is, the better the feature in general.

CLASSIFICATION

Here the feature evaluation gets a bit trickier, since there is no universally agreed-upon way to perform classification. There are a plethora of methods to accurately evaluate a classification feature, the most important of which are the following:

- **Index of Discernibility.** This metric was developed especially for this purpose. Although it was originally created to assess whole datasets, it also works well with individual features and all kinds of classification problems. It takes values in [0, 1] and is distance-based. The publicly available versions of this metric are the Spherical Index of Discernibility (original metric), the Harmonic Index of Discernibility (simpler and somewhat faster), and the Distance-based Index of Discernibility (much faster and more scalable).

- **Fisher's Discriminant Ratio**. This metric is related to linear discriminant analysis, and also doubles as a feature evaluation measure. It works with individual features only and is easy to compute.

- **Similarity index**. This simple metric works with discreet features only. It takes values in [0, 1] and is very quick to calculate.

- **Jaccard Similarity**. This simple yet robust metric is also applicable to discreet features only. It takes values in [0, 1], is quick to compute, and focuses on an individual class of the target variable.

- **Mutual Information**. This is a well-researched metric for both discreet and continuous variables. It yields positive values and is fast to compute (though its use on continuous variables is not as easy, since it involves complex intervals). It's also simple to normalize it so that it yields values [0, 1].

Although uncommon, it is possible to combine a pair (or more) of these metrics for a more robust evaluation of a feature. If you want to evaluate feature combos to see how well they work together, your only option is the Index of Discernibility.

FEATURE EVALUATION TIPS

Whichever metric you choose, keep in mind that although a feature's estimated value is a proxy to its performance, it is not absolute. Poor features have been proven to be essential for robust classifications, as they seem to fill the information gaps of other features. So, no feature evaluation metric can be 100% accurate in predicting a feature's value in practice. However, you can effectively use feature evaluation to eliminate the obviously useless features from your dataset, conserving resources and making the stages that follow easier.

SUMMARY

- Data engineering is an essential part of the data science pipeline, and although it can be time-consuming and monotonous, it can save you a lot of time in the long run.

- Data frames are popular data structures that can handle missing values (represented as NA) effectively, using the `isna()` function to identify them. It's also easy to load data into them, using the `readtable()` command, as well as to save them into delimited files, using the `writetable()` function.

- Accessing data from `.json` files can be accomplished using the JSON package and its `parse()` command. You can create a `.json` file using the `print()` command of the same package. Data extracted from a `.json` file is made available as a dictionary object.

- Cleaning up data is a complex process comprising the following elements, depending on the sort of data we have:
    - **Numeric data:** eliminate missing values, handle outliers.
    - **Text data:** remove unnecessary characters, remove stop words (in the case of text analytics).

- Formatting data (casting each variable as the most suitable type) is important as it saves memory resources and helps prevent errors later on.

- Transformations are commonplace in data engineering and depend on the kind of data at hand:
    - **Numeric data:** normalization (making all features of comparable size), discretization (making a continuous feature discreet), binarization (turning a discreet feature into a set of binary ones), and making a binary feature continuous (for binary classification problems only).
    - **Text data:** case normalization (making all characters lower or upper case) and vectorization (turning text into binary arrays).
- Feature evaluation is essential in understanding the dataset at hand. Depending on the type of modeling that you plan to do afterwards, there are

different strategies for accomplishing feature evaluation, the most important of which are:

- o Index of Discernibility – continuous features.
- o Fisher's Discriminant Ratio – continuous features.
- o Similarity Index – discreet features.
- o Jaccard Similarity – discreet features.
- o Mutual Information – both discreet and continuous features.

CHAPTER CHALLENGE

1. What is the importance of data engineering in a data science project?

2. What are the main advantages of data frames over matrices?

3. How can you import data from a `.json` file?

4. Suppose you have to do some engineering work on a data file that is larger than your machine's memory. How would you go about doing this?

5. What does data cleaning entail?

6. Why are data types important in data engineering?

7. How would you transform numeric data so that all the variables are comparable in terms of values?

8. What data types in Julia would you find most useful when dealing with a text analytics problem?

9. Suppose you have some text data that you are in the process of engineering. Each record has a string variable containing the presence or not of certain key words and key phrases. How would you save that file efficiently so that you could use it in the future and also share it with the engineering team?

10. How would you evaluate the features in the `OnlineNewsPopularity` dataset? What about the ones in the `Spam` dataset?

Once the data has been molded into shape, you can now explore the dataset. Exploring allows you to get to know the pieces of information that lurk underneath the surface of noise that often plagues datasets. After some inevitable detective work (which is part of the data exploration process), you may begin to forge some features along the way, enriching your dataset and making things a bit more interesting.

Yet before you can create anything, you must first "listen" to the data, trying to discern the signals that are there and form a mental map of the data terrain that you will be working with. All this will not only give a good perspective of the dataset, but will enable you to make better guesses about what features to create, what models to use, and where to spend more time, making the whole process more efficient.

In this chapter we'll examine how we can use descriptive statistics, plots, and more advanced statistics (especially hypothesis testing) to obtain useful insights that will shape our strategy for analytics.

LISTENING TO THE DATA

"Listening" to the data involves examining your variables, spotting potential connections among them, and performing comparisons where you see fit. This may sound like an irksome task but it doesn't have to be. In fact, most seasoned data scientists consider this one of the most creative parts of the data science process. That's probably because it involves both analytical (mainly statistical) and visual processes. Whatever the case, all this work will naturally pique your curiosity, leading you to ask some questions about the data. Some of these questions will find their way into scientific processing, giving rise to hypothesis formulation and testing, which is another essential part of data exploration.

This process is not as simple as it may seem. Data exploration starts with observation of what's there, followed by searching for things that are not apparent. This paves the way for data discovery, which we will examine in detail in later chapters. For now, let us focus on the main aspects of data exploration: descriptive statistics, hypothesis testing, visualization, and fitting everything together in a case study.

The purpose of all this, as we saw in Chapter 5, is to get some idea of what the dataset's signals are like, and what we will be able to do with them. Also, it will give us an opportunity to assess the quality of the variables and see what we can work with in the subsequent stages.

PACKAGES USED IN THIS CHAPTER

Before we begin, let's look at the packages we will be using in this chapter: `StatsBase` (for Statistics), `Gadfly` (for all the visuals), and `HypothesisTests` (a great statistical package specializing in hypothesis tests, currently the only one on its category). You can delve deeper into `HypothesisTests` here: http://bit.ly/29f0hb6. Install all these packages and load them into memory. Each package will allow us to perform one of the aforementioned tasks.

```
In[1]: Pkg.add("StatsBase")
    Pkg.add("Gadfly")
    Pkg.add("HypothesisTests")
In[2]: using StatsBase
    using Gadfly
    using HypothesisTests
    using DataFrames
```

We encourage you to check out the references on the footnotes for each one of the new packages, to get a better feel for what they enable you to do. After working through the material in this chapter, you can also check out the examples on each package's webpage. These will familiarize you with all of their different parameters, which is a task beyond the scope of this book.

COMPUTING BASIC STATISTICS AND CORRELATIONS

Let's begin our data exploration endeavors by doing some basic statistics and correlations on one of our datasets. For our examples we'll make use of the `magic` dataset introduced in Chapter 2. Let's start by importing its data from its `.csv` file to a matrix called `X`:

```
In[3]: X = readcsv("magic04.csv")
```

Just like in the previous chapters, we invite you to execute all the code of this chapter in IJulia, although you can run it on any other IDE, or even the REPL, depending on your programming experience.

As you may remember from Chapter 2, this dataset comprises eleven variables: ten continuous (the inputs) and one binary (the target). Also, the `.csv` file has no headers. First, we need to do some basic pre-processing on the data so that Julia can recognize it for what it is: a series of numeric variables (in this case, the inputs) and a categorical one (in this case, the target). While we are at it, let's split the dataset into input and output arrays (let's call them `I` and `O`) so that they look something like this:

```
I Array:
28.7967    17.0021     2.6449      0.3918      0.1982      27.7004
    22.011     -8.2027     40.092      81.8828
31.6036    11.7235     2.5185      0.5303      0.3773      27.2722
    23.8238     -9.9574     7.3609      205.261
162.052    137.031     4.0612      0.0374      0.0187      117.741
    -64.858     -45.216     77.96 257.788
23.8172    9.5728      2.3385      0.6147      0.3922      27.2107
    -7.4633     -7.1513     10.449      117.737
75.1362    30.9205     3.1611      0.3168      0.1832      -5.5277
    28.5525     21.8393     4.648 357.462
O Array:
g
```

```
g
g
g
g
```

You can accomplish this by running the snippet in listing 7.1.

```
In[4]: N, n = size(X)                    #1
    I = Array(Float64, N, n-1)
    O = X[:, end]
    for j = 1:(n-1)
      for i = 1:N
    I[i,j] = Float64(X[i,j])         #2
      end
    end
#1 Get the dimensions of the X Array (N = rows / data points, n =
    columns / features)
#2 Transform the data in the X Array into Floats
```

Listing 7.1 Preparing the data of magic for exploration.

VARIABLE SUMMARY

Looking at this data doesn't tell you much, apart from the fact that there are no missing values and that the inputs are floats. It does, however, lead to some questions about the data. What is the center point of each variable? What is its dispersion like? What is the shape of the distribution it follows? How are the variables related to each other? To answer these questions we need to employ a couple of basic statistics techniques, namely the variable summary and the correlations matrix. Once the answers are obtained, you'll be prepared to deal with the data in an effective and more meaningful way.

You can get a summary of the variables of the dataset using the following command:

```
describe(x)
```

where x is an array or a DataArray/DataFrame structure (either a particular variable of your dataset or the whole dataset). This command will display a list of descriptive statistics: the mean, the median, the maximum, the minimum, etc.

Let's apply describe() to each one of the input variables of magic as follows:

```
In[5]: for i = 1:size(I,2)
           describe(I[:,i])
       end
```

As the target variable is of the character type, there isn't much that describe() can do for you. In fact, it's going to throw an error, since the corresponding method does not handle character variables (you could, however, transform it into a discreet numeric one, if you want to be able to calculate descriptive stats on it). We could transform 0 to a type that describe() will work with, but this wouldn't be as meaningful. For example, what would a mean value of 0.5 for the target variable tell you about that variable? Not much.

It is clear that the majority of the variables in this dataset possess a positive skewness (you can cross-check that by running the skewness_type() function we built in Chapter 3, in which case you'd get a series of "positive" strings as your output). To have a more accurate estimate of this you can use the function skewness() on any one of these variables. For the first variable you could type:

```
In[6]: println(skewness(I[:,1]))
```

You can get the same information provided by describe() using another function called summarystats(). The only difference is that the latter produces an object where all this information is stored (this object is of SummaryStats type, in case you are wondering). This may be useful if you wish to reference a particular stat of a variable. Say that you wish to use the mean of the first variable of the input data, for example:

```
In[7]: summarystats(I[:,1]).mean
```

Note that `summarystats()` works only on array structures, so if you want to apply it on a `DataArray`, you will need to convert it to an array first using the following general command:

```
convert(Array, DataFrameName[:VariableName])
```

It doesn't take a seasoned data scientist to see that the data here is all over the place and that it could use some normalizing. However, this shouldn't affect our exploration; the inherent patterns of the variables, as they are expressed in correlation-like metrics, are numeric variables that have nothing to do with the nature of the original variables explored.

CORRELATIONS AMONG VARIABLES

The famous adage that "less is more" is also applicable in data science, especially when it comes to datasets. This is because redundant features frequently exist. One of the most common ways of picking them out is by exploring the relationships among the variables of the dataset. To make this happen you need to apply a correlation measure.

Pearson's correlation r (also known as correlation coefficient ϱ) is by far the most popular tool for this. Although Julia is familiar with it, you may need a refresher. If that's the case, you can check out this great webpage that describes it thoroughly: http://bit.ly/29to3US. Here's the tool in action:

```
cor(x,y)
```

  where x and y are arrays of the same dimensionality.

```
cor(X)
```

  where X is the whole dataset (`Array{T, 2}`, where `T <: Number`).

So, for our case, we'd get the following output when applying `cor()` to our input data:

```
In[8]: C = cor(I)
```

You could also print the result in the console using `println(cor(I))` but the corresponding output isn't particularly easy to understand. Despite its popularity, Pearson correlation leaves a lot to be desired (unless you are dealing with tidy data, following closely some distribution). Its biggest issue is that it is heavily affected by outliers in the dataset, while it doesn't handle logarithmic data well.

On the plus side, it is fast, and unless you are a mathematician, you don't take correlations at face value anyway (they are more like guidelines than anything else). A couple of interesting alternatives to Pearson's correlation, designed to tackle data regardless of its distribution makeup, are the following:

- Spearman's rank correlation, typed as `corspearman(x,y)`. For more information, check out this webpage: http://bit.ly/29mcSwn

- Kandell's tau rank correlation, typed as `corkendall(x,y)`. For more information, see: http://bit.ly/29pJztd.

Pairs of variables that you find to be strongly correlated with each other (such as 1 and 2, 3 and 4, 4 and 5, etc.) will require special consideration later on, as you may want to remove one of the variables within each pair. Usually correlations that have an absolute value of 0.7 or more are considered strong.

All these correlation metrics apply to continuous variables. For nominal variables, you must apply a different kind of metric (once each variable is converted into a binary variable). A couple such metrics are the Similarity Index or Simple Matching Coefficient (http://bit.ly/29nneL9) and the Jaccard Similarity or Jaccard Coefficient (http://bit.ly/29n41vH). The Jaccard Coefficient is particularly useful for datasets having a class imbalance.

COMPARABILITY BETWEEN TWO VARIABLES

Let's take a break from our data exploration efforts and look into some theory that may help you make more informed choices about which approach to use when comparing two variables. Just because two variables both exist in an array and Julia is happy to do mathematical computations with them, that doesn't necessarily mean that they mix very well. This is especially important to know if you want to use them together for a feature, or for some statistical test. So how do two variables compare with each other? Overall we have the following distinct possibilities:

- The two variables are of (even slightly) different type, e.g. Float64 and Int64. In this case you can't work with them directly, though it is possible to use them together in plots.

- The two variables are both numeric but have different variances. In this case you can work with them and create all kinds of plots containing them, but you may not be able to perform some statistical tests. Also, it would not be a good idea to get rid of one of them, even if they are similar (i.e. they correlate well with each other).

- The two variables are both numeric and have roughly the same variance. In this case the variables are as comparable as they can get. Apart from general wrangling and plotting, you can do all kinds of statistical tests with them.

- The two variables are both categorical. When this happens we can still compare them, regardless of what kind of values they have. In this case you can use specialized techniques like the chi-square test.

This information may not be directly applicable to a dataset, but it's always useful to have it in mind as it allows you to better discern things.

PLOTS

Plots are fundamental to data exploration, mainly because they are intuitive and can convey a lot of information at a single glance. In addition, they can be an excellent source of insights, and ideal for summarizing your findings (e.g. for reporting). There are various ways to construct plots in Julia, the most popular of which is through the use of the Gadfly package. Other alternatives include the up-

and-coming Plotly tool (http://bit.ly/29MRdKD), Python's tool called Bokeh (http://bit.ly/29RrRjo), and two tools created by the Julia team: one called Winston (http://bit.ly/29GCtOM) and the other called Vega (http://bit.ly/2a8MoRh). Once you are comfortable enough with Gadfly, we encourage you to investigate these options at your own time.

There are no strict rules when it comes to using plots. As long as you can depict the information you want to show, feel free to use any kind of plot you want. Of course, some are better suited to certain scenarios than others, but that's something you'll learn as you gain more experience in data exploration. Generally you'll always want to name your plots (usually in the caption that accompanies them) and have them available in a printable form (usually a `.png`, `.gif`, or `.jpg` file, though `.pdf` is also an option).

GRAMMAR OF GRAPHICS

One thing to keep in mind when creating graphics is that the process of building a graphic is highly standardized in most packages. This standard of graphic-creation has been developed by Leland Wilkinson and has been described thoroughly in his book, "The Grammar of Graphics" (1999 and 2005). `Gadfly` follows this paradigm, so let's take a closer look at it.

Basically, a plot can be seen as a collection of objects describing the data it is trying to represent. Each one of these objects represents a layer and is defined in the function used to create the plot (naturally, the data used to create the plot is also a layer). These layers are the following:

- Aesthetic mappings (guide)
- Geometry
- Statistical transformation
- Position adjustment (scale)
- Data.

Try to identify these layers, through their corresponding objects, in the examples in the sections that follow.

PREPARING DATA FOR VISUALIZATION

Before we start plotting, we'll need to format the data so that it is in the form of a data frame, since `Gadfly` is not particularly fond of arrays. For that, it will be best to create a list of the variable names, as this allows for easier referencing and better understanding of the variables at hand:

```
In[9]: varnames = ["fLength", "fWidth", "fSize", "fConc", "fConc1",
    "fAsym", "fM3Long", "fM3Trans","fAlpha", "fDist", "class"]
```

Now, we can bind everything in a data frame object, after reloading the data:

```
In[10]: df = readtable("magic04.csv", header = false)             #1
    old_names = names(df)
    new_names = [symbol(varnames[i]) for i = 1:length(varnames)] #2
    for i = 1:length(old_names)
      rename!(df, old_names[i], new_names[i])                    #3
    end
#1 obtain the data from the .csv file and put it in a data frame
    called df
#2 create an array containing the symbol equivalent of the variable
    names (from the array varnames)
#3 change the names of the data frame df to the newer ones in the
    array new_names
```

BOX PLOTS

Box plots are useful for depicting the highlights of the distribution of each variable in a simple and intuitive form. However, although `Gadfly` officially supports them, they don't work with the current version of Julia. We encourage you to check them out once this issue is ironed out by visiting the corresponding webpage: http://bit.ly/29gH9cE.

BAR PLOTS

Contrary to what the name suggests, bar plots are rarely found in bars. These plots are useful in classification problems when you want to compare values of a discreet variable, or specific statistics of any variable (e.g. means, variances) across various classes. In this case, the plot makes it clear that our dataset is imbalanced, as there are about 6000 more instances of class h (see Figure 7.2 below).

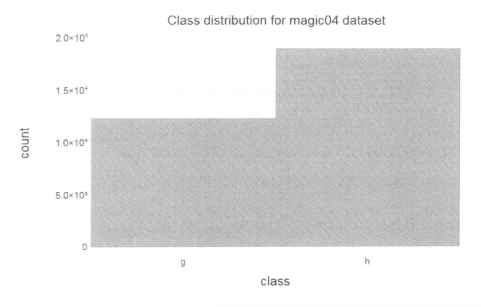

Figure 7.2 A bar plot of class distribution of the dataset.

If you wish to create some plots of this type, Julia can make this happen with the help of the following Gadfly function:

```
In[11]: plot(df, x = "class", Geom.bar, Guide.ylabel("count"),
    Guide.title("Class distribution for Magic dataset"))
```

Although the Guide.X parameters are entirely optional, they are helpful for your audience as they make the plot more easily interpretable.

LINE PLOTS

Line plots are similar to bar plots; the only difference is that the data points are connected sequentially, instead of with the X axis. They are applicable in similar cases and rarely encountered in data exploration. Nevertheless, they can prove useful for plotting time series data. Here is an example of a line plot for the class distribution of our dataset (Figure 7.3):

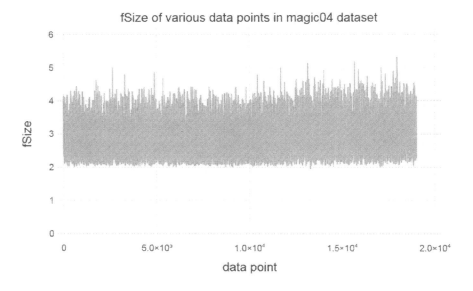

Figure 7.3 A line plot of fSize feature across all of the data points of the `magic` dataset.

You can create this yourself using the following simple piece of code:

```
In[12]: plot(df, y = "fSize", Geom.line, Guide.xlabel("data
    point"), Guide.ylabel("fSize"), Guide.title("fSize of various
    data points in Magic dataset"))
```

SCATTER PLOTS

Basic scatter plots

These are one of the most useful of all the plots, as they pinpoint potential relationships between two variables. These are particularly useful for establishing connections between variables, and for finding good predictors for your target variable (especially in regression problems, where the target variable is continuous). Scatter plots don't always have a clear pattern and often look something like the plot in Figure 7.4.

From this plot it is clear that there is no real relationship between these variables. If the points of this plot formed more of a line or a curve, then there might be some kind of dependency evident. In this case, the dependency is practically non-existent, so it would be best to keep both of these as independent variables in our prediction model. A correlation analysis (using any correlation metric) would provide additional evidence supporting this conclusion.

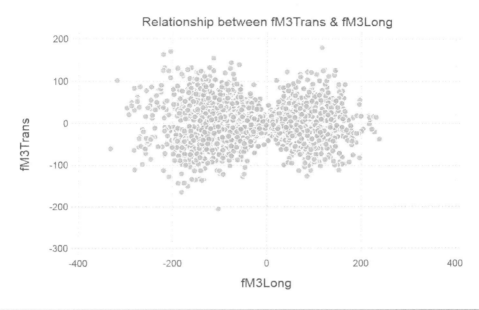

Figure 7.4 A scatter plot for features 7 and 8. Clearly there is little relationship (if any at all) between the fM3Long and fM3Trans variables.

You can create a scatter plot between two features in our dataset, like the one in Figure 7.4, using the following code:

```
In[13]: plot(x = df[:fM3Long], y = df[:fM3Trans], Geom.point,
    Guide.xlabel("fM3Long"), Guide.ylabel("fM3Trans"),
    Guide.title("Relationship between fM3Trans & fM3Long"))
```

Scatter plots using the output of t-SNE algorithm

It is truly fascinating how this simple yet brilliant algorithm developed by the Dutch scientist Laurens van der Maaten is rarely mentioned in data science books and tutorials. It has been used extensively in the data exploration of large companies like Elavon (US Bank) and Microsoft. Prof. Van der Maaten's team has implemented it in most programming platforms, including Julia, so there is no excuse for ignoring it! You can find the latest package here: http://bit.ly/29pKZUB. To install it, clone the package on your computer using the following command, as it is not an official package yet:

```
In[14]: Pkg.clone("git://github.com/lejon/TSne.jl.git")
```

In short, t-SNE is a mapping method that takes a multi-dimensional feature space and reduces it to 1, 2 or 3 dimensions. From here, the data can be plotted without having to worry about distorting the dataset's geometrical properties in the process.

It was first introduced to the scientific world in 2008 through a couple of papers, the most important of which was published in the Journal of Machine Learning Research and can be read at http://bit.ly/29jRt4m. For a lighter introduction to this piece of technology, you can check out Professor Van der Maaten's talk about his algorithm on YouTube: http://bit.ly/28KxtZK.

For our dataset we can get a good idea of how its data points relate to the two classes by examining the resulting plot, which looks like something similar to the one in Figure 7.5 (we say "similar" because every time you run the algorithm it will produce slightly different results, due to its stochastic nature).

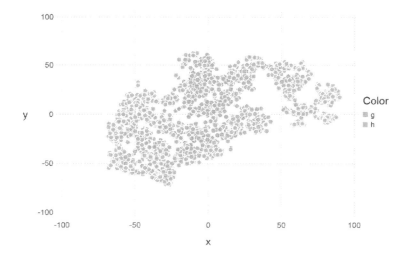

Figure 7.5 A scatter plot based on the output of the t-SNE algorithm on the `magic` dataset. You can view the plot in full color online at http://bit.ly/1LW2swW.

This plot clearly indicates that there is a significant overlap between the two classes, making classification a challenging task. The h class is more or less distinct in some regions of the feature-space, but for the most part g and h are interlaced. Therefore, it would behoove us to apply a more sophisticated algorithm if we want a good accuracy rate for this dataset.

Although the method is ingenious, the documentation of its Julia implementation remains incomplete. Here is how you can use it without having to delve into its source code to understand what's going on:

1. Normalize your dataset using mean and standard deviation.

2. Load the tSNE package into memory using tsne().

3. Run the main function: Y = tsne(X, n, N, ni, p), where X is your normalized dataset, n is the number of dimensions that you wish to reduce it to (usually 2), N is the original number of dimensions, ni is the number of iterations for the algorithm (default value is 1000), and p is the perplexity parameter (default value is 30.0).

4. Output the result:

```
In[14]: labels = [string(label) for label in O[1:length(O)]]
In[15]: plot(x = Y[:,1], y = Y[:,2], color = labels)
```

If you are unsure of what parameters to use, the default ones should suffice; all you'll need is your dataset and the number of reduced dimensions. Also, for larger datasets (like the one in our example) it makes sense to get a random sample as the t-SNE method is resource-hungry and may take a long time to process the whole dataset (if it doesn't run out of memory in the meantime). If we apply t-SNE to our dataset setting n = 2 and leaving the other parameters as their default values, we'll need to write the following code:

```
In[16]: using TSne
In[17]: include("normalize.jl")
In[18]: include("sample.jl")
In[19]: X = normalize(X, "stat")
In[20]: X, O = sample(X, O, 2000)
In[21]: Y = tsne(X, 2)
In[22]: plot(x = Y[:,1], y = Y[:,2], color = O)
```

In our case the labels (vector o) are already in string format, so there is no need to create the labels variable. Also, for a dataset of this size, the t-SNE transformation is bound to take some time (the tsne() function doesn't employ parallelization). That's why in this example we applied it to a small sample of the data instead.

Scatter plots are great, especially for discreet target variables such as classification problems. For different types of problems, such as regression scenarios, you could still use them by including the target variable as one of the depicted variables (usually y or z). In addition, it is best to normalize your variables beforehand, as it is easy to draw the wrong conclusions about the dataset otherwise.

HISTOGRAMS

Histograms are by far the most useful plots for data exploration. The reason is simple: they allow you to see how the values of a variable are spread across the spectrum, giving you a good sense of the distribution they follow (if they do follow such a pattern). Although useful, the normal distribution is rather uncommon, which is why there are so many other distributions created to describe what analysts observe. With Julia you can create interesting plots depicting this information, like the one shown in Figure 7.6.

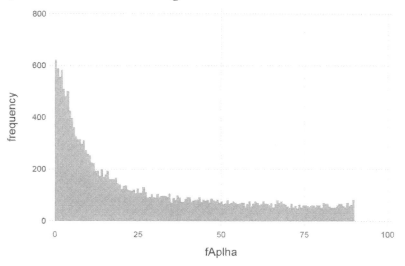

Figure 7.6 A histogram of feature 9 (fAlpha). Clearly this feature follows a distribution that is nowhere near normal.

You can get Julia to create a histogram like this one by using the following code:

```
In[23]: p = plot(x = df[:fAlpha], Geom.histogram,
    Guide.xlabel("fAplha"), Guide.ylabel("frequency"))
```

If you want a coarser version of this plot with, say, 20 bins, you can add the bincount **parameter, which by default has a rather high value:**

```
In[24]: p = plot(x = df[:fAlpha], Geom.histogram(bincount = 20),
    Guide.xlabel("fAplha"), Guide.ylabel("frequency"))
```

From both versions of the histogram, you can see that the fAlpha variable probably follows the power law, so it has a strong bias towards smaller values (to be certain that it follows the power law we'll need to run some additional tests, but that's beyond the scope of this book).

Exporting a plot to a file

Exporting plots into graphics or PDF files is possible using the Cairo package. This is a C-based package that allows you to handle plot objects and transform them into three types of files: PNG, PDF, or PS. (Cairo may not work properly with early versions of Julia.) For example, we can create a nice .png and a .pdf of the simple plot myplot using the following code:

```
myplot = plot(x = [1,2,3,4,5], y = [2,3.5,7,7.5,10])
draw(PNG("myplot.png", 5inch, 2.5inch), myplot)
draw(PDF("myplot.png", 10cm, 5cm), myplot)
```

The general formula for exporting plots using Cairo is as follows:

```
draw(F("filename.ext", dimX, dimY), PlotObject)
```

In this code, F is the file exporter function: PNG, PDF, or PS, and filename.ext is the name of the desired image file. dimX and dimY are the dimensions of the plot on the X and Y axis, respectively. If they are left undefined, Julia assumes number of pixels, but you can also specify another unit of measurement, such as inches or cm, by adding the corresponding suffix. Finally, PlotObject is the name of the plot you want to export.

Alternatively, if you run your plotting script in the REPL you can save the created graphic from your browser, where it is rendered as an `.html` file. This file is bound to be larger than a typical `.png` but it is of lossless quality (since the plot is rendered whenever the page is loaded) and incorporates the zoom and scroll functionality of the `Gadfly` plots in the Julia environment. In fact, all the plots included in this chapter were created using this particular process in the REPL, attesting to the quality of browser-rendered plots.

HYPOTHESIS TESTING

Suppose you are a data scientist and you want to check whether your hypotheses about the patterns you see in your data (i.e. the particular variables you are focusing on) hold "true". You notice that the sales variable is different at certain days of the week but you are not sure whether that's a real signal or just a fluke. How will you know, and avoid wasting your manager's valuable time and your expensive resources? Well, that's why hypothesis testing is here.

Testing basics

In order to harness the power of hypothesis testing, let's quickly review the theory. Hypothesis testing is an essential tool for any scientific process, as it allows you to evaluate your assumptions in an objective way. It enables you to assess how likely you are to be wrong if you adopt a hypothesis that challenges the "status quo." The hypothesis that accepts the status quo is usually referred to as the null hypothesis, and it's denoted H0. The proposed alternative is creatively named the alternative hypothesis, and it's denoted H1.

The more you can convince someone that H1 holds "true" more often than H0, the more significant your test is (and your results, as a consequence). Of course you can never be 100% certain that H1 is absolutely "true", since H0 has been considered valid for a reason. There is a chance your alternative hypothesis is backed by circumstantial evidence (i.e. you were lucky). Since luck has no place in science, you want to minimize the chances that your results were due to chance.

This chance is quantified as alpha (α), a measure of the probability that your alternative hypothesis is unfounded. Naturally, alpha is also a great metric for significance, which is why it is the primary significance value of your test. Alpha values that correspond to commonly used significance levels are 0.05, 0.01, and 0.001. A significance of $\alpha = 0.01$, for example, means that you are 99% sure that your alternative hypothesis holds truer than your null hypothesis. Obviously, the smaller the alpha value, the stricter the test and therefore the more significant its results are.

Types of errors

There are two types of errors you can make through this schema:

- Accept H1 while it is not "true". This is also known as a false positive (FP). A low enough alpha value can protect you against this type of error, which is usually referred to as type I error.

- Reject H1 even though it is "true". Usually referred to as a false negative (FN), this is a usually a result of having a very strict significance threshold. Such an error is also known as a type II error.

Naturally you'll want to minimize both of these types of errors, but this is not always possible. The one that matters most depends on your application, so keep that in mind when you are evaluating your hypotheses.

Sensitivity and specificity

Sensitivity is the ratio of correctly predicted H1 cases to total number of H1 cases. Specificity is the ratio of correctly predicted non-H1 cases to total number of non-H1 cases. In practice, these two metrics are variables that we calculate. These variables are not arbitrarily large or small, since they cannot be larger than 1 or smaller than 0. This is often expressed as "taking values in" a given interval. So, here is how the four distinct cases of a test result relate to sensitivity and specificity:

Test Result	Relationship to S & S
true positive result (correctly predicted H1 cases)	sensitivity
false negative result (missed H1 cases)	1-sensitivity
true negative result (H0 cases predicted as such)	specificity
false positive result (H0 cases predicted as H1 ones)	1-specificity

Table 7.1 The relationship between sensitivity and specificity and corresponding test results.

We will come back to sensitivity and specificity when we'll discuss performance metrics for classification, in Chapter 9.

Significance and power of a test

These concepts are useful for understanding the value of a test result, although they provide little if any information about its importance. That's something that no statistical term can answer for you, since it depends on how much value you bring to your client.

Significance, as we saw earlier, is how much a test's result matters—a sign that the result is not some bizarre coincidence due to chance. It is measured with `alpha`, with low `alpha` values being better. So, if your test comes up with what is called a `p` value (the probability that we obtain this result by chance alone) that is very small (smaller than a predetermined threshold value of alpha, such as 0.01), then your result is statistically significant and possibly worth investigating further. You can view significance as the probability of making a type I error.

Similarly, you can consider the power of a test as the chance that a test would yield a positive result, be it a true positive or a false positive. Basically, it's the probability of *not* making a type II error. Naturally, you would want your test to have a small value for significance and a high value for power.

KRUSKAL-WALLIS TESTS

The Kruskal-Wallis (K-W) test is a useful statistical test that checks the levels of a factor variable to see whether the medians of a corresponding continuous variable are the same, or at least one pair of them is significantly different. Such a test is particularly handy for cases like in the `magic` dataset, when the target variable is a nominal one; it is usually even more applicable in cases where there are several different values (at least three).

In general, you'd apply the K-W test using the following function of the `HypothesisTests` package:

```
KruskalWallisTest{T<:Real}(g::AbstractVector(T))
```

where `g` is a one-dimensional array (or AbstractVector) comprising the groups of the continuous variable that is tested.

You can learn more about the K-W test by reading the documentation created by the Northern Arizona University, found at http://bit.ly/28OtqhE. If you wish to dig deeper, we recommend Prof. J. H. McDonald's excellent website on biostatistics, found at http://bit.ly/28MjuAK.

T-TESTS

One of the most popular techniques to test hypotheses is the t-test. This type of statistical test enables you to compare two samples (from the same variable) and see if they are indeed as different as they appear to be. One of its main advantages is that it can handle all kinds of distributions, while it is also easy to use (compared to some statistical tests that require a prerequisite training course in statistics). That's one of the reasons why the t-test is one of the most commonly encountered tests out there, especially for continuous variables.

Let's consider two examples of the same variable `sales` we discussed in our hypothetical case at the beginning of the section. We can plot their distributions as in Figure 7.7. They need not be so neat, since we make no assumptions about the distributions themselves—as long as the number of data points is more than 30. Still, the plot alone cannot answer our question: are the sales on the two different days different enough to be considered a signal or is it just noise–random fluctuations due to chance?

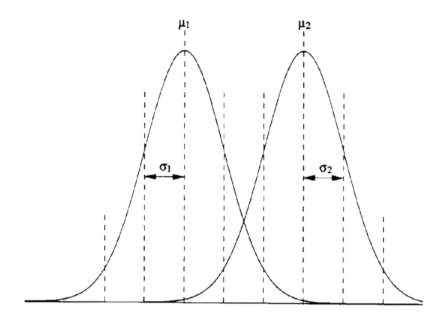

Figure 7.7 The distributions of two sets over a given variable. Although the two samples appear to be different (their means are not the same), this can only be confirmed through the use of a statistical test, such as the t-test.

Fortunately, the t-test can give us the answer to this question, along with a measure of how likely it is to be wrong (alpha value). Julia can work a t-test as follows, depending on whether the variances of the two distributions are the same:

```
pvalue(EqualVarianceTTest(x, y))
pvalue(UnequalVarianceTTest(x, y))
```

where x and y are one-dimensional arrays containing the data samples in question.

Of course, we can split our data in a zillion different ways. One meaningful distinction is based on the class variable. This way we can see if a particular continuous feature is different when it applies to the data points of class g compared to the data points of class h. Before we run the test, we need to split the data into these two groups, and then compare their variances. In this example we'll look at the 10th feature (fDist), but the same process can be applied to any feature in this dataset.

```
In[25]: ind1 = findin(df[:class], ["g"])
In[26]: ind2 = findin(df[:class], ["h"])
In[27]: x_g = df[:fDist][ind1]
In[28]: x_h = df[:fDist][ind2]
In[29]: v_g = var(x_g)
In[30]: v_h = var(x_h)
```

It's now clear that the two samples are different in variance; the second sample's variance is about 36% more than the first sample's. Now we'll need to apply the second variety of the t-test, when the variances of the two distributions are not the same:

```
In[31]: pvalue(UnequalVarianceTTest(x_g, x_h))
```

The result Julia returns is an exceptionally small number (~7.831e-18), which indicates a very low probability that this difference in means is due to chance. Needless to say, that's significant regardless of the choice of alpha (which can take values as small as 0.001, but rarely smaller). In other words, there's a better chance that you'll be struck by a lightning three times in a row than that the means of this feature are different by chance alone (according to the National Lightning Safety Institute, the chances of getting struck by a lightning, in the US, are about 1 in 280000, or 0.00035%.) The impact of this insight is that this feature is bound to be a good predictor, and should be included in the classification model.

CHI-SQUARE TESTS

The chi-square test is the most popular statistical test for discreet variables. Despite its simplicity, it has a great mathematical depth (fortunately, you won't have to be a mathematician in order to use it). Despite the somewhat complex math involved, a chi-square test answers a relatively simple question: are the counts among the various bins as expected? In other words, is there any imbalance in the corresponding distributions that would suggest a relationship between the two discreet variables? Although such a question can occasionally be answered intuitively (particularly when the answer is significantly positive), it is difficult to assess the borderline case without a lot of calculations. Fortunately Julia takes care of all the math for you, through the following function from StatsBase:

```
ChisqTest(x, y)
```

where x and y are rows and columns, respectively, of a contingency table of two variables. Alternatively, you can pass to Julia the whole table in a single variable X, which is particularly useful when tackling more complex problems where both variables have three or more unique values:

```
ChisqTest(X)
```

Since we don't have any discreet variables in our dataset, we'll create one for illustration purposes, based on the fLength feature. In particular, we'll break it up into three bins: high, medium, and low, based on an arbitrary threshold. The high bin will include all data points that have a value greater than or equal to $\mu + \sigma$; the low bin will contain anything that is less than or equal to $\mu - \sigma$; all the remaining points will fall into the medium bin.

Try this out as an exercise in data-wrangling. Use the .>= and .<= operators for performing logical comparison over an array; to find the common elements of two arrays, along with the intersect() function. With some simple logical operations we end up with the contingency table shown in Table 7.2.

Class / fLength	Low	Medium	High	Total
g	0	11747	585	12332
h	34	4778	1876	6688
Total	34	16525	2461	19020

Table 7.2 A contingency table showing counts of "Low", "Medium," and "High" values of the fLength feature, against the class variable.

Based on the above data (which is stored in, say, the two-dimensional array C, comprising of the values of the first 2 rows and the first 3 columns of the table), we can apply the chi-square test as follows:

```
In[32]: ChisqTest(C)
```

Julia will spit out a lot of interesting but ultimately useless information regarding the test. What you need to focus on is the summary that's buried somewhere in the test report:

```
Out[32]: Test summary:
         outcome with 95% confidence: reject h_0
         two-sided p-value:     0.0 (extremely significant)
```

Clearly there is no way that these counts could have been generated by chance alone, so we can safely reject the null hypothesis (which Julia refers to as `h_0`) and conclude that there is a significant relationship between `fLength` and the `class` variable. Again, this means that we may want to include it (or the original feature it was created from) in our model.

The result of the chi-square test will not always be so crystal clear. In these cases, you may want to state beforehand what your significance threshold (alpha) will be and then compare the p-value of the test to it. If it's less than the threshold, you can go ahead and reject the null hypothesis.

OTHER TESTS

Apart from the aforementioned tests, there are several others that are made available through the `HypothesisTests` package. These may appeal to you more if you have a mathematical background and/or wish to discover more ways to perform statistical analysis using Julia. We encourage you to explore the package's excellent documentation (http://hypothesistestsjl.readthedocs.org) and practice any of the tests that pique your interest. You can find additional information about the various statistical tests at reputable Stats websites, such as http://stattrek.com.

STATISTICAL TESTING TIPS

The world of statistical testing is vast, but by no means exhaustive. That's why it's been a fruitful field of research since its inception. As the realm of big data makes these techniques more valuable, its evolution is bound to continue. Still, the tests mentioned in this chapter should keep you covered for the majority of the datasets you'll encounter. Remember that there is no "perfect score" for a given problem; it is not uncommon for someone to try out several statistical tests on her data before arriving at any conclusions. Furthermore, the results of these tests are better used as guidelines than strict rules. Often, a pair of variables may pass a certain test but fail others, so they definitely cannot be a substitute for human judgment. Instead, they can be useful tools for drawing insights and supporting your own intuitions about the data at hand.

CASE STUDY: EXPLORING THE ONLINENEWSPOPULARITY DATASET

We will practice applying all of these tools on another dataset, start to finish. We'll return to the previously mentioned OnlineNewsPopularity dataset, which is a classic case of a regression problem. As we saw in Chapter 2, this problem aims to predict the number of shares of various online news articles based on several characteristics of the corresponding posts. This is particularly important for the people creating these articles, as they want to maximize their impact in social media. Let's first load it into a dataframe, for more intuitive access to its variables (which in this case are already in the .csv file as a header):

```
In[33]: df = readtable("OnlineNewsPopularity.csv", header = true)
```

By examining a few elements of this dataframe it becomes clear that the first variable (url) is just an identifier, so we have no use for it in our models, nor in the exploratory part of our analysis.

Variable stats

Now let's dig into the various descriptive statistics of our dataset, including the target variable:

```
In[34]: Z = names(df)[2:end] #1
In[35]: for z in Z
        X = convert(Array, df[symbol(z)]);
        println(z, "\t", summarystats(X))
```

```
      end
#1 Exclude the first column of the data frame (url) as it is both
   non-numeric and irrelevant
```

From all these, it is clear that the variables' values are all over the place, so we should go ahead and normalize them as we saw in the previous chapter:

```
In[36]: for z in Z
         X = df[symbol(z)]
         Y = (X - mean(X)) / std(X) #1
         df[symbol(z)] = Y
       end
#1 This is equivalent to normalize(X, "stat"), which we saw
   earlier.
```

Other than that, there is nothing particularly odd about the variables that begs any additional work. One thing to keep in mind is that some of the variables are binary, even though they are coded as floats in the data frame. We don't need to normalize the features since they are already on the same scale as the other (normalized) features. There are no consequences.

Before we move on to the visualizations, let's see how the different variables correlate with the target variable:

```
In[37]: n = length(Z)
In[38]: C = Array(Any, n, 2)
In[39]: for i = 1:n
           X = df[symbol(Z[i])]
           C[i,1] = Z[i][2:end]
           C[i,2] = cor(X, df[:shares])
        end
```

The above code produces a two-dimensional array that contains the names of the variables and their corresponding correlation coefficients with the target variable (shares). Clearly the relationships are all weak, meaning that we'll need to work harder to build a decent prediction model for this dataset.

VISUALIZATION

All that statistical talk is great, but what do our features look like and how do they compare with the target variable? Let's find out with the following code:

```
In[40]: for i = 1:n
    plot(x = df[symbol(Z[i])], Geom.histogram,
      Guide.xlabel(string(Z[i])), Guide.ylabel("frequency"))
    plot(x = df[symbol(Z[i])], y = df[:shares], Geom.point,
      Guide.xlabel(string(Z[i])), Guide.ylabel("shares"))
    end
```

The result is a series of histograms accompanied by scatter plots with the target variable, a few of which are shown in Figure 7.8.

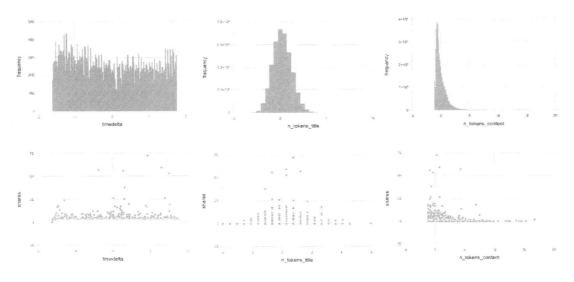

Figure 7.8 Histograms of the first three variables, and scatter plots between them and the target variable.

The histograms indicate that the majority of the features don't have particularly strong relationships with the target variable, although there is some signal there. This confirms the correlations (or lack thereof) we calculated in the previous paragraph.

HYPOTHESES

Clearly the traditional approach to hypothesis creation and testing we discussed previously won't apply here, since we don't have a discreet target variable. However, with a little imagination we can still make use of the t-test, bypassing the limitations of any distribution assumptions. We can split the target variable into two parts (high and low values) and see whether the corresponding groups of values of each variable are significantly different.

This is similar to the correlation coefficient approach, but more robust, as it doesn't search for a linear relationship (which would have been pinpointed by the correlation coefficient). The big advantage is that it manages to show whether there is an underlying signal in each variable, without getting too complicated. (The next level of complexity would be to run ANOVA and MANOVA models, which go beyond the scope of data exploration.) So, let's see how the HypothesisTests package can shed some light onto this dataset through the code in listing 7.1:

```
In[41]: a = 0.01                                                      #1
In[42]: N = length(Y)
In[43]: mY = mean(Y)
In[44]: ind1 = (1:N)[Y .>= mY]
In[45]: ind2 = (1:N)[Y .< mY]
In[46]: A = Array(Any, 59, 4)
In[47]: for i = 1:59
            X = convert(Array, df[symbol(Z[i])])
            X_high = X[ind1]
            X_low = X[ind2]
            var_high = var(X_high)
            var_low = var(X_low)
            if abs(2(var_high - var_low)/(var_high + var_low)) <= 0.1 #2
                p = pvalue(EqualVarianceTTest(X_high,X_low))
            else
                p = pvalue(UnequalVarianceTTest(X_high,X_low))
            end
            A[i,:] = [i, Z[i], p, p < a]
            if p < a
                println([i, "\t", Z[i]]) #3
            end
```

```
      end
#1 Set the significance threshold (alpha value)
#2 Check to see if variances are within 10% of each other
   (approximately)
#3 Print variable number and name if it's statistically significant
```

Listing 7.1 A code snippet to apply t-tests to the `OnlineNewsPopularity` dataset.

Clearly the majority of the variables (44 out of 59) can accurately predict whether the target variable is high or low, with 99% certainty. So, it has become clear that the variables of the dataset are not so bad in terms of quality overall; they just don't map the target variable in a linear manner.

T-SNE MAGIC

Although t-SNE was designed for visualization of feature spaces, mainly for classification problems, there is no reason why we cannot apply it in this case–with a small twist. Instead of mapping the dataset onto a two- or three-dimensional space, we can use t-SNE on a one-dimensional space. Although this would be completely useless for visualization, we can still use its output in a scatter plot with the target variable and check for any type of relationship between the two. This will become more apparent once you try out the code snippet in Listing 7.2.

```
In[48]: using("normalize.jl")
In[49]: X = convert(Array, df)
In[50]: Y = float64(X[:,end])
In[51]: X = float64(X[:,2:(end-1)])
In[52]: X = normalize(X, "stat")
In[53]: Y = normalize(Y, "stat")
In[54]: X, Y = sample(X, Y, 2000)
In[55]: X1 = tsne(X, 1)
In[56]: plot(x = X1[ind], y = Y[ind], Geom.point)
```

Listing 7.2 Code snippet to apply t-SNE to the `OnlineNewsPopularity` dataset.

This code produces a highly compressed dataset (X1) that summarizes the whole normalized dataset into a single feature, and then plots it against the target variable (which we call Y in this case). This result is shown in Figure 7.9. Although the relationship between the inputs (X1) and the target is weak, it is evident that smaller values of X1 generally yield a slightly higher value in Y.

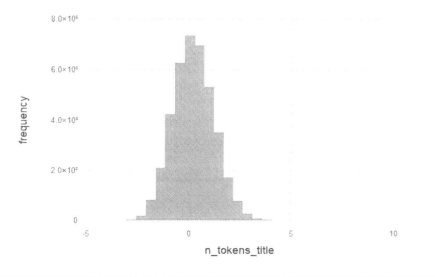

Figure 7.9 Scatter plot of T-SNE reduced dataset against target variable.

CONCLUSIONS

Based upon all of our exploratory analysis of the OnlineNewsPopularity dataset, we can reasonably draw the following conclusions:

- The distributions of most of the variables are balanced.

- Normalizing the variables is imperative.

- There is a weak linear relationship between each input variable and the target variable.

- The inputs of the dataset can predict whether the target variable is generally high or low, with statistical significance (a = 0.01).

- Using a scatter plot based on t-SNE, we can see that the relationship of all the input variables with the target variable is reversely proportional (albeit weakly).

SUMMARY

- Data exploration is comprised of many different techniques. The most important of these are descriptive statistics (found in the `StatsBase` package), plots (`Gadfly` package), and hypothesis formulation and testing (`HypothesisTests` package).

Descriptive Statistics:

- You can uncover the most important descriptive statistics of a variable `x` using the `StatsBase` package, by applying the following functions:
  - `summarystats(x)` – This function is great for storing the stats into an object, so that you can use them later.
  - `describe(x)` – This function is better for getting an idea of the variable through the display of the stats on the console.

- You can calculate the correlation between two variables using one of the functions that follow:
  - `cor(x, y)` – The Pearson method is best suited to distributions that are normal.
  - `corspearman(x, y)` – The Spearman method will work with any kind of distribution.
  - `corkendall(x, y)` – Kandell's tau method is also good for any kind of distribution.

- To create a correlation table with all possible correlations among a dataset's variables, apply one of the above correlation functions with a single argument, the dataset array.

Plots:

- There are several packages in Julia for plots, the most important of which are: `Gadfly`, `Plotly`, `Bokeh`, `Winston`, and `Vega`.

- Before creating any visuals with `Gadfly`, it is best use a data frame to store all your variables.

- In all `Gadfly` plots, you can label your creations using the following parameters in the `plot()` function:
  - `Guide.xlabel("Name of your X axis")`.
  - `Guide.ylabel("Name of your Y axis")`.
  - `Guide.title("Name of your plot")`.

- You can create the following plots easily using `Gadfly`:
  - **Bar plot:** `plot(DataFrameYouWishToUse,`
    `x = "IndependentVariable", Geom.bar)`.
  - **Line plot:** `plot(DataFrameYouWishToUse,`
    `y = "DependentVariable", Geom.line)`.
  - **Scatter plot:** `plot(x = DataFrameName[:IndependentVariable],`
    `y = DataFrameName[:DependentVariable], Geom.point)`.
  - **Histogram:** `plot(x = DataFrameName[:VariableName],`
    `Geom.histogram)`.

- You can visualize a whole dataset regardless of its dimensionality using the t-SNE algorithm in the `tSNE` package.

- You can save a plot you have created and stored in an object using the `Cairo` package. Alternatively, you can screen capture the plot, or run the command on the REPL and save the HTML file it creates in your web browser.

Hypothesis Testing:

- Hypothesis tests are a great way to reliably test an idea you may have about the relationships between variables. They can be run using tools in the `HypothesisTests` package. The most commonly used hypothesis tests are the following:
  - **t-test:** `pvalue(EqualVarianceTTest(x, y))`, or in the case of different variances in your variables, `pvalue(UnequalVarianceTTest(x, y))`.
  - **chi-square test:** `ChisqTest(X)`.

- Hypothesis tests are evaluated based on two factors, neither of which map the value of the results. Instead they show the scientific validity of the test. These factors are the following:

  - Significance (alpha): The probability that your test makes a type I error. Significance is usually defined as thresholds corresponding to the alpha values of 0.05 (most common), 0.01, and 0.001 (least common).

  - Power: The probability of not making a type II error. Power corresponds to how likely it is that your test yields a positive result (which can be either correct or incorrect).

- Apart from the t-test and the chi-square test, there are several other statistical tests you can use; these are described in detail in the `HypothesisTests` documentation.

CHAPTER CHALLENGE

1. What action could be taken based on the identification of high correlation between two variables in a dataset?

2. When can you prove the null hypothesis in a test?

3. In a classification problem, under which conditions can you use correlation to see how well a feature aligns with the class variable?

4. Explore a dataset of your choice and note down any interesting findings you come up with.

5. Can a t-test be applied on variables following irregular distributions?

6. Suppose we have a medical dataset comprising data of 20 patients. Can we draw any statistically significant conclusions about its variables using the standard test? Why?

7. What would be the best plot to use for depicting a dataset's feature space?

8. What is the main use case for the t-SNE function?

Contrary to what many people think, more data is not always better. This is particularly true when it comes to additional features (or dimensions). Take for example Sherlock Holmes, the famous fictional detective, who managed to solve the most baffling cases. Although his observation skills were unparalleled, a big part of his success was due to his ability to focus on the most essential aspects of the problem, eliminating all the unnecessary information. This is the human equivalent of dimensionality reduction in all its glory.

Of course, keeping all the features in a dataset can be a good thing in certain cases. Most of the benchmark datasets used to test a new machine learning system are dense in feature sets, with each one of their features contributing to the end result. In data science, though, the datasets worked with are often very large–not just in the number of data points, but also in their dimensionality. This makes the signal seem like a needle in a haystack of noise. A good data scientist takes this haystack and removes as much of the hay as possible before starting his modeling work, making the job much easier.

There are many ways to accomplish this "haystack thinning." Some methods entail merging features together into more meaningful meta-features, while others involve examining and evaluating the original features and keeping only those that seem most relevant.

An alternative method focuses on whether we should use the features by themselves, or use them in tandem with the target variable. These two methods are usually referred to as unsupervised and supervised respectively.

In this chapter we will cover the following topics:

- Principal Component Analysis as one of the popular methods of reducing dimensionality

- Feature evaluation and selection as a worthwhile alternative to dimensionality reduction

- Additional dimensionality reduction approaches.

Let us now examine some specific methods based on these approaches to dimensionality reduction.

PRINCIPAL COMPONENTS ANALYSIS (PCA)

One of the most popular methods used for dimensionality reduction is PCA, a method developed in statistics. Its premise is that because information in a dataset is expressed as variance, the axes upon which most of this variance is measured must be the ones richest in information; therefore it is these axes we should focus on. This method has the following advantages:

- PCA requires no assumptions about the distribution(s) of the dataset.

- PCA has a high compression rate (with good fidelity when information is uncompressed).

- There is no need for labels in the dataset as PCA works using only the inputs.

- PCA has a strong mathematical background.

- There is no need to normalize the data before applying PCA.

The output of this method is a feature set consisting of a number of meta-features, ordered by importance (with the first one being the most information-rich). The exact number of meta-features, also referred to as "principal components," is usually determined by a parameter of the method. As you would expect, the higher this number, the less information is lost in the process. However, adding more meta-features follows the law of diminishing returns; this is why, in most cases, we focus on a small number of meta-features.

Fortunately, the implementation of PCA in Julia is optimized so as to find the best number of meta-features on its own, making the implementation of the method even more straightforward. Of course, you can always add an extra parameter for a more aggressive dimensionality reduction, if you so prefer. We'll look into the specifics of this method shortly.

PCA is mainly used for visualization purposes, and is popular among all kinds of analysts due to its simplicity. However, the method is not free of drawbacks, including:

- The resulting meta-features are linear combinations of the original ones that often lack interpretability

- PCA doesn't scale well, making it impractical for very large datasets containing thousands of features.

Regardless of the inherent weaknesses of this method, it is a powerful tool that is also easy to use. Should you wish to learn more about it, we suggest that you read about it in any statistics book, or check out L.I. Smith's comprehensive online tutorial at http://bit.ly/MU8WV7.

One last thing to keep in mind about PCA is that it is ideal for reconstructing the original feature set, if needed, as the error would be minimal. This is why it is often used for image processing with much success. Let us now look at how Julia can make use of this technique with one of our datasets.

APPLYING PCA IN JULIA

As we saw in previous chapters, the `OnlineNewsPopularity` dataset is rather large when it comes to features, and not all of them seem to be relevant to the target variable, which is the number of shares a given news article receives. Julia can help us reduce the size of the feature set to make the dataset easier to handle.

One way to do this is through the use of PCA, which can be found in the `MultivariateStatistics` package, which we first need to install and load:

```
In[1]: Pkg.add("MultivariateStats")
In[2]: using MultivariateStats
```

We'll omit the outputs for most of the commands in the examples of this chapter, leaving only the cases where we need to comment on the outputs of these commands. Once we have installed the `MultivariateStats` package, we'll load the data from the corresponding .csv file:

```
In[3]: cd("d:\\data\\OnlineNewsPopularity")                    #1
In[4]: X = readcsv("OnlineNewsPopularity.csv")[2:end,2:end]    #2
#1 you'll need to update this to the corresponding folder in your
    computer
#2 get the numeric data only
```

Since the header info (first row) and the identifier attribute (first column) aren't necessary for this example, we'll load only the rest of the dataset. Now it's time to convert the data to floats and split it into a training and a testing set. Although the splitting is not entirely necessary to run the PCA method, it's the best way to perform the dimensionality reduction in practice. This is because the test set is not always part of the original dataset, often becoming available at later stages of the project, long after we have created our models.

For the purposes of this example we will convert the output variable into a binary one, to demonstrate how dimensionality reduction works for classification problems. This process, however, does not affect the PCA method at all, since PCA does not make use of the target variable in any way.

```
In[9]: N, n = size(X)
    n -= 1                              #1
    I = Array(Float64, N, n)
    O = X[:, end]
    for j = 1:(n-1)
      for i = 1:N
       I[i,j] = Float64(X[i,j])
      end
```

```
       end
In[10]: Itr = I[ind[1:z],:]
        Ite = I[ind[(z+1):end],:]
        Otr = O_bin[ind[1:z]]                               #2
        Ote = O_bin[ind[(z+1):end]]                         #2
In[11]: M = fit(PCA, Itr'; maxoutdim = 10)                  #3
Out[11]: PCA(indim = 59, outdim = 4, principalratio = 0.99367)

#1 remove output column in the col. count (so, now n = number of
     features)
#2 this will be useful later on
#3 limit the total number of variables in reduced feature set to 10
```

At this point we have the dimensionality reduction framework, based on the training data, stored in the object called M. Notice that in the output Julia provides a brief summary of this mathematical model. We've learned that indim, the number of dimensions that go into the model, is 59 (=n), while outdim, the number of dimensions that come out of the model is just 4. This may appear strange since we asked for 10, but the Julia code aims to yield the optimum number of variables that is within our parameters. 10 is the maximum number of variables that can come out of the model; since Julia could get the job done with fewer, the PCA framework created just four.

The principalratio variable indicates what proportion of the overall variance of the data is covered by the selected (four) principal components, which in this case is a bit over 99%. This means that less than 1% of variance cannot be expressed by the reduced feature set, which is truly impressive. This type of variance is called residual variance. By adding more features to the PCA model we could limit the residual variance further, but remember the law of diminished returns that was mentioned earlier. Every additional principal component will be less and less useful, and will be adding less and less to the principalratio figure.

We have managed to reduce the feature set by (59 - 4) / 59 = 93%, in terms of features, with minimal loss of information (as expressed in the overall variance). Let's see now how we can implement this framework to the data we need to work with in the later parts of the pipeline:

```
In[12]: Jtr = transform(M, Itr')'
Out[12]: 31715x4 Array{Float64,2}:
    -1.1484e5   24619.6 -675.339     -29135.1
     95645.0   -57635.1 8347.65       16974.2
    -53198.3    -93375.1     36341.9   43627.4
```

Here we've taken the feature set of the original training data and applied the PCA model using the `transform()` function of this package. This yields a matrix consisting of four features, as expected. We had to transpose the feature matrix before applying the `transform()` function, since it expects the data to be formatted a bit differently. We can do the same with the feature set of the testing data as follows:

```
In[13]: Jte = transform(M, Ite')'
```

And there you have it. The dataset has been quickly and painlessly reduced in dimensionality. Of course the new features are a bit counter-intuitive, but rest assured that most of the information contained in the original features is still there. You can learn more about the intricacies of the PCA-related objects in the package's documentation, which is well-maintained: http://bit.ly/28OuXEk.

INDEPENDENT COMPONENTS ANALYSIS (ICA): MOST POPULAR ALTERNATIVE OF PCA

Although PCA is great if you need to reconstruct the original feature set from the reduced one, we rarely have the need to do this in most data science applications. Usually it's more valuable to have independent features, particularly if we are using certain statistical models that have feature independence as an assumption. One way to accomplish a dimensionality reduction that allows for independence is through the ICA method.

At the core of the ICA technique lies the mutual information metric, a handy measure of how good two features are together. In other words, ICA ensures that the extracted features it yields are as informative as possible, when used together. It is a crude estimation of how much value (measured in bits) would be added to a feature if it were used in tandem with another feature.

ICA tries to maximize this metric in its outputs. In other words, it tries to create feature combos (meta-features) that optimize the value of the information they collectively contain. This results in statistically independent features that are also non-Gaussian in nature. ICA is a theoretically sound approach to dimensionality reduction and has gained a lot of traction in the past decade, so it's definitely worth having in your toolbox.

As for implementation, the same package that supports PCA also provides tools for applying the ICA method to your data. The use of the main functions is identical to that of the corresponding functions in PCA; you still build the model using `fit()` and apply it using `transform()`. You just need to use ICA instead of PCA as the first parameter of `fit()`, in order to create the ICA model. You can learn more about ICA from the documentation webpage of the `MultivariateStatistics` package: http://bit.ly/29PLfdT.

FEATURE EVALUATION AND SELECTION

The PCA and ICA methods fall under the umbrella of *unsupervised* approaches, as they don't require a target variable in order to function. This has its advantages (e.g. they can work on all kinds of datasets and can add a lot to data exploration), but if there is additional information present, it makes sense to take it into account when reducing dimensionality. To accomplish this, we need to perform feature evaluation as a preliminary stage of the dimensionality reduction process, and then make a selection of the most promising features (or extracted features). These are often referred to as *supervised* approaches.

Overview of the methodology

In the majority of data science projects, the objective is to predict a particular variable (target). It logically follows that the more closely a feature is related to that variable, the more useful it will be for the models we create. Let's say you're trying to evaluate the effectiveness of a health diagnostic method that aims to predict whether a patient is healthy or not. You probably wouldn't use that person's favorite TV show as a feature–but you might use the number of hours he watches TV per day.

The feature evaluation and selection approach to dimensionality reduction ensures that only relevant features make the cut, and that all noisy ones are removed. So, in this example, we would compare all the features we have against the target variable and keep the ones that relate most closely to it, while discarding all the ones that are statistically independent of it.

There are various methods to evaluate a feature, as we have briefly seen in the previous chapter. We can use one of the following:

- Fisher's Discriminant Ratio (FDR)

- Index of Discernibility (latest open-source version: DID)

- Similarity Metrics
  - Correlation
  - Cosine similarity
  - Jaccard and other binary similarity metrics.

Although uncommon, it is possible to use combinations of these metrics for a more accurate evaluation of the features at hand. The method(s) you choose will depend on the data available. Specifically, depending on your features and your target variable, you might use the following:

	Target is a float	Target is a discreet variable
Features are floats	Cosine similarity or some other non-binary similarity metric, such as Pearson's Correlation	DID, FDR, Mutual Information
Features are binary	This combination isn't possible! Your problem must be incorrectly modeled.	Jaccard similarity, binary similarity, or a symmetric variant of either of these

Once you have decided which metric to use for evaluation, you need to set a threshold beyond which a feature will be accepted in the reduced feature set. This is usually arbitrary and depends on the problem at hand. Naturally, the higher the threshold, the smaller the reduced feature set will be. Alternatively, you can set the number of features you wish to have in the reduced feature set (let's call this number K). In this case you need to sort all the features based on the evaluation metric and select those with the K highest values.

Using Julia for feature evaluation and selection using cosine similarity

Now let's take our `OnlineNewsPopularity` dataset once more and see how we can perform dimensionality reduction using the feature evaluation and selection approach. In particular, we'll examine how we can harness the information of the continuous target variable (float type) in how we assess the individual features.

First, we'll need to define the cosine similarity function that we need for assessing the features:

```
In[14]: function cossim(x::Array, y::Array)
    # Cosine Similarity Function
    nx = norm(x)
    ny = norm(y)

    if (nx == 0) | (ny == 0)
      return NaN
    else
      return dot(x,y) / (nx * ny)
    end
  end
```

This is a quick and dirty way of building the metric, but it works fine for the purposes of this example and shows how Julia can be flexible, when needed. If we wanted to take a few extra steps, we could build a more error-proof version of the function. This would involve ensuring that the metric would be applied only to data that would make sense to use (e.g. all numeric vectors). You can improve this method so that Julia will reject irrelevant inputs (e.g. arrays of characters) as a practice exercise.

Now that our evaluation method is in place, we can use it to assess the features in our dataset. First, let's initialize the vector containing the feature scores in relation to the target variable:

```
In[15]: V = Array(Float64, n)
```

Some people prefer to initialize a vector with zeros, using the zeros() function, but array() is faster and makes more sense in this case study, as we populate every single one of the elements of V:

```
In[16]: for i = 1:n
    V[i] = cossim(Itr[:,i], Otr)
    end
```

After a bit of waiting, we should obtain a populated vector containing the evaluation of each of our 59 features. We can preview the first few of these numbers and calculate the average cosine similarity of the whole dataset as follows:

```
In[17]: abs(V[1:5]), mean(abs(V))
Out[17]:
    ([0.2052250978962261,0.2325465827311343,0.17498156181682142,0.0
    3124251651392406,0.03769500008408716],0.14725725376572263)
```

Since cosine similarity (like many other similarity measures) takes both positive and negative values, it makes sense to use the absolute value (abs() function). This is because a feature with a very negative similarity would still be valuable, since it would carry a signal, just like in the correlation cases.

Based on the above output, the cosine similarities of the features are low, with an average value of approximately 0.15. This warns us that predicting the popularity of a news article given this data will not be a trivial problem; we will need to make our threshold relatively low, say 0.2:

```
In[17]: th = 0.2
    feat_ind = (abs(V) .>= th)
    sum(feat_ind)
Out[17]: 20
```

In this case we find the 20 features ranking over 0.2 in terms of cosine similarity. Should we need fewer or more, we can adjust the threshold accordingly. To find out exactly which features made the team, we can use the `find()` command:

```
In[18]: show(find(feat_ind))
    [1,2,7,11,12,23,24,26,27,42,44,46,47,48,49,50,52,53,54,58]
```

The feature selection method is bound to yield somewhat different results when you run it, since the data points selected for the subset we are using will be different. Of course, you could use all the data points, but this would be cheating; it would ensure good performance even if the model is bad.

Using Julia for feature evaluation and selection using DID

Now let's try performing feature evaluation and selection for a dataset where the target variable is discreet (i.e. binary or nominal). In this example we will make use of the Distance-based Index of Discernibility method (DID for short), using a binary target variable based on the number of shares.

The DID metric is recommended for various reasons. First of all, it is distribution agnostic and therefore widely applicable in all kinds of data. It's also fast to calculate. Finally, it's intuitive and easy to interpret. Actually, transforming a continuous feature to a binary (or some other kind of discreet variable) is commonplace in data science. By employing this tactic, we illustrate that the data scientist is versatile and examines the data from various angles.

We can arbitrarily define this binary variable as being "true" for shares being equal or greater than 10,000, and "false" otherwise. One interpretation of this variable would be the articles' viral status. Considering that these are news articles, even 10,000 shares could be enough to consider them viral. Let's put Julia to work to make this happen:

```
In[19]: ind = (O .>= 10000) # cases of "viral" result
    O_bin = falses(N) # initialize binary Array
    O_bin[ind] = true
```

Next, we can separate the now binary outputs into training and testing, using the same randomized sampling we did previously (by employing the same array `z` as before):

```
In[20]: Otr = Array(O_bin[ind[1:z]])
        Ote = Array(O_bin[ind[(z+1):end]])
```

Now, we need to load the essential functions in order to apply the DID metric:

```
In[21]: include("C:\\users\\Zacharias\\Documents\\Julia\\DID.jl")
```

Be sure to adjust the path before you attempt to load the DID script. Finally, we can evaluate all the features individually, using the same logic as before:

```
In[22]: for i = 1:n
          V[i] = DID(Itr[:,i], Otr)[1]
        end
```

If you look closely at the code of the `DID.jl` script, you'll notice that `DID()` requires three inputs, the last one being the sample size. If you are not too particular, just utilize the default value of 10,000 data points (which is plenty for most datasets) as it's robust. However, because a different sample is used every time you run the metric, you can expect some variance in its output (which shouldn't affect the results much). Also note that `DID()` yields two outputs: the overall score (a float64 variable) and the intra-class discernibility matrix, showing how discernible each pair of classes is (a float64 matrix variable). Although insightful, the second output is not required for most applications, which is why we have the [1] index at the end of the line where the `DID()` function is used.

Like we did in the cosine similarity example, let's take a look at what these feature evaluations look like:

```
In[23]: V[1:5], mean(V)
[0.5068131108916679,0.22245264761577588,0.04160899480072447,0.16882
    573283040755,0.0754911973187614]0.19675244105321787
```

As DID scores are by definition between 0 and 1, there is no need to apply the `abs()` function on them. It seems that the features are not particularly powerful for predicting whether a news article becomes viral; generally, DID scores below 0.5 are not great for two-class problems. Therefore, if we are to perform some meaningful dimensionality reduction, we need to adjust our expectations accordingly. Let's try using a threshold value of 0.35:

```
In[24]: th = 0.35
    feat_ind = (V .>= th)
    sum(feat_ind)
Out[24]: 10
```

We've found ten features that appear promising. Let's look at which indexes they correspond to:

```
In[25]: show(find(feat_ind)) # features in reduced feature set
    [1,14,25,31,32,33,42,54,56,58]
```

The two methods yield a different list of selected features, even though we applied them on the exact same subset of the dataset. The reason for this is twofold. First of all, different metrics provide different evaluations of the features. Secondly, the target variables in the two cases are inherently different (one is a float and the other is a Boolean), capturing different levels of information of the original dataset.

Pros and cons of the feature evaluation and selection approach

This set of methods, although widely used by the most knowledgeable data scientists, is not all fun and games. Whether it is worthwhile for your data is not always obvious. This decision is made easier by carefully considering the various advantages and disadvantages of this methodology, which are shown in Table 8.1.

Pros	Cons
Speed	Doesn't take into account dependencies among the features of the dataset
Very few parameters	No mathematical proof behind it
Easily scalable	Requires target variable
Interpretability	

Table 8.1. Pros and cons of the feature evaluation and selection approach to dimensionality reduction.

OTHER DIMENSIONALITY REDUCTION TECHNIQUES

There are a few other options for dimensionality reduction that are worth considering. Two of the most important ones are the following:

- Genetic algorithms

- Discernibility-based approach.

Both of these methods are sophisticated and often computationally expensive. However, this is the price to pay for building a robust reduced feature set that closely approximates the optimum. (Although theoretically possible, in practice it is unrealistic to obtain the optimum selection of features.)

Overview of the alternative dimensionality reduction methods

We'll briefly discuss two of the most powerful and sophisticated dimensionality reduction methods: those based on genetic algorithms and those based on discernibility. Both of these approaches make use of groups of features at a time, aiming to capture the information contained in the relationships among the various features of the dataset. As these are more advanced topics, we will not go into much detail, but we will provide you with references where you can learn more.

Genetic algorithms

The genetic algorithm (GA) approach has been around for many years and is one of the most popular family of AI algorithms founded in biomimicry. In summary, GA involves a series of optimization algorithms that work on discreet variables. So, if you want to optimize a bunch of nominal parameters of a system and you have a continuous variable that they relate to (referred to as "fitness function"), GA is a promising approach. Since the dimensionality reduction problem (when expressed as a feature selection task) is inherently a discreet optimization problem, the GA-based approach makes perfect sense.

Your best option for working with GA is the `GeneticAlgorithms` package (http://bit.ly/29lG0l2). Using this package, your `abcde` array would be the indexes of the features available, as a Boolean vector. As for the fitness function, you can use any similarity metric you wish that can take a set of features as an input. You can define the details of this in the function called `fitness()`.

GA is a specialized AI topic which requires a bit of studying if you wish to understand and implement it. A great place to start is on Professor Obitko's site: http://bit.ly/29p3Tt9.

Discernibility-based approach

Unlike GA (or any other sophisticated approach out there), the discernibility-based method is straightforward and doesn't require any background whatsoever, while its parameters are few and self-explanatory.

Unlike the individual feature evaluation use of the DID metric, the strategy discussed in this section involves the evaluation of several features at once–a trait most feature evaluation metrics don't share. The use of the metric in this setting goes as follows:

1. Evaluate the whole feature set.

2. Establish one of the following termination parameters:
    a) The proportion of the discernibility score that you want to maintain in the reduced feature set, OR
    b) the total number of features.

3. Apply a search strategy to optimize the reduce feature set's DID, such as:
    a) Start from the most promising feature and build up the feature set by adding and removing features, OR
    b) start from the whole feature set and remove most needless features.

Should you wish to explore this approach in more detail, you can read up on the topic in Chapter 5 of the material found at http://bit.ly/28O5qMY. Although the discernibility concept and its original implementations predate the DID metric, they all follow the same framework. Therefore, all feature evaluation methods that applied to the SID and HID metrics will also apply to DID and any other discernibility metrics.

When to use a sophisticated dimensionality reduction method

It is clear that no dimensionality reduction approach is a panacea, since they each have a different use case. This is why it is crucial that you become familiar with all of them. Overall, the sophisticated methods we described are good for complex cases where there is substantial non-linearity. GAs are particularly good for very large feature sets, but their plethora of parameters may intimidate some data scientists. If you have the time to experiment with various settings and understand the dataset well enough, go ahead and try this approach. If, however, you just want to get a working solution to the problem without becoming a digital geneticist of sorts, the discernibility-based approach would be a fine alternative.

These methods described are just a few of the most robust ones out there. There are several other worthy approaches available, so we recommend you remain on the lookout for alternatives. Even if you never use any of the sophisticated dimensionality reduction methods, it is good to know that they exist and that if your default approaches fail, there is something else you can use.

SUMMARY

- Dimensionality reduction is often an essential part of data science, as it condenses the dataset at hand, making efficient use of data analysis methods. As a bonus, the reduced dataset takes up less storage space and fewer resources in general.

- There are two main approaches to dimensionality reduction: using only the features (unsupervised), and using the features in combination with the target variable (supervised).

Unsupervised dimensionality reduction methods:

- The most popular unsupervised dimensionality reduction technique is principal components analysis (PCA). This statistical method works well with a small to moderate number of features. It maximizes the variance of the dataset explained by the extracted meta-features.

- Independent component analysis (ICA) is a worthy alternative to PCA; similarly, it does not utilize the target variable. ICA works by maximizing the mutual information metric, instead of the variance. It also provides meta-features.

Supervised dimensionality reduction methods:

- The supervised dimensionality reduction methods can be further categorized into basic (involving individual evaluation of features), and sophisticated (involving evaluation of features in groups).

- Basic methods evaluate each feature, depending on the type of the target variable, and select the ones with the highest scores.
    - Continuous: Cosine Similarity, Pearson Correlation, or some other similarity metric
    - Discreet: Fisher Discriminant Ratio, Index of Discernibility, or Mutual Information

- Sophisticated
    - Continuous: Genetic Algorithms (GA) based approach
    - Discreet: Index of Discernibility or GA based approach

- There is no silver bullet when it comes to the dimensionality reduction method to use. Your choice depends on your data and the available resources.

CHAPTER CHALLENGE

1. You are given a dataset consisting of one million rows and ten thousand features. Would you perform dimensionality reduction? If so, what method would you use? Why?

2. A project you are working on involves a dataset of one million rows and 500 features. Would you perform dimensionality reduction? If so, what method would you use? Why?

3. After a lot of refining of your original gene expression data, you have created a dataset consisting of 200 rows and five thousand features. What dimensionality reduction would you use on this dataset? Why?

4. You are given a dataset consisting of ten thousand rows and 20 features. Would you use dimensionality reduction on this dataset? Why?

5. A statistics researcher has developed a dimensionality reduction method that guarantees to find the best possible reduced feature set, by examining all possible combinations. Would you use this method for a data science project? Why?

6. What is the main advantage of feature evaluation based approaches to dimensionality reduction, over the popular statistical ones (e.g. PCA)?

7. A brilliant researcher has developed a method that can process data with high efficiency and performance, as long as the inputs are statistically independent of each other. Which dimensionality reduction method would you use to turn your dataset into a manageable size? Why?

8. You are given a dataset consisting of one million features and 100 million rows. Many of the features are correlated to each other. You have plenty of time to come up with an insight about the dataset, and the objective is to have the highest accuracy possible in the model that runs the reduced dataset. Which approach would you take? Why?

CHAPTER 9
Sampling Data and Evaluating Results

In the era of big data, sampling has become a popular and essential part of the data science pipeline. Even if you can get all the available data to fit into a large data structure, it may be ill-advised (unless you already have an adequate model at your disposal). Just because the cloud and large computer clusters make it possible, doesn't mean that you should use all the available data as-is. You shouldn't even need all of your data to see whether a feature holds value; a sample can make the whole process much more efficient.

Equally important is the evaluation of the results of your models. Although there are some obvious techniques we have used already, there is much more to it, as not all data science problems involve the same goals. Besides, when it comes to evaluating results, there are often conflicting objectives which must be considered.

In this chapter we'll examine the following topics:

- The various ways we can perform sampling

- Evaluation metrics for classifiers

- Evaluation metrics for regression systems

- K-fold Cross Validation.

SAMPLING TECHNIQUES

Although we have glanced at sampling throughout the book, we've merely scratched the surface. Sampling can be a sophisticated process for certain problems. In this section we'll examine the two main types of sampling and how we can employ Julia for these tasks. In all cases of sampling used in data science, we make use of randomization, as this yields more unbiased samples.

Basic sampling

This is the type of sampling we have been using so far. It works well for the majority of cases and it is very fast in its implementation, particularly in a language like Julia. Because it is such a simple way to create samples, you don't need a package for it. However, there are a variety of options available in the StatsBase package, using the sample() function. We recommend you load that function into memory using the import StatsBase.sample command, as we'll be extending it later with a custom function.

The idea behind basic sampling is to take a random subset of the original data and yield the features and the target variable values that correspond to it. The only parameter we need to use is the number of data points we expect to have in the sample (e.g. 1000). So, if we were to take the magic dataset, for instance, and apply basic sampling, we would type:

```
In[1]: p = 0.1
    n = round(Int64, 19020*p)
    ind = sample(1:19020, n)
    SampleData1 = data[ind,:]
```

Where the value multiplied by p is the number of elements in the sample, rounded to the nearest integer. Alternatively, you can use the built-in function randperm(n), which provides you with a random permutation of a range from 1 to n. So, in the case of the magic dataset we could type:

```
In[1]: ind = randperm(19020)[1:n]
    SampleData2 = data[ind,:]
```

Both of these methods are fast, but the latter is preferable if you don't want to worry about external packages (that often tend to be difficult to remember when you need them!).

Stratified sampling

Stratified sampling is a bit trickier as it aims to preserve the class structure of the dataset, when classes are available. However, you can use any discreet variable instead of a class, if you want to apply this type of sampling to a dataset (e.g. the gender variable for a demographics dataset). The objective is to create a sample with a distribution of a given variable similar to that of the original dataset.

Again, the only parameter we need to address is the number of elements that need to be included in the sample. As this is not a trivial task, we need to make use of an external script (like the `sample.jl` included in this book, which extends the `sample()` function of the `StatsBase` package) as currently there is no package that provides this method. So, applying stratified sampling to the `magic` dataset would look like this:

```
In[3]: StratifiedSample = sample(data[:,1:10], data[:,11], n)
```

This works only because we have extended the `sample()` function using the `sample.jl` script. If you were to run this snippet with the default `sample()` function of the `StatsBase` package, you would get an error. The output of this function yields two distinct arrays of the sample: one for the features and one for the labels. You could easily merge the two by employing the built-in `hcat()` function:

```
In[4]: SampleData3 = hcat(StratifiedSample[1], StratifiedSample[2])
```

In this example stratified sampling may be an overkill, but there are several real-world scenarios where this approach would be appropriate and necessary. If a particular class is very small compared to the other classes, its signal may be weakened or lost altogether through the basic sampling approach.

PERFORMANCE METRICS FOR CLASSIFICATION

Once we have completed a classification task, we end up with a vector of predicted labels that correspond to the test set we have run through a classification system. But how close were we to the actual labels? To answer this question in a reliable and insightful way, we employ a series of metrics. Let's look at each one of them more closely.

Confusion matrix

Although this is not strictly a classification metric, a confusion matrix (or table) is essential for evaluating a classifier's performance. The matrix should indicate how close the predictions were to the actual labels, and divulge some insight as to where the errors (misclassifications) lie. This will not only allow us to go deeper into the classifier's performance, but also get a better understanding of the dataset. This is especially true if we run several classifications on the same data, using different parameters and different classifiers. Let us now see how Julia can produce a confusion matrix for a basic classification experiment (so that you can check it by hand, for more in-depth understanding of the methods described in this section). First, let's create the predictions and the labels' vectors:

```
In[5]: t = [1, 1, 1, 1, 2, 2, 2, 2, 2, 2, 2, 2]
       y = [1, 2, 2, 2, 2, 2, 2, 2, 1, 2, 2, 1]
Now, let's calculate the corresponding confusion matrix:
In[6]: CM = confusmat(2, t, y)
Out[6]: 2x2 Array{Int64,2}:
    1 3
    2 6
```

The target variable can be anything (e.g. a string, a character), but for this function of the MLBase package to work, it must be encoded as an array of integers. If you are unsure about how to accomplish this, please refer to Chapter 6.

In this simple example, we can deduce that the classifier has mediocre performance, since there are a lot of cases where class 1 was predicted as class 2 and vice versa. In general, the closer the confusion matrix is to a diagonal matrix, the better the performance of the classifier. Let us see how we can quantify this rule of thumb, using a series of metrics based on the confusion matrix.

Accuracy metrics

Basic accuracy

In the beginning of the book, as well as in the "Caffeine for the Force" case study, we looked briefly at this metric for evaluating the performance of various classifiers. It is the simplest metric for this task and it works well for relatively balanced datasets (i.e. datasets where the classes are of comparable size).

In essence, this metric calculates the proportion of correct classifications over the total number of classifications. By correct classifications, we mean cases where the predictions and the labels are the same. This corresponds to the diagonal of the confusion matrix. So, in our previous example, the accuracy of the classification is `(1 + 6) / length(t) = 7 / 12` equals roughly `0.583`. The same result can be obtained through the `correctrate()` function of the `MLBase` package:

```
In[7]: correctrate(t, y)
Out[7]: 0.58333333334
```

The same result would be obtained if you reversed the inputs of the function by accident, since Julia has no way of knowing which labels are the ground truth and which are the predicted ones.

Accuracy is often referred to as "accuracy rate" and it always takes a value between 0.0 and 1.0 (usually expressed as a percentage). Usually an accuracy higher than $1/q$, where q is the number of classes, is considered satisfactory (although you'd like to get as close to 1.0 as possible). Unfortunately, the accuracy metric performs poorly when the dataset is heavily unbalanced, yielding misleading results. For instance, in a fraud detection scenario, even a horrible classifier is bound to produce accuracy rates close to 1 simply by defaulting to the dominant class, which in this case would be "safe transaction."

Weighted accuracy

Although accuracy on its own is a very blunt metric (considering every hit or miss of exactly the same value), it has a modified version that works well for even the most challenging datasets: weighted accuracy. One benefit of weighted accuracy is that it makes some data points more important than others, as is often the case in unbalanced datasets, where the smaller class usually holds the most value.

In the previous example, if we were more interested in predicting the first class correctly, we would assign higher weights to the elements of the corresponding test set. The weights are normalized. Their exact values don't matter all that much, since it is the ratio of the weight of one data point to another that affects the overall score. So, in our example, we could apply weighted accuracy by first defining and normalizing the weights:

```
In[8]: w = [4, 1]
    w ./= sum(w)
Out[8]: 2-element Array{Float64,1}:
    0.8
    0.2
```

Now, we need to apply them to the calculation of the accuracy rate:

```
In[9]: 2*sum(diag(CM) .* w) / 12
Out[9]: 0.333333333333333
```

Note that "2" corresponds to the number of classes and "12" to the total number of classifications. In general, the formula for the weighted accuracy metric would be:

```
q*sum(diag(CM) .* w) / N
```

If you plan to use weighted accuracy often, it would be helpful to code it into a function such as the following:

```
function wa{T <: Real}(t::Array{Int64, 1}, y::Array{Int64, 1},
    w::Array{T, 1})
  q = length(unique(t))
  N = length(t)
  CM = confusmat(q, t, y)
  return q*sum(diag(CM) .* w) / N
end
```

In the example, we chose the first class to be much more important than the second one, making the overall performance of the classifier vastly different. Before, the classifier seemed decent; after the application of the weights it seems subpar for this particular problem. If we were to reverse the weights and make the second class more important, the weighted accuracy would swing in the opposite direction, taking a value of about 0.833. It is important to choose the weights carefully if you want the weighted accuracy to provide meaningful and insightful results.

Precision and recall metrics

Accuracy often fails to capture how well a classifier performs for a particular class, as it focuses on delivering the classifier's overall performance. If we wish to zoom in on a particular class we'll need to make use of alternative metrics, such as precision and recall.

Precision depicts how reliable a classifier is for predicting a particular class. Mathematically it is defined as the number of hits over the total number of predictions for that particular class: TP / $(TP + FP)$. So, for the given example, the precision of the classifier for class 1 is 1 / $(1 + 2)$ = 0.333. In general, you can use the confusion matrix CM to calculate the precision of class c using the snippet:

```
CM[c,c] / sum(CM[:,c])
```

Recall shows how many of the cases of the particular class the classifier got right. Mathematically this is equivalent to the number of hits over the total number of cases for that class, predicted or otherwise: TP / $(TP + FN)$. For our example, the recall of the classifier for class 1 is 1 / $(1 + 3)$ = 0.25. The code to calculate recall in the general case is:

```
CM[c,c] / sum(CM[c,:])
```

Clearly, both the precision and the recall for class 1 are not excellent. The precision and recall of class 2 will be larger, since overall the performance of the system is 0.583 and there are only two classes. Of course, to know exactly what they are we'll need to do the corresponding calculations.

F1 METRIC

Although precision and recall capture important information about the performance of a classifier for a given class, neither of them provides a good snapshot of the bigger picture. One can easily tweak a classifier so that it has amazing precision or amazing recall, but it is extremely difficult to get a very good score for both (unless you actually improve the classifier or the features significantly). Any metric that took into account both precision and recall would be able to deliver a more holistic view of the classifier's performance.

One such metric (the most popular one) is the F1 metric, which is expressed as a number between precision and recall, leaning toward whichever one is smaller. This is expressed mathematically using the harmonic mean (which you can read more about at http://bit.ly/29p4FpY), or in terms of the confusion matrix: `F1 = 1/(1+(FP+FN)/(2TP)) = 2TP/(2TP+FP+FN)`. In the aforementioned example the F1 of the classifier would be: `2*1/(2*1+2+3) = 2/7 = 0.286`. This general formula for the F1 metric can be expressed in Julia as:

```
2*CM[c,c] / (sum(CM[:,c]) + sum(CM[c,:]))
```

Alternatively, you can just calculate the harmonic mean of `R(CM,c)` and `P(CM,c)`.

Not surprisingly, the F1 metric for class 1 of this classification is not good either, as both the precision and the recall for that class are relatively low. Yet even if one of them were satisfactory, the other one would pull the F1 metric to a low value. As an exercise, you can calculate the F1 metric of this classification for the second class of this classification experiment.

MISCLASSIFICATION COST

Rarely do all errors have the same importance. In security applications, for example, if you misclassify a normal person as an intruder, it's not the end of the world (though that person may get frustrated). If you misclassify an intruder for a normal person, though, you'll make the headlines–and not in a positive way!

Defining the cost matrix

Mathematically we can express this difference in the importance of errors as different misclassification costs, usually arranged in a matrix. Obviously in such a setup, the diagonal of the matrix would be all zeros (since this corresponds to the correct classifications), with all the remaining elements being some non-negative numbers. This is often referred to as a cost matrix and in our example it could be something like this:

```
0 10
3  0
```

You can store this in Julia as:

```
C = [0 10; 3 0]
```

Note that this is unrelated to the classifier used and it is usually arbitrary defined (unless we know how much each type of mistake would cost us). Also, the cost is not necessarily in a particular currency; it is usually the relative size of each cost that is important. Even if you double the whole matrix, it shouldn't affect your view of the classifier's performance over a series of classification experiments.

Calculating the total misclassification cost

In order to make use of the cost matrix, we need to combine it with the confusion matrix we calculated earlier. You can do this by applying the following simple piece of code:

```
In[10]: total_cost = sum(CM .* C)
Out[10]: 36
```

This number may not mean much to us, but if the cost matrix is populated in a meaningful way, this result would be more insightful. For example, if the numbers in C represented thousands in lost revenue, the above output would mean that this classifier's imperfect performance would cost us $36,000. When optimizing for the total misclassification cost we want as small a number as possible.

RECEIVER OPERATING CHARACTERISTIC (ROC) CURVE AND RELATED METRICS

ROC Curve

The ROC curve is one of the most common methods for assessing a classifier's performance for cases with just two classes, particularly if you are new to the field.

It doesn't take any parameters and provides you with an insightful plot that you can share with your supervisors and anyone else who doesn't need to see all of the details.

Contrary to what its name suggests, it's not usually a curve, but more like a zig-zag line. It basically shows how well a classifier performs in terms of true positives and false positives, under various conditions. Usually the classifier is applied with a different set of parameters and its performance is noted as a point in the plot. Afterward, all the points are connected, resulting in a plot called the ROC curve. The closer the curve lies to the top-left corner of the plot, the better the classifier is overall.

In Figure 9.1 you can see a typical ROC curve. The dotted line across the plot shows the performance of a naive classifier as a reference. The closer the curve is to that line, the worse the classifier's performance is.

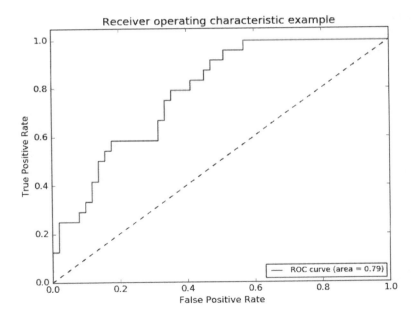

Figure 9.1. A typical ROC curve of a classifier.

In order to create a ROC curve, though, you'll need more than just the predicted labels of the classification. You'll also require the probabilities of each data point's classification. This is basically a measure of how confident the classifier is for a particular label, and in many cases is the score that defines the label (this score is sometimes referred to as "degree of confidence"). Let us first generate an array p with these probabilities (this would normally come from the classifier as one of its outputs):

```
In[11]: p = [0.6, 0.55, 0.65, 0.6, 0.7, 0.65, 0.9, 0.75, 0.55,
        0.65, 0.8, 0.45]
```

You can generate ROC curves in Julia using the following code, after you've loaded the ROC package:

```
In[12]: using ROC
In[13]: z = (y .== t)
    rc = ROC.roc(p, z)
```

Since the roc() function exists in the MLBase as well, we should make it explicit to Julia that we want to use the function from the ROC package, which is why we call this function by adding "ROC." in front of it.

Now, let's create a plot based on the ROC object we have created:

```
In[14]: plot(rc)
```

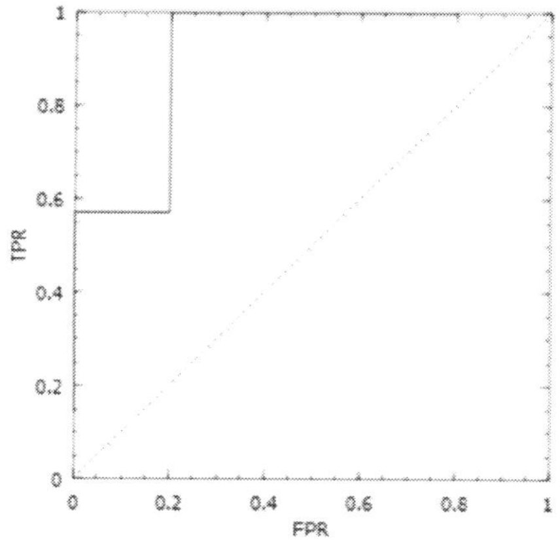

Figure 9.2. The ROC curve of the classifier in our example.

The MLBase package also has a few functions for the ROC curve, but if you want to create a plot of the curve itself, the easiest way is through the ROC package. Still, once you are comfortable with Julia, we recommend you give it a try as it is much better documented than the ROC package.

AUC Metric

Since the ROC curve itself doesn't tell us much about exactly how well a classifier performs, we often need to quantify its insight through a metric. AUC, which stands for area under curve, is the most popular metric as it shows exactly that, taking values between 0 and 1. The higher its value, the better the classifier performed in this particular experiment. Let's look at how we can calculate AUC using Julia:

```
In[15]: AUC(rc)
Out[15]: 0.7142857142857143
```

Usually scores over 0.7 are considered satisfactory. In this fictitious example the classifier performed acceptably based on the AUC metric, though there is plenty of room for improvement. The relatively good performance is partly due to the fact that the classifier was not confident about the cases where it failed to provide a correct prediction. It is important to keep in mind that although this imaginary classifier performed decently overall, it may still not be a good choice for the problem at hand; take the evaluation of AUC with a grain of salt.

Gini Coefficient

This is another metric that stems from the ROC curve; it shows how a classifier's performance compares to the random classifier represented by the straight line in the ROC plot. It takes values between -1 and 1, with 0 representing a performance as good as a random guess. The Gini Coefficient is calculated by the formula $G = 2AUC - 1$, where AUC is the area under the ROC curve metric, as we saw previously. Generally, a positive Gini Coefficient is good. However, it is not an absolute metric, since we may be interested in how a classifier performs for a particular class–something that this metric fails to capture.

In Julia there is no function that yields the Gini Coefficient of a classification, but if you want to calculate it you can use the AUC() function as a basis:

```
In[16]: function GC(roc_curve) = 2*AUC(roc_curve) - 1
In[17]: GC(rc)
Out[17]: 0.4285714285714286
```

Clearly, evaluation of this fictitious classification experiment is pretty good (about 43% better than chance), though there is still a lot of room for improvement.

PERFORMANCE METRICS FOR REGRESSION

Since the regression aspect of machine learning is a whole new animal, it comes with its own set of metrics. This is because the output of a regressor is a continuous variable, just like the target variable that it tries to predict. None of the classification metrics would work properly (if at all).

Regression performance metrics basically compute how different the prediction is from the target (this difference is also known as error). The lower they are, the better the performance of the regressor. The most widely-used metrics are the mean square error (MSE) and the sum squared error (SSE). There are a few reasons that performance metrics for regression tend to focus on squared errors:

- There's no need to worry about the sign of the error, since the square function eliminates it

- They take care of extreme errors as these are magnified

- The error function is easy to apply a derivative on, making it ideal for certain optimization methods.

MSE Metric and its variant, RMSE

By taking all the aforementioned squared errors and averaging them, we obtain the MSE metric. If we were to take the square root of this value, we would get the RMSE metric, which is a variant of MSE. RMSE is often used in physics, particularly in signal processing.

In Julia we can compute the MSE and RMSE metric as follows. First we need to get some sample data going:

```
In[18]: t = [0.0, 0.5, 1.0, 1.5, 2.0, 2.5, 3.0, 2.0, 3.0, 2.5, 1.5,
       3.0]
       y = [-0.5, 0.6, 1.4, 1.2, 1.9, 2.6, 3.1, 2.4, 2.9, 2.5, 1.3,
       2.8]
```

The first vector (t) has the target values, while the second (y) has the corresponding predictions. Next, we need to calculate the squared errors (se) based on these vectors:

```
In[19]: se = (t - y).^2
```

Now, we can calculate MSE and RMSE easily by executing the following code:

```
In[20]: mse = mean(se)
Out[20]: 0.06583333333333334
In[21]: rmse = sqrt(mse)
Out[21]: 0.2565800719723442
```

Here are a couple of functions for calculating the MSE and RMSE metrics swiftly. Unfortunately, they aren't yet contained in a reliable package.

```
MSE(t::Array{Float64, 1}, y::Array{Float64, 1}) = mean((t-y).^2)
RMSE(t::Array{Float64, 1}, y::Array{Float64, 1}) = sqrt(mean((t-
     y).^2))
```

SSE METRIC

If we were to add the squared errors instead of taking their average, we would end up with the SSE metric. This is also popular when evaluating the performance of a regression system. Though it correlates perfectly with the MSE metric (so there is no need to calculate both), it may be useful in some cases where you need to calculate performance several times (e.g. through an optimization process), as it is slightly faster to compute. Here is how Julia can help you make use of this metric by using the squared errors vector we calculated previously:

```
In[22]: sse = sum(se)
```

```
Out[22]: 0.79
```

Should you want to wrap this whole process in a function, you could use something like this:

```
SSE(t::Array{Float64, 1}, y::Array{Float64, 1}) = sum((t-y).^2)
```

OTHER METRICS

All the performance metrics for regression are basically variants of the Euclidean distance between the predicted targets and the actual ones. So it is not difficult to create your own performance metrics, if you want to dig deeper into the evaluation of your regressor's performance.

For example, instead of the vanilla-flavored mean used in MSE, you could use the harmonic or even the reverse harmonic mean (which is not canon in statistics, despite its utility) on the squared errors. These two alternative metrics will be milder and harsher on the extreme errors performed by the regression system being assessed, respectively. Here are the corresponding functions for these metrics:

```
function harmean{T<:Real}(X::Array{T,1}, tol::Float64 = 0.1)
# tol = tolerance parameter for avoiding "division by 0" errors
    return length(X) / sum(1./(X + tol)) - tol
end
function revharmean{T<:Real}(X::Array{T,1}, tol::Float64 = 0.1)
# Reverse Harmonic Mean
    return maximum(X) + minimum(X) - harmean(X, tol)
end
function HSE{T<:Real}(y::Array{T,1}, t::Array{T,1})
# Harmonic mean of Squared Error
SE = (y-t).^2
return harmean(SE)
end
function RHSE{T<:Real}(y::Array{T,1}, t::Array{T,1})
# Reverse Harmonic mean of Squared Error
SE = (y-t).^2
return revharmean(SE)
end
```

Feel free to explore other alternatives as well. At the end of the day, the data science field is work in progress, so who is to say that the best performance metric for regression isn't yet to be discovered? Besides, it may be the case that a custom performance metric works better for your data science problem.

K-FOLD CROSS VALIDATION (KFCV)

KFCV is an evaluation strategy that allows you to check whether a particular machine learning system achieves good generalization by performing a series of experiments on it. The experiments make use of the whole dataset by partitioning it into K roughly equal parts, which are used as the test set in K different iterations. In order to obtain useful results from KFCV in the case of classification problems, we often must perform stratified sampling.

The logic of KFCV is that if a machine learning system happens by chance to perform well at a particular sample, it might fool us into believing that it is a reliable one. However, it would be practically impossible to repeat this lucky break again and again, over mutually exclusive test sets. So, if a classifier or regressor has a lucky run, it may influence the results of a single experiment, but not of the whole series of experiments dictated by KFCV.

The selection of the K parameter in KFCV can be tricky. There is no "right answer" since it depends, as usual, on the problem at hand. Usually a K value of 10 provides adequate results (which is why it is the default option in the corresponding script for this task).

If we were to choose the maximum possible value for K (i.e. the total number of data points in the dataset), we would end up with a special evaluation technique that is referred to as Leave-One-Out validation. This is particularly useful for very small datasets, where sampling the data doesn't make much sense as it would compromise the signal in the data. Although well-documented, this particular evaluation method is rarely used in data science (you could say that data scientists tend to "leave it out" of their toolbox!).

If you want to learn more about KFCV, we recommend studying a set of slides prepared by Professor Gutierrez-Osuna; they can be found at http://bit.ly/1gOxGwp. Also, even though you can use any kind of sampling for KFCV when dealing with classification problems, we strongly recommend that you go with stratified sampling; it is easy to get a biased sample at some point, after repeating the process K times.

Applying KFCV in Julia

You can use Julia to apply K-fold Cross Validation to your data using the provided script `KFCV.jl` (unfortunately, there isn't a decent implementation of the KFCV method in any of the available packages at this time). Here is how you can do this for the `magic` dataset, using `K = 10`.

First you need to make sure that the `KFCV.jl` file is on your working directory. Then you can go ahead and load it:

```
In[23]: include("KFCV.jl")
```

Finally, you can apply it on your data as follows:

```
In[24]: P, T, PT, TT = KFCV(data[:,1:(end-1)], data[:,end], 10);
```

The semicolon at the end is optional, but can help keep your notebook more usable (if you don't use the semicolon, Julia will flood your notebook with data that you don't need to view).

The outputs of this function are all arrays consisting of 10 elements. Each one of these outputs are respectively:

- P: The training inputs (features) for each KFCV experiment

- T: The training outputs (labels) for each KFCV experiment

- PT: The testing inputs (features) for each KFCV experiment

- TT: The testing outputs (labels) for each KFCV experiment.

KFCV tips

Although KFCV is better than any single test you can run on a machine learning system (even with stratified sampling), it is not a panacea. There are times that a classifier or a regressor would perform relatively well on a series of KFCV experiments; this is why we recommend you run a number of KFCVs—enough to yield statistical significance. However, as the data you use for developing your model gets larger, the need for repeated KFCV runs diminishes.

Also, if you want to compare two classifiers or two regressors to each other, you are better off using the same KFCV partitioning for both systems. This is particularly important if both machine learning systems are of about the same level of performance.

SUMMARY

Sampling:

- Sampling provides a smaller dataset that is more practical to work with, while at the same time preserving (to some extent) the signals of the original dataset.

- Basic sampling is indifferent to the class structure and works fine with relatively balanced datasets. It is the most common way of sampling for regression problems.

- Stratified sampling takes into account the number of elements in each class and produces a sample that has the same class distribution. It is particularly suitable for unbalanced datasets and for K-fold Cross Validation.

- Evaluate results by determining the performance of a classifier or a regressor.

Classification:

- There are several metrics for evaluating a classifier, the most important of which are accuracy (basic and weighted), precision, recall, F1, total cost (based on a cost matrix), and the ROC curve (along with its related metrics). Most of these are related to the confusion matrix of a particular classification.

- Confusion matrix is a $q \times q$ matrix showing how well a classifier performs in predicting the correct labels and where the various errors lie (q = number of classes). The elements in the diagonal correspond to all the correct classifications.

- Accuracy is a basic metric that takes the ratio of the number of the correct classifications over the total number of predictions. It takes values between 0 and 1 (the higher the better). It works well for balanced datasets.

- Weighted accuracy is a variant that takes into account the importance of each class and shifts the value of the metric accordingly. This is good for unbalanced datasets, or datasets where we care more for the predictions related to certain classes mainly. The weights are defined arbitrarily.

- Precision is a metric that shows how reliable a classifier is for a particular class.

- Recall is a measure that depicts how many of the elements of a particular class are classified correctly.

- F1 is the harmonic mean of precision and recall, expressing the performance of a classifier for a given class.

- Cost matrix is a $q \times q$ matrix showing how much each misclassification costs (its diagonal is full of zeros). This is very similar to the weighted accuracy and is used to calculate the overall cost of all the errors made by a given classifier for a particular dataset. The costs are defined in an arbitrary way.

- An ROC curve is a plot that shows how well a classifier does overall, when it comes to problems with two classes.

- The AUC metric (short for area under curve) is a measure of a binary classifier's performance, based on the ROC curve. It takes values between 0 and 1 (the higher the better).

- The Gini Coefficient is another metric that is based on the ROC curve and shows how well a binary classifier performs compared to random guessing. It takes values between -1 and 1 (the higher the better), with any positive value being better than random classification.

Regression:

- Regression is evaluated using some variant of the distance of the predicted values to the actual values. The most common metrics used are mean square error (MSE), and sum of square error (SSE).

- Square error is a vector consisting of the errors of the various data points the regressors has predicted, raised to the power of two. The errors themselves are the differences between the actual values and the predicted values.

- MSE is the arithmetic average of the squared errors of in a regression problem.

- RMSE is the square root of the MSE in a regression problem.

- SSE is the sum of all the squared errors in a regression problem. This is equivalent to the square of distance between the predictions and the actual values, expressed as vectors.

K-fold Cross Validation (KFCV):

- This evaluation strategy involves several runs of a classification or regression experiment in such a way that we obtain a holistic view of its performance, ensuring that the results are not because of the particular training and testing sets used.

- With KFCV, the dataset is partitioned into K approximately equal parts. Each one of them is used as a test set in the K experiments that follow.

- The value of K in KFCV depends on the dataset size. Larger datasets require a small K, while smaller datasets are better off with a larger K.

- The Leave-One-Out evaluation strategy is a special case of KFCV, where the K parameter is equal to the size of the dataset. This is suitable for very small datasets and is not often used in data science.

CHAPTER CHALLENGE

1. Can you use stratified sampling for a dataset with a continuous variable as a target?

2. Which sampling method would you use for a heavily unbalanced dataset? Why?

3. What aspect of sampling yields the least bias in the sample created?

4. Is it possible to have a normalized version of the total cost (based on the misclassification cost approach), taking values between 0 and 1? How would you go about implementing this?

5. Could you use a ROC curve for a three-class problem?

6. Would it be possible to use KFCV for any problem? Give an example to justify your answer.

CHAPTER 10
Unsupervised Machine Learning

One of the fundamentals of data science is finding patterns in the data at hand. As you may remember from Chapter 5, this is accomplished mainly during the data exploration part of the pipeline. Although the various statistical methods and plots yield much useful insight, sometimes we must employ a more sophisticated approach. This is particularly useful if we have certain expectations about the data (such as different groups or patterns that should exist) and wish to explore them further.

This lends itself to what is known as unsupervised learning: the kind of machine learning where labels are unknown or nonexistent altogether. The aim of this strategy is to find these labels in a way that makes sense for the data at hand, while also uncovering the structure of the dataset. In this chapter we'll explore this topic in some depth to examine how unsupervised learning can be done in Julia effectively.

In this chapter we will examine the following topics:

- The basics of unsupervised learning, including the underlying distance metrics

- The K-means method for clustering

- The density concept and the DBSCAN clustering technique

- Hierarchical clustering

- Validation metrics for clustering

- Tips for applying unsupervised learning effectively.

Before we continue, make sure that the `Clustering` package is installed on your system.

Unsupervised Learning Basics

Unsupervised learning is extremely important for a variety of reasons. First of all, it provides insight about patterns in the data that you would not be able to pinpoint with other methods. This is particularly useful during the data exploration stage where you are uncertain what signals the data contains. You could find these signals with other means, but it would take a significant amount of additional effort.

This brings us to the next point, which is the amount of time unsupervised learning saves. This extends beyond data exploration to something that's even more important when it comes to productionalizing your work. A classic example is figuring out the labels of a dataset, which is possible with one of the methods of unsupervised learning. There are numerous ways of finding labels (the most obvious of which is hiring some people to do it manually), but these methods don't scale well. Unsupervised learning is both fast and scalable, while it is cheap comparatively.

Finally, this machine learning approach allows us to organize the data at hand and understand it better. At the same time we can make more meaningful plots that can shed additional light on the problem we are trying to solve. And unlike conventional plots, unsupervised learning techniques provide you with a variety of metrics. There are several unsupervised learning techniques, all of which have their niche. The most important of these are the following:

- **Clustering,** a group of processes that identify groups in the data

- **Association rule discovery,** a method that identifies collections of features values that appear often together

- **Mixture decomposition,** a statistical methodology that aims to identify parametric densities of individual populations constituting a "superpopulation."

There are several other methods that qualify as unsupervised learning, though they are seldom encountered in data science projects. In this chapter we will focus on the first type of unsupervised learning, as it is the most commonly used and is crucial in providing actionable information about the data at hand.

Clustering types

There are two main types of clustering, depending on the inner workings of the clustering method: partitional and hierarchical. The first type splits the data into a number of mutually exclusive groups (usually denoted as K), while the second one creates a tree where the most similar elements are grouped together gradually. Partitional clustering is particularly useful for creating a labels vector that could be used later on for classification. Both partitional and hierarchical clustering are excellent tools for data exploration.

Apart from this categorization, there are other ways to differentiate the clustering methods. One way to categorize clustering methods is as hard or as fuzzy, depending on whether a data point belongs to a cluster exclusively or to some degree. Another descriptor is deterministic or stochastic, depending on whether the algorithm used employs randomness or not.

In all the clustering methods, the points compared are evaluated as to how similar (or dissimilar) they are to each other, in order to determine whether they belong to the same group or not. For this we usually use a distance metric, such as Euclidean distance. However, there are several other alternatives, as we'll see in the following section.

Distance metrics

There are several metrics that can be used to express the distance between two data points, the most important of which are listed below. For all the examples we make use of two float vectors `x` and `y` of equal dimensionality. In order to utilize these metrics in Julia, you'll need to add and load the `Distances` package (check http://bit.ly/29vRs0A for more information).

- **Euclidean distance.** This is the default distance metric, which works well for small dimensionalities. It is always non-negative and without an upper limit. It is good practice to normalize its inputs, to avoid biased results.

- **Cosine distance.** This is the corresponding distance metric to the cosine similarity measure we have seen previously: `cos_dist = 1 - cos_sim`. It is good for cases where there are vast differences in particular parts of the vectors compared, and works well with all kinds of dimensionalities. Cosine distance takes values between 0 and 2, inclusive, and doesn't require normalization beforehand.

- **Manhattan distance (aka City-Block distance).** This is very much like the Euclidean distance but it uses absolute values instead of squares, when computing the distances in each dimension. It takes non-negative values without an upper limit, and just like Euclidean distance, it is a good idea to normalize its inputs before calculating this distance metric.

- **Jaccard distance.** This is an interesting metric that works not only on numeric data but also on Boolean data. It is defined as `JD = 1 - J(x,y)`, where `J` is the Jaccard similarity we have seen in a previous chapter. The above formula is equivalent to `JD = 1 - sum(min(x, y)) / sum(max(x, y))`. Jaccard distance takes values between 0 and 1, inclusive. Just like cosine distance, this distance metric doesn't require normalization beforehand.

- **Other.** There are several other distances you can use, depending on the data you have. You can view them in the documentation of the `Distances.jl` package: http://bit.ly/29vRs0A.

So, if we have a couple of vectors x = [1.0, 2.0, 3.0] and y = [-1.0, 2.5, 0.0], we could calculate their distance in Julia using some of the above metrics:

```
In[1]: d = evaluate(Euclidean(), x, y)
Out[1]: 3.640054944640259
In[2]: d = evaluate(CosineDist(), x, y)
Out[2]: 0.6029666664116279
In[3]: d = evaluate(Cityblock(), x, y)
Out[3]: 5.5
In[4]: d = evaluate(Jaccard(), x, y)
Out[4]: 0.8461538461538461
```

GROUPING DATA WITH K-MEANS

K-means is probably the most commonly used clustering technique, due to its simplicity and speed. Using a single parameter, K, it splits the data into K different groups (referred to as clusters), based on how close each data point is to the cluster center. The cluster centers change in every iteration of the algorithm, based on the data points that belong to these clusters; they are usually calculated as the means of the values of the data points in them (hence the name of the algorithm). The original clusters are defined randomly, making every run of the K-means algorithm yield slightly different results. The algorithm stops once the cluster centers don't change significantly or until a maximum number of iterations has been reached.

Although in the original version of K-means the cluster centers are calculated based on the mean of the data points that belong to them, there are a few variants of the method where different averaging metrics (such as the median) are used. Also, there is a powerful variant of K-means that uses fuzzy logic, so each data point belongs to all possible clusters with some membership value, known as C-means. Although these variations are tempting, we'll limit ourselves to the most basic method of K-means in this section, as this is the one most often used in practice. In Figure 10.1 you can see a typical output of the K-means algorithm (which is representative of other partitional clustering algorithms, too).

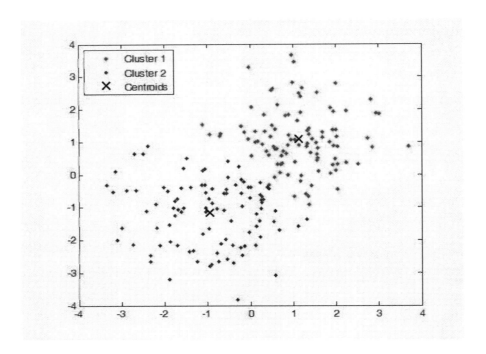

Figure 10.1 An example of a typical K-means clustering output.

K-MEANS USING JULIA

For K-means in Julia we'll be using the `Clustering` package, which also includes some other clustering techniques (see http://bit.ly/29vRs0A for details on the package's contents). Once you add it and load it into memory you can start using it on your data.

Let's look at how we can apply it to the `OnlineNewsPopularity` dataset. Here we will work under the hypothesis that there are two distinct categories of news articles (the popular ones and the not-so-popular ones), so we'll use `K = 2`:

```
In[5]: using Clustering
In[6]: data =
    readdlm("d://data//OnlineNewsPopularity//OnlineNewsPopularity.c
    sv", ',');
In[7]: F = map(float, data[2:end,2:60]) #make all features floats
In[8]: F = normalize(F, "linear")
In[9]: Z = kmeans(F', 2)
```

We need to transpose the inputs (features) since the `kmeans()` function takes its data in a different form (each row being a different feature and each column a data point). Also, since there are several outputs, it is best to put them all in a single data structure (variable Z) so that later we can retrieve them individually through that variable. Specifically, if we were interested in the cluster labels, we would type:

```
In[10]: labels = assignments(Z); show(labels[1:10])
    [1,1,1,1,1,1,1,1,1,2]
```

Of course, there are several more values in the labels vector, but here we just view the first ten to get an idea of what the labels vector looks like. The numbers that correspond to the two clusters are arbitrarily chosen by the algorithm and may not be the same in the next run. It is often the case that even if the clusters are more or less identical, the same data points that are shown here as 1s may be later labeled as 2s.

We could manually count all these labels to get an idea of how large each cluster is. Thankfully, the package has a specialized function, `counts()`, that you can apply to accomplish this task easily:

```
In[11]: c = counts(Z); show(c)
    [31208,8436]
```

What about the centers of the clusters? We can obtain them from the outputs data structure with the `.centers` identifier:

```
In[12]: C = Z.centers; show(C[1:5,:])
    [0.505558031543492 0.3821391822047006
    0.39736453412433603 0.40946961999592846
    0.06286506180190116 0.07051594966020513
    0.0007965795130288157 0.00072829082065273
    0.0009634138252223355 0.0009300011157573742]
```

Naturally, there are several more rows in the centers variable (C): one for each feature of the dataset. However, due to space limitations, we show here just the first five rows, for the two cluster centers. By examining the cluster centers more closely we can see that certain variables (e.g. the first one, `timedelta`) play a more important role in keeping the clusters distant, as the difference in the centers' coordinates in the corresponding dimensions is larger. This may provide additional insight, as those variables seem to divulge more useful information related to the dataset's structure. We would expect, then, that these variables will work better as predictors later on.

K-MEANS TIPS

Although the K-means method works well in the majority of situations, it fails to produce meaningful results in some cases. Specifically, when the number of clusters (K) is off, the resulting labels may be nonsensical. So, before you run this algorithm (or any of its variants), be sure to have a good idea of what you are looking for.

In a sentiment analysis problem, for example, a good value for K would be 2 (positive and negative sentiment), or 3 (positive, negative, and neutral sentiment). Asking K-means to provide clusters for $K = 10$ for this problem may not make much sense, which would be reflected in the very small differences in the coordinates of the cluster centers. It is a good idea to carefully consider how you will interpret the results, since Julia can only help you so much with your partitional clustering endeavors.

DENSITY AND THE DBSCAN APPROACH

Although it is one of the most fundamental concepts in physics, density hasn't been properly implemented in the world of data science, with many people still confusing it with probability density. In essence, density kernels are heuristics that approximate the true density of a particular data point. Unless you already know a lot about the dataset, finding the optimum parameters of such a kernel is a challenge.

With that being said, even the crude implementations of this concept manage to work decently and make a new generation of clustering algorithms possible (although density has the potential to enhance the data analytics field).

The aim of density is to provide a reliable measure of how crowded a particular part of the feature-space is. Naturally, the more data points there are in a particular area, the higher the density and the lower the entropy of the dataset, as it is closely linked to order. Density is basically the most direct way of pinpointing a signal in the data, and it is based on tangible measurements.

In clustering, density is used in algorithms like DBSCAN, which we will cover in more depth in the next section. As density is closely linked to distances, you need to have a distance matrix calculation function handy, like the one we provide in the corresponding notebook of this chapter.

DBSCAN ALGORITHM

DBSCAN is probably the most well-known alternative to K-means. It stands for Density Based Spatial Clustering of Applications with Noise, and is a very robust partitional clustering method. The fundamental premise behind this algorithm is that we expect every cluster to be defined by a probability distribution that is lighter near the edges and darker in the center.

This translates into a higher probability of picking a point near the center of a cluster than near a cluster's boundaries. This simple idea has powerful implications, as it can filter out the noisy elements of the dataset and construct the clusters based on the most concrete (i.e. dense) ones.

DBSCAN takes as its input the distance matrix of the dataset's points, along with two parameters, d and K. The first parameter corresponds to how far around a data point we want to look for the density estimation. (There is an objective way to pick this parameter for all density estimations, but as there is no scientific reference for it, we'll leave it out.) Naturally, d is a float.

The second parameter represents the density threshold that distinguishes dense from sparse data points (this too can be objectively defined, but there is not scientific canon for it either). Specifically, it refers to the number of data points in the area examined (i.e. K is an integer). Both d and K relate to the data at hand; there are no default values recommended by the creators of the algorithm.

Unlike K-means, DBSCAN does not require as a parameter the number of clusters, as it finds the optimum partitioning based on the density values of the various data points.

APPLYING DBSCAN IN JULIA

Let us now see how we can apply DBSCAN in Julia (using the `Clustering` package as before). Due to potential memory limitations, we are going to work with just the first 10,000 data points of the dataset. First, let's calculate the distance matrix of these points:

```
In[13]: D = dmatrix(F[1:10000,:]);
```

Now, let's find their average distance:

```
In[14]: mean(D)
Out[14]: 4.874257821045708
```

It would be a good idea to use a lower d parameter (e.g. 3.0). As for the K parameter, a value around the total number of dimensions should work well (e.g. 60). So, we can apply DBSCAN as follows:

```
In[15]: Z = dbscan(D, 3.0, 60)
```

Let's see what the labels look like by using the same functions as in the K-means example:

```
In[16]: labels = assignments(Z); show(labels[1:10])
    [1,1,1,1,1,1,1,1,1,1]
```

It looks like the first cluster is dominant. Let's see what the cluster sizes are like:

```
In[17]: c = counts(Z); show(c)
     [8699,1149]
```

So, for this two-cluster model, the results are similar to the results of the K-means method. Should we change the parameters, though, we may discover a different cluster setup.

HIERARCHICAL CLUSTERING

Hierarchical clustering doesn't assume a specific number of clusters, like most algorithms of partitioning clustering. A valuable data exploration tool, it examines how the data points relate to each other and constructs a tree showing how these relationships apply to larger and larger groups, starting from a single data point. This yields a graph with the various points of the dataset connected in pairs, with the most similar ones linked together. You can see a typical hierarchical clustering output in Figure 10.2.

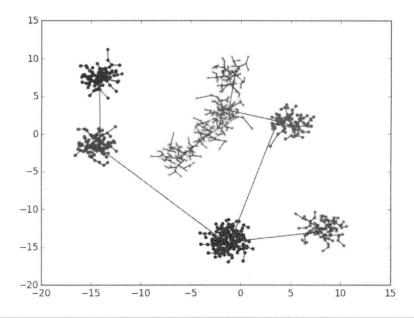

Figure 10.2 A typical hierarchical clustering tree output.

Although the output of a hierarchical clustering algorithm is not all that useful in finding the labels of the data at hand, it can be useful in understanding the data. It can potentially indicate the optimum number of clusters (i.e. pinpointing the optimal K parameter in K-means). Due to the limitations of the plotting package used on the back end (PyPlot), visuals of the cluster hierarchy are visible only for two dimensional data. Let's see how we can apply this clustering technique in Julia using the corresponding package.

Applying hierarchical clustering in Julia

To perform hierarchical clustering we'll need to make use of the QuickShiftClustering package. First let's load this package, as well as the PyPlot package, which is used for plotting the hierarchical tree:

```
In[18]: using QuickShiftClustering
        using PyPlot
```

Since we'll need to do some dimensionality reduction in order to view a meaningful plot based on the clustering, we'll also make use of the MultivariateStats package:

```
In[19]: using MultivariateStats
```

Now we can create the tree for the hierarchical clustering. To avoid spending too much time waiting for the results (particularly in the final stage of the process), we'll limit the data used to a sample of 300 data points and 2 features. First, we'll get the first two meta-features using a PCA model:

```
In[20]: M = fit(PCA, F'; maxoutdim = 2)
```

Next, we'll create a transformed sample of the dataset, having two dimensions (the above features of the PCA model) and 300 data points:

```
In[21]: G = transform(M, F[1:300,:]')'
```

Afterward, we can run it through the quickshift() function to get a hierarchical clustering model:

```
In[22]: Z = quickshift(G')
```

We can get the labels of the clustering using the `quickshiftlabels()` function:

```
In[23]: labels = quickshiftlabels(Z);
```

The output of this function is not particularly meaningful, since it is used mainly in creating the plot that follows. To create this plot, we'll make use of the `quickshiftplot()` function:

```
In[24]: quickshiftplot(Z, G', labels)
```

You can see the various links of the data points and how they all merge together to form larger and larger groups of data, with ever-bigger links forming, until everything in the dataset is connected (Figure 10.3). It becomes clear that the groupings we saw in the previous clustering approaches are meaningful after all, since there are two distinct clusters of data points (possibly corresponding to the normal and viral news, respectively).

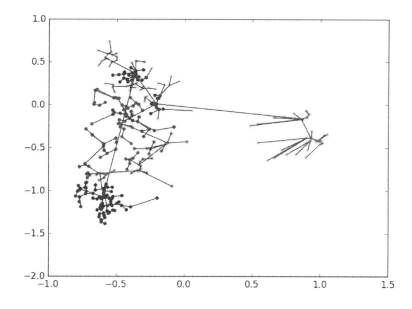

Figure 10.3 An output plot for the QuickShiftClustering clustering model.

A word of caution: although the `Clustering` package also includes methods to handle hierarchical clustering (`hclust()` and `cutree()` functions), they are still works-in-progress; at the time of this writing they don't perform as expected. We recommend you avoid using both until they have become fully functional and have some documentation on the package web page.

When to use hierarchical clustering

Although not as popular as K-means or DBSCAN, this is a particularly useful clustering strategy for a few use cases where partitional methods cannot deliver. Namely, it is ideal for data exploration and for parameter searching for other clustering algorithms. For example, if you are not sure how many clusters you need to take into account (K), hierarchical clustering can prove useful. Also, by taking pairs of features at a time, you can see how the different features affect the cluster structure and therefore get an idea of which ones are more informative.

VALIDATION METRICS FOR CLUSTERING

Although the objective of clustering is usually to acquire some insight from the available data so as to perform more efficient analytics later on, sometimes we need to evaluate the performance of a clustering system. To do this we can employ a number of metrics, the most popular of which are silhouettes (sometimes referred to as Silhouette Width) and Variation of Information. In this section we'll examine how the first one works, as it is more useful.

SILHOUETTES

Silhouettes are popular and robust metrics for assessing how well-defined clusters are, with applications extending to classification as well. A silhouette is basically a ratio of distances that takes values between -1 and 1, with higher values showing that a data point or a cluster is better off being in the cluster it is in. Values below 0 are particularly concerning as they hint toward a complex dataset, or a bad clustering. You can read more about silhouettes in the research article where the concept was first introduced: http://bit.ly/28QQ8aq.

We have implemented this metric in Julia with a function called `sil()`, which takes the cluster assignments (labels) and the pairwise distance matrix (D) as its inputs. Taking our previous example from the DBSCAN classification we have:

```
In[25]: sil(labels, D)
Out[25]: (-0.23285061303777332, [-0.159633,-0.207085,-0.17854,
    -0.180267,-0.226897,-0.185112,-0.231703,-0.195578,-0.13228,
    -0.243666 … -0.250058,-0.264992,-0.185843,-0.23381,-0.22416,
    -0.163046,-0.278264,-0.229035,-0.250064,-0.24455])
```

The outputs of this method are the silhouette of the whole dataset and the silhouettes of the various data points (the latter are stored in a vector). It appears that this particular clustering is not ideal. This may be caused by the cluster imbalance and/or the geometry of the dataset.

Clustering validation metrics tips

Although the aforementioned metrics for evaluating clustering performance have been implemented in the `Clustering` package, we recommend you avoid using them as they are not yet completely functional. Though well-documented, these metrics may throw errors at random, even with inputs that come straight out of the clustering algorithms of this package.

Overall, clustering performance is more of an academic research topic than something that is used in practice, particularly if you care only about the data exploration application of clustering. However, if you are dealing with a complex dataset and you wish to delve deep into its geometry, or have a data product that depends heavily on clustering, several clustering experiments are in order. To make sure that these experiments are as useful as possible, it would behoove you to carry out proper validation procedures as well. We recommend you implement the Variation of Information as an exercise, once you feel comfortable with Julia programming.

EFFECTIVE CLUSTERING TIPS

Although clustering is as straightforward as it gets in machine learning, it takes a bit of skill to get the most out of it. There are certain things that you need to keep in mind in order to obtain useful insights and avoid getting a diluted signal. Specifically, things like handling high dimensionality and performing normalization can be crucial when it comes to getting your data ready for a clustering algorithm, no matter how effective the algorithm.

Dealing with high dimensionality

High dimensionality can be detrimental to clustering since distance metrics (particularly Euclidean distance and its variants) don't work on high-dimensional space as expected. All the distances become very large and their range diminishes, making the clusters sparse and practically meaningless. Also, any signal that exists in the dataset gets diluted and is not clearly reflected in the created clusters.

The best way to handle this issue is to remove excessive dimensions (features with weak signals) and/or extract meta-features that capture all the information of the original features of the dataset, as we saw in the previous chapter and in the hierarchical clustering example. Generally, a feature space that allows for large variance in the data points of the dataset also allows for a robust clustering. This often results in feature sets having less than 100 features, though the exact number depends on the nature of the dataset.

NORMALIZATION

Keep in mind that data needs to be normalized in the majority of cases when running a clustering algorithm. Unless you are using cosine distance, or some other distance metric that works with all kinds of data, you need to ensure that what you put into the clustering algorithm is of the same scale. Otherwise, you may end up with biased and counter-intuitive outputs.

We recommend you use a normalization method that yields values between 0 and 1. This is particularly useful if you plan to include binary features, which are by their nature in this value spectrum.

VISUALIZATION TIPS

It is important to always create a visualization of the output of a partitional clustering algorithm, even if this means reducing the dimensionality further (e.g. through PCA, as we saw previously). Examining the cluster centers can be useful as well, since these are the "typical" elements of each cluster, even if data points having these exact values may not exist in the dataset. All this is bound to be helpful for interpreting the results and making the most of the whole process.

SUMMARY

- Unsupervised learning involves data analytics that take place without a target variable.

- Unsupervised learning yields useful insights about the dataset and helps us understand it better, making supervised learning much more manageable and oftentimes more fruitful.

- There are various types of unsupervised learning, including clustering, discovery of association rules, and mixture decomposition.

- Clustering is by far the most popular type of unsupervised learning and has been thoroughly researched.

- There are many ways to categorize clustering methods, the most common of which is partitional vs. hierarchical, which focuses on the objective of the clustering process. Other categorizations consider the various aspects of the algorithms involved, such as deterministic vs. stochastic.

- Partitional clustering involves generating a number of groups (partitions) that are mutually exclusive, each containing the most similar data points, while being as dissimilar from the other groups as possible. The number of groups is a parameter of most partitional clustering methods.

- The vast majority of these methods are stochastic in nature. Partitional clustering is useful not only for data exploration but for creating a target variable for classification. Partitional clustering methods are available in the `Clustering` package of Julia.

    o   K-means is the most popular partitional clustering algorithm, splitting the dataset into `K` clusters based on the distances among the data points involved. It is extremely fast and works well with relatively simple datasets. You can apply K-means in Julia using the code: `kmeans(data, K)`, where `data` is the dataset (features are depicted as rows) and `K` is the number of clusters.

    o   DBSCAN is a more powerful partitional clustering algorithm that makes use of the density concept to handle more challenging datasets. It is not as fast as K-means but is more effective overall, and it doesn't require input of the number of clusters. You can use Julia to run DBSCAN by typing: `dbscan(D, d, K)`, where `D` is the pairwise distance matrix, `d` is the minimum density value beyond which a data point is considered dense, and `K` is the number of nearby data points to be considered in the density calculation.

- Hierarchical clustering is an alternative clustering methodology that involves the gradual grouping of the data points until a single cluster is reached. This is in the form of a tree structure that shows all possible meaningful groupings on a 2D plane.

- Hierarchical clustering is useful for exploratory purposes mainly. You can make use of hierarchical clustering in Julia by using the `QuickShiftClustering` package as follows: `quickshift(data)`, where `data` is the dataset (features are depicted as rows, like before). You can view the resulting tree structure using the code: `quickshiftplot(Z, data, labels)`, where `Z` is the output of the `quickshift()` function, and `labels` is the assigned labels of the clustering algorithm (output of `quickshiftlabels(Z)`).

- All clustering methods make use of some kind of dissimilarity metric such as Euclidean distance. There are several such metrics available in the `Distances` package of Julia.

- Validating a clustering system's output is possible through various metrics, the most popular of which are silhouettes and Variation of Information. Currently only the silhouettes method is fully functional in Julia (see notebook).

- Silhouette is a distance-based metric that ranges from -1 and 1 and shows how close a data point is to its assigned cluster, compared to other clusters. The higher its value the better. You can make use of it in Julia through the custom function `sil()`: `sil(labels, D)`, where `labels` is a vector containing the assigned labels from the clustering model, and `D` is the pairwise distance matrix.

- In order to perform clustering more effectively, consider the following:
  o Keep the number of features relatively low (as low as possible without losing a lot of information).
  o Normalize all the featured and meta-features used in the clustering process.
  o Create visuals to better comprehend the various clusters and how they relate to each other.
  o Examine the cluster centers to gain additional insight about the nature of the clusters.

CHAPTER CHALLENGE

1. Why are distances important for clustering?

2. Which clustering method would you use for a very complex dataset?

3. Why can't the metrics covered in Chapter 9 be used for evaluating the output of a clustering system?

4. Can all types of data be clustered? What do you need to keep in mind before doing this?

5. How is partitional clustering different from t-SNE (Chapter 7)?

6. Is clustering essential for data science? Why?

7. How does dimensionality affect clustering performance? What remedies are there for this?

8. How can you emphasize a particular feature in a normalized dataset so that it plays a more pronounced role in the clustering process?

Supervised machine learning is truly the core of data science, as all of the directly applicable insights stem from the outputs of this part of the process. Its most common types are classification and regression, depending on the nature of the target variable.

It would be quite a feat to do this topic justice, as there are so many different methods that fall under its umbrella. However, we'll cover the most commonly used ones and demonstrate how they can be implemented in Julia, relying on the following packages: `DecisionTree`, `BackpropNeuralNet`, `ELM` and `GLM`. Make sure that you have them installed on your computer before going through the examples in this chapter.

In this chapter we will examine the following topics:

- Rationale and overview of supervised learning

- Decision trees (classification)

- Regression trees

- Random forests

- Basic neural networks (ANNs)

- Extreme Learning Machines (ELMs)

- Statistical models for regression

- Other supervised learning methods.

We'll be working with both the `Magic` and the `OnlineNewsPopularity` datasets, so make sure that you have loaded these into memory, too. We'll also use a couple of auxiliary functions for some essential data engineering, so make sure that you load the files `sample.jl` and `normalize.jl` into memory. Finally, make sure that you load a few other auxiliary functions, such as `MSE()`, located in the first part of this chapter's notebook file.

Supervised learning involves getting the computer to create a generalization based on some labeled data, and then use that generalization to predict the labels of a set of unlabeled data. There are several ways of doing this, each one representing a particular supervised learning method. Although there are two main methodologies of supervised learning, classification and regression, it is sometimes the case that a supervised learning system does both.

The goal of this type of machine learning is to be able to make accurate and reliable predictions. We could learn the labels of an unlabeled dataset via unsupervised learning, but this would be limited to more obvious structural patterns in the dataset. If we have some additional information in the form of labels, then we can harness these invaluable assets only through specialized methods: the supervised learning algorithms.

Although many people use logistic models (e.g. logistic regression) for this purpose, we will veer away from those. Logistic models are by far the weakest methods out there; apart from easy interpretability, they don't have any other real advantages. If you're interested in logistic models, you can easily implement them yourself.

Modern machine learning started when data analysts wanted to go beyond what logistic models could offer. In the rest of the chapter we'll focus on more interesting methods, examining their role in data science as well as how they are implemented in Julia. However, we won't be looking much at the use of ensembles (combinations of supervised learning systems), as this is a more sophisticated approach that requires substantial machine learning expertise.

Decision Trees

A decision tree is basically a series of rules that is applied to the dataset, eventually leading to a choice between two or more classes. It is like playing the "20 questions" game, but with a limited set of objects that you are trying to guess, and without a strict number of questions that can be asked.

Mathematically, decision trees are graphs (we'll talk more about graphs in the next chapter) that are designed to examine a limited number of possibilities, in order to arrive at a reliable conclusion about what class each data point is in. These possibilities are modeled as nodes and edges, as you can see in the example in Figure 11.1. In this figure, different fruits are classified based on their color, shape, size and taste. Not all of these characteristics are used for each classification; the ones that are used depend on the output of each test (node).

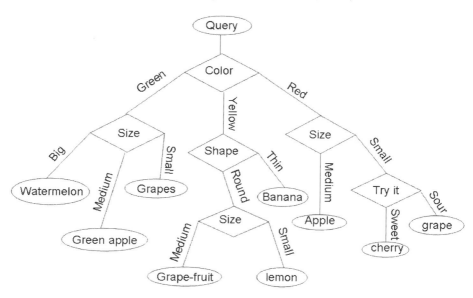

Figure 11.1 An example of a typical decision tree. Used with permission from www.projectrhea.com.

Decision trees are great for cases where the features are rich in information, more or less independent from each other, and not too large. They are excellent for interpretability and easy to build and use. Also, due to their nature, they don't require any normalization in the data they use.

Implementing decision trees in Julia

You can implement decision trees in Julia by making use of the `DecisionTree` package as follows:

```
In[1]: using DecisionTree
```

Next, we'll need to define some parameters for the decision trees we use. The first one is the combined purity parameter, which refers to the proportion of correct labels in a leaf node. Although it's tempting to make this equal to 1.0, it's unwise because overfitting will unmistakably result. A very low value would not work, either. Usually a value of 0.9 works well for the majority of applications.

```
In[2]: CP = 0.9
```

Since we'll be doing some cross-validation as well, we'll need to define the corresponding parameter for it.

```
In[3]: K = 5
```

Before we move on, let's define a couple more parameters, namely the tree depth (`td`) and the number of leaves to be used for averaging in regression applications (`nl`). The tree depth is mainly for viewing purposes, and applies to a single decision tree. Even though it is not absolutely necessary, it can be useful in understanding and interpreting the decision tree we build. Some good values for these parameters are the following (feel free to experiment with other ones if you want):

```
In[4]: td = 3
       nl = 5
```

Now, let's see how the decision trees are built and used to classify the `magic` dataset. First, let's build a tree and tidy it up using the `build_tree()` and `prune_tree()` functions respectively:

```
In[5]: model = build_tree(T1, P1)
    model = prune_tree(model, CP)
```

The "pruning" of the tree is not truly essential, but it is useful as it keeps the tree simple and therefore less prone to overfitting. The output of all this is the following:

```
Out[5]: Decision Tree
    Leaves: 1497
    Depth: 30
```

Believe it or not, this is a relatively small decision tree, especially considering that we are using the dataset as-is. Naturally, if we were to perform some dimensionality reduction, the resulting tree would be even smaller. The above command is not guaranteed to produce the exact same tree on your computer, due to the stochastic nature of the decision tree. Let's now see what this bonsai of ours looks like:

```
In[6]: print_tree(model, td)
Feature 9, Threshold -0.3096661121768262
L-> Feature 1, Threshold 1.525274809976256
  L-> Feature 9, Threshold -0.6886748399536539
    L->
    R->
  R-> Feature 7, Threshold -2.3666522650618234
    L-> h : 99/99
    R->
R-> Feature 1, Threshold -0.16381866376775667
  L-> Feature 3, Threshold -1.0455318957511963
    L->
    R->
  R-> Feature 1, Threshold 0.42987863636363327
    L->
    R->
```

From this short preview of the built tree, it becomes clear that feature 1 (fLength) plays an important role in distinguishing between the two classes of radiation observed by the telescope. This is because it appears on the first leaf and because it appears more than once. We can also note the thresholds used in all the leaves shown here, to better understand the feature. Perhaps we'll eventually want to make this feature discreet. If that's the case, the thresholds used here could be a good starting point. Now let's see how all this can be used to make some predictions, using the `apply_tree()` function:

```
In[7]: pred = apply_tree(model, PT1)
Out[7]: 1902-element Array{Any,1}:
    "g"
    "g"
    "g"
    "g"
    "g"
```

This will yield an array populated by the predicted labels for the test set. The type of the output as well as the values themselves will be the same as the original targets, i.e. "g" and "h" for each one of the two classes. What about the certainty of the classifier, though? This can be made available through the `apply_tree_proba()` function, as long as we provide the list of class names (Q):

```
In[8]: prob = apply_tree_proba(model, PT1, Q)
Out[8]: 1902x2 Array{Float64,2}:
    1.0      0.0
    1.0      0.0
    1.0      0.0
    1.0      0.0
    0.985294  0.0147059
```

Each one of the columns of the output corresponds to the probability of each class. This is similar to the output of a neural network, as we'll see later on. Actually, the decision tree calculates these probabilities first and then chooses the class based on the probabilities.

As all this may not be enough to assess the value of our classification bonsai, we may want to apply some KFCV to it. Fortunately, the `DecisionTree` package makes this much easier as it includes a cross validation function, `nfoldCV_tree()`:

```
In[9]: validation = nfoldCV_tree(T_magic, F_magic, CP, K)
```

The result (which is too long to be included here) is a series of tests (K in total), where the confusion matrix as well as the accuracy and another metric are shown. Afterwards, a summary of all the accuracy values is displayed, to give you a taste of the overall performance of the decision trees. Here is a sample of all this, from the final cross validation round:

```
2x2 Array{Int64,2}:
 2138 327
  368 971
Fold 5
Classes: Any["g","h"]
Matrix:
Accuracy: 0.8172975814931651
Kappa:   0.5966837444531773
```

This may not satisfy the most demanding data scientists out there–those who rely on more insightful metrics, like the ones we described in Chapter 9, where performance metrics are discussed. Generally, though, the confusion matrix will prove valuable when calculating the metrics we need, so we don't have to rely on the accuracy provided by the cross validation function of this package.

Decision tree tips

Although decision trees are great for many problems, they have some issues that you ought to keep in mind. For example, they don't deal well with patterns that are not in the form of a rectangle in the feature space. These patterns produce a large number of rules (nodes), making them cumbersome and hard to interpret. Also, if the number of features is very large, they take a while to build, making them impractical. Finally, due to their stochastic nature, it is difficult to draw conclusions about which features are more useful by just looking at them.

Overall, decision trees are decent classification systems and are worth a try, particularly in cases where the dataset is relatively clean. They can be ideal as a baseline, while they can work well in an ensemble setting as we'll see later on in the Random Forests section.

REGRESSION TREES

The regression tree is the counterpart of the decision tree, applicable in regression problem-solving settings. Instead of labels, they predict values of a continuous variable. The function of regression trees relies on the fact that decision trees can predict probabilities (of a data point belonging to a particular class). These probabilities are by nature continuous, so it is not a stretch to transform them into another continuous variable that approximates the target variable of a regression problem. So, the mechanics underneath the hood of the regression trees are the same as those of the decision trees we saw previously. Let's now look at how all this is implemented in Julia, via the DecisionTree package.

Implementing regression trees in Julia

We can build and use a regression tree in Julia using the same functions as in the decision tree case. The only difference is that when building a regression tree, we need to make use of the number of leaves parameter (nl) when applying the build_tree() function. This basically tells Julia to treat the target as a continuous variable, and approximate it by taking the average of the number of leaves. So, if we were to train a regression tree model in this fashion we would type:

```
In[10]: model = build_tree(T2, P2, nl)
```

Like before, we would get something like this as an output:

```
Out[10]: Decision Tree
    Leaves: 14828
    Depth: 19
```

Although this is a decision tree object as far as Julia is concerned, its application lies in regression. So, if we were to apply it on our data, here is what would happen:

```
In[11]:  pred = apply_tree(model, PT2)
Out[11]: 1902-element Array{Float64,1}:
    1500.0
    5700.0
```

```
5200.0
1800.0
426.0
```

This output would go on for a while, with all of the elements of the output array being floats, just like the targets we trained the model with (T2). Let's see how well these predictions approximate the actual values (TT2):

```
In[12]:   MSE(pred, TT2)
Out[12]: 2.2513992955941114e8
```

This is not bad at all, considering how varied the target variable is. Naturally, this can be improved by tweaking the regression tree a bit. However, for now we'll focus on other, more powerful supervised learning systems.

Regression tree tips

As you might expect, regression trees have the same limitations as their classification counterparts. So although they can be great as baselines, you will rarely see them in production. Nevertheless, it is important to learn how to use them, as they are the basis of the next supervised learning system we'll examine in this chapter.

RANDOM FORESTS

As the name eloquently suggests, a random forest is a set of decision or regression tree systems working together. This is by far the most popular ensemble system used by many data scientists, and the go-to option for the majority of problems. The main advantage of random forests is that they generally avoid overfitting and always outperform a single tree-based system, making them a more comprehensive alternative. Configuring them, however, can be a bit of a challenge. The optimum parameter settings (number of random features, number of trees, and portion of samples used in every tree) depends on the dataset at hand.

Random forests are modestly interpretable, but they lack the ease of use and interpretability of single-tree systems. Random forests tend to obtain better generalizations, making them suitable for challenging problems, too. As a bonus, mining the trees in a random forest can yield useful insights about which features perform better, as well as which ones work well together. Also, they are generally fast, though their performance heavily depends on the parameters used.

Implementing random forests in Julia for classification

You can implement random forest using the following Julia code and the `DecisionTree` package. First, let's get some parameters set: the number of random features in each training session (nrf), the number of trees in the forest (nt), and the proportion of samples in every tree (ps):

```
In[13]: nrf = 2
        nt = 10
        ps = 0.5
```

Next, we can build the forest based on the data of the `magic` dataset, using the `build_forest()` function and the above parameters:

```
In[14]:  model = build_forest(T1, P1, nrf, nt, ps)
Out[14]: Ensemble of Decision Trees
    Trees:    10
    Avg Leaves: 1054.6
    Avg Depth: 31.3
```

Contrary to what you might expect, the forest has significantly fewer leaves on each of its trees, but many more branches (expressed as depth). This is because of the parameters we chose, and for a good reason. If we were to use all the features on each tree and all of the data points, we would end up with a bunch of trees that would be similar to each other. Although such a forest could be better than any individual tree, it wouldn't be as good as a forest with more diversity in its members.

This diversity lies not just in the structure of the trees, but also in the rules that each one encompasses. Just like in nature, a diverse forest with a large variety of members tends to flourish in terms of performance. In this case, our mini-forest of ten diverse trees is far more robust than any tree we could build individually, in the same number of attempts.

It is not expected that you'll blindly believe this (we are all scientists, after all). Instead, let's test this claim out by making use of this classification forest, using the `apply_forest()` function as follows:

```
In[15]: pred = apply_forest(model, PT1)
```

The prediction output would be similar to that of a single decision tree, which is why we omit it here.

Just like in the decision tree case, we can also calculate the corresponding probabilities of the above classification, this time using the `apply_forest_proba()` function:

```
In[16]: prob = apply_forest_proba(model, PT1, Q)
```

Here is what these probabilities would look like in the case of the random forest:

```
Out[16]: 1902x2 Array{Float64,2}:
    1.0 0.0
    0.5 0.5
    0.9 0.1
    0.6 0.4
    0.9 0.1
```

Note how the probabilities are far more discreet than the ones in the single decision tree. That's because they are based on the outputs of the individual trees that make up the forest; since they are ten in total, the probabilities would be in the form `x / 10`, where `x = 0, 1, 2, ..., 10`.

Let's see how the forest performs overall now. To do that, we'll use the corresponding cross validation function, `nforldCV_forest()`:

```
In[17]: validation = nfoldCV_forest(T_magic, F_magic, nrf, nt, K,
        ps)
```

Like in the decision tree case, this function provides a long output, including this sample:

```
2x2 Array{Int64,2}:
 2326 118
 408  952
Fold 5
Classes: Any["g","h"]
Matrix:
Accuracy:  0.8617245005257623
Kappa:    0.6840671243518406
Mean Accuracy: 0.8634069400630915
```

We don't need to look at everything to see how this result is much better than that of a single decision tree. Of course, the difference is much greater if the baseline is lower. Whatever the case, a random forest is bound to perform much better, at least in terms of overall performance as measured by the accuracy metric.

Implementing random forests in Julia for regression

Let's look at how random forests can be applied in a regression setting, ultimately outperforming a single regression tree. Since we'll be using the same parameters as in the previous examples, we can just go straight into the building of the regression random forest. Use the build_forest() function, but this time with the number of leaves parameter (nl) also added to the mix:

```
In[18]:  model = build_forest(T2, P2, nrf, nt, nl, ps)
Out[18]: Ensemble of Decision Trees
    Trees:    10
    Avg Leaves: 2759.9
    Avg Depth: 34.3
```

This time we get a set of denser trees (more leaves), that are also slightly longer (more depth). This change is to be expected, since a regression tree is generally richer in terms of nodes in order to provide accurate approximations of the target variable, which is also more complex than that of a classification task.

Let's now see how all this plays out in the predictions space. Like before, we'll use the `apply_forest()` function:

```
In[19]: pred = apply_forest(model, PT2)
```

Finally, let's take a look at how this forest of regression trees performs overall by applying KFCV. We'll use the `nfoldCV_forest()` function like before, but with the number of leaves parameter (`nl`) added in its inputs:

```
In[20]: validation = nfoldCV_forest(T_ONP, F_ONP, nrf, nt, K, nl,
        ps)
```

Here is part of the output:

```
Fold 5
Mean Squared Error:    1.5630249391345486e8
Correlation Coeff:   0.14672119043349965
Coeff of Determination: 0.005953472140385885
```

If we were to take the average of all the mean squared errors of the five tests, we would end up with a figure close to 1.40e8. This is much smaller than the MSE of the single regression tree we saw previously (about 2.25e8), as we would expect.

Random forest tips

Despite their popularity, random forests are not the best supervised learning systems out there. They require a lot of data in order to work well, and the features need to be uncorrelated to some extent. Also, it is virtually impossible to tweak them so that they work well for heavily unbalanced datasets, without altering the data itself.

An advantage of random forests is that if we examine them closely, we can glean some useful insight about the value of each feature. This is made possible by the frequency of each feature being used in a leaf node. Unfortunately the current implementation of random forests in the `DecisionTree` package doesn't allow this.

Overall, decision forests are good for baseline measures, and are fairly easy to use. Additionally, the `DecisionTree` package is powerful and well-documented, so it is definitely easy to explore this kind of supervised learning systems further.

BASIC NEURAL NETWORKS

Even up until fairly recently, this was an esoteric part of machine learning that few people cared about and even fewer understood. Despite this, neural networks are by far the most influential and the most robust alternative to statistical learning. Fancy math aside, neural networks are abstraction models that emulate processes of the human brain by using a hierarchical structure of mathematical processes.

Instead of biological cells, neural networks have mathematical ones, which share the same name as their counterparts: neurons. Instead of transmitting electrical signal through neurotransmitters, they use float variables. Finally, instead of an excitation threshold corresponding to a cell's choice of whether to propagate the signal it receives, they have a mathematical threshold and a series of coefficients called weights. Overall, they are a functional abstraction of the physiological neural tissues, and they do a good job processing information in a similar manner. In Figure 11.2 you can see a typical artificial neural network (ANN).

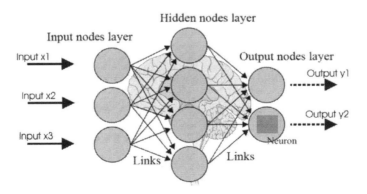

Figure 11.2. A typical artificial neural network (ANN).

ANNs are basically graphs that perform classification and regression, like tree-based systems, but employ a series of more sophisticated algorithms. A neural network is a graph that can both represent the dataset it is trained on, while simultaneously using this information for predictions. Structurally, ANNs have their neurons organized in layers; the basic ANNs have three to four layers, one or two of which are hidden. These hidden layers represent the meta-features that a neural network builds and uses for its predictions.

We encourage you to learn more about ANNs, paying close attention to how they are trained and the overfitting issues that may arise. And although it's generally a good idea to read the documentation of Julia packages, in this case it would be best if you didn't, since the example in the `BackpropNeuralNet` package may lead you to the wrong conclusions about how ANNs work.

Implementing neural networks in Julia

Let's see now how we can get a basic ANN working using the `BackpropNeuralNet` package on the `magic` dataset. First, we need to prepare the data, particularly the target variable, since an ANN only works with numeric data (the ones in this package work with just floats). In order to get the ANN to understand the target variable we need to transform it into a n x q matrix, where n is the number of data points in either the training or the testing set, and q the number of classes. Each row must have 1.0 at the column of the corresponding class. We have coded this transformation into a simple function called `vector2ANN` (see the first part of the notebook).

For now we need to define some parameters for the ANN, namely the number of nodes in each layer and the number of iterations for the training (usually referred to as epochs):

```
In[21]: nin = size(F_magic,2) # number of input nodes
    nhln = 2*nin # number hidden layer nodes
    non = length(Q) # number of output nodes
    ne = 1000 # number of epochs for training
```

Some constants for the dataset will also come in handy:

```
In[22]: N = length(T1)
    n = size(PT1,1)
    noc = length(Q) # number of classes
```

Now we can transform the target variable using the `vector2ANN()` function, for the training set:

```
In[23]: T3 = vector2ANN(T1, Q)
```

Finally, we are ready to work with the ANN itself. Let's start by loading the package into memory:

```
In[24]: using BackpropNeuralNet
```

Next, we need to initialize an ANN based on the parameters we defined previously, using the `init_network()` function. The initial form of the ANN is a bunch of random numbers representing the various connections among its nodes. This provides us zero information up front, and may even be confusing for some people. For this reason we repress the output of this command by adding a semicolon at the end:

```
In[25]: net = init_network([nin, nhln, non]);
```

Now comes the more time-consuming part: training the neural net. Unfortunately, the package provides just the most fundamental function (`train()`), without any explanation of how to use it. Running it once is fast, but in order for the neural network to be trained properly, we need to apply it several times, over all the data points of the training set (curiously, the function works only with a single data point). So, here is the code we need to run to get the training of the ANN going:

```
In[26]: for j = 1:ne
    if mod(j,20) == 0; println(j); end #1

    for i = 1:N
        a = P1[i,:]
        b = T3[i,:]
        train(net, a[:], b[:])
    end
end
```

If the total number of iterations (ne) is large enough, there is a chance for the ANN to train properly. However, this can be an unsettling process since we don't know whether the training is working or whether it has crushed the Julia kernel. In order to get some kind of update, we insert the statement in #1 that basically provides us with the iteration number every 20 iterations. If we find that the ANN hasn't been trained properly, we can run this loop again, since every time the train() function is executed, it works on the existing state of the ANN, rather than the initial one.

Once we are done with the training, we can test the performance of the ANN using the following commands:

```
In[27]: T4 = Array(Float64, n, noc)
    for i = 1:n
      T4[i,:] = net_eval(net, PT1[i,:][:])
    end
```

The above loop records the output of the neural network for each data point in the testing set. However, the format of this output is a matrix, similar to the one we used for the target variable when we trained it. To turn it into a vector we need to apply ANN2vector(), an auxiliary function we have developed for this purpose:

```
In[28]: pred, prob = ANN2vector(T4, Q)
```

This function provides the predictions, a vector similar to the original class variable, along with a probabilities vector as a bonus. The probabilities vector shows the corresponding probability for each prediction. We can now evaluate the performance of the ANN using the accuracy metric:

```
In[29]: sum(pred .== TT1) / n
```

Clearly this performance leaves a lot to be desired. This is probably due to either insufficient training, suboptimal parameters, or a combination of these. Ideally, we would train the ANN until the error on the training set falls below a given threshold, but this approach requires a more in-depth view of the topic that is well beyond the scope of this book.

Neural network tips

Many data scientists are polarized on this topic, and it has attracted a lot of attention in the past few years. The intention here is not to discredit this technology but to pinpoint its limitations. Even though it is probably one of the best systems in your toolbox, it does have some problems that make it less than ideal for certain data science applications. With this in mind, let's look into ANNs in more depth.

First of all, they have a tendency to overfit, particularly if you don't know how to pick the right parameters. So if you are new to them, don't expect too much, in order to avoid disappointment. If you do spend enough time with them, however, they can work wonders and quickly become the only supervised learning systems you use. Whatever the case, be prepared to spend some time with them if you want to achieve noteworthy performance for your classification or regression task.

ANNs tend to be slow to train, particularly if you have a lot of data. So, they are better suited for large systems (ideally computer clusters). If you want to train one on your laptop, be prepared to leave it on for the rest of the afternoon, or night, or even weekend, depending on the dataset at hand.

In order to achieve particularly good generalization from an ANN, you'll need a lot of data. This is partly to avoid overfitting, and partly because in order for the ANN to pick up the signal in your dataset, it must notice it several times, which happens best when you have a large number of data points. Alternatively, you can oversample the least represented patterns, but you have to know what you are doing, otherwise you might decrease the overall performance of the classification or regression task.

Overall ANNs are great, particularly when carefully configured. However, you may need to do some work to make them perform well. For example, you can put a series of ANNs together in an ensemble and be guaranteed a good performance. You'll need to have resources to spare, though, as most ANNs in data science are computationally expensive, with ensembles of them even more so. Therefore, it's best to save them for the challenging problems, where conventional supervised learning systems yield mediocre performance.

EXTREME LEARNING MACHINES

The use of Extreme Learning Machines, or ELMs for short, is a relatively new network-based method of supervised learning, aiming to make the use of ANNs easier and their performance better. Although they have been heavily criticized by academics due to their similarity to another technology (randomized neural networks), this does not detract from their value.

ELMs work well and are one of the best alternatives to ANNs and other supervised learning methods. In fact, the creators of this technology claim that its performance is comparable to that of state-of-the-art deep learning networks, without their computational overhead.

Essentially, ELMs are tweaked versions of conventional ANNs with the main difference being the way they are trained. In fact, ELMs have reduced the training phase into an extremely nimble optimization task (which is probably where they get their controversial name), giving them a solid advantage over all other network-based methods.

This is achieved by first creating a series of random combinations of features, which are represented by one or more layers of nodes (the hidden layers of the ELM). Then, an optimal combo of these meta-features is calculated so as to minimize the error in the output node. All the training of the ELM lies in the connections between the last hidden layer and the output layer. This is why two separately trained ELMs on the same data may have significant differences in their weights, matrices, and even their performance. This doesn't seem to bother many people, though, since the speed of ELMs makes it easy to try multiple iterations of the same ELM on the same data before the final model is picked.

You can learn more about this intriguing technology at the creators' website: http://bit.ly/29BirZM, as well as through the corresponding research papers referenced there.

IMPLEMENTING ELMS IN JULIA

The implementation of Extreme Learning Machines in Julia is made easy through the use of the ELM package (http://bit.ly/29oZZ4u), one of the best ML packages ever created in this language. Its unprecedented simplicity and ease of use is only surpassed by its excellent documentation and cleanness of code. Also, for those of you interested in researching the topic, the author of the package has even included a reference to a key article on the field. So, let's get started by formatting the target variable in a way that is compatible with the ELMs:

```
In[30]: T5 = ones(N)
        T6 = ones(n)
In[31]: ind_h = (T1 .== "h")
In[32]: T5[ind_h] = 2.0
In[33]: ind_h = (TT1 .== "h")
In[34]: T6[ind_h] = 2.0
```

With the above code, we have turned the target variable into a float having values 1.0 and 2.0 for the two classes, respectively. Naturally, the numbers themselves don't have particular significance. As long as you represent the classes with floats, the ELM will be fine with them.

Now we can proceed with loading the ELM package into memory through the familiar code:

```
In[35]: using ELM
```

Next, we need to initialize an ELM by using the ExtremeLearningMachine() function. The only parameter we need is the number of nodes in the hidden layer, which in this case is 50. This number can be any positive integer, though it usually is larger than the number of features in the dataset.

```
In[36]: elm = ExtremeLearningMachine(50);
```

Finally the time has come to train the ELM using the features and the modified target variable. We can do this using the `fit()` function. However, since a function with the same name exists in another package, we need to specify to Julia which one we want, by putting the package name in front of it:

```
In[37]: ELM.fit!(elm, P1, T5)
```

Unlike an ANN, an ELM will train in a matter of seconds (in this case milliseconds), so there is no need to insert a progress reporting statement anywhere. Once our system is trained, we can get a prediction going by using the `predict()` function on the test data:

```
In[38]: pred = round(ELM.predict(elm, PT1))
```

Note that we have applied the `round()` function as well. This leads to a threshold of 1.5 for the class decision (anything over 1.5 gets rounded up to 2.0 and anything below 1.5 becomes 1.0), which is an arbitrary choice for a threshold, even if it is the most intuitive one. However, it is a good starting point, as we can always change the threshold when we refine the model.

The `predict()` function will yield the predictions of the ELM, which will be floats *around* the class designations (1.0 and 2.0). Some of them will be lower than a given class, while others will be higher. One practical way to flatten them to the class designations is through rounding them. You could also do this flattening manually by introducing a custom threshold (e.g. anything below 1.3 gets classified as 1.0, while anything over or equal to 1.3 becomes 2.0).

Although this approach doesn't provide you with a probability vector for the predictions, this is still possible with a couple of lines of code (see Exercise 11). However, we don't need the vector in order to calculate the accuracy of the ELM, which we can do as follows:

```
In[39]:  sum(pred .== T6) / n
Out[39]: 0.8180862250262881
```

That's not too shabby for a supervised learning system relying entirely on random meta-features, an arbitrary selection of its parameter, and a few milliseconds of training. Needless to say, this performance can be improved further.

ELM TIPS

Although ELMs are by far the easiest and most promising network-based alternative right now, they are not without their issues. For example, you may have a great signal in your data but the ELM you train may not pick it up on the first instance that you create. Also, just like ANNs, they are prone to overfitting, particularly if your data is insufficient. Finally, they are a fairly new technology so they're still experimental to some extent.

It's quite likely that the ELMs implemented in the current ELM package will become obsolete in the months to come. There are already multi-layer ELMs out there that appear to be more promising than the basic ELMs we have worked with here. So, if the ELM you create doesn't live up to your expectations, don't discard the technology of ELMs altogether.

Although ELMs are bound to perform significantly better than ANNs on the first attempt, this does not mean that they are necessarily the best option for your supervised learning task. It is possible that with proper parameters an ANN performs better than an ELM. So, if you are into neural networks (particularly the more complex ones), don't be discouraged by their initial performance. Just like every supervised learning system, they require some time from your part before they can shine. Fortunately, ELMs are not as demanding in this respect.

STATISTICAL MODELS FOR REGRESSION ANALYSIS

We already saw a couple of regressors earlier, where tree-based models managed to approximate a continuous variable at a somewhat impressive level. Now we'll look at one of the most popular regression models that is specifically designed for this task, although it can double as a classification system, making it somewhat popular among the newcomers to data science.

Although its classification counterpart is mediocre at best, this regressor is robust and employs a lot of statistics theory along with powerful optimization algorithms, the most common of which is gradient descent. All this is wrapped up in a framework that is known as statistical regression and is often the go-to solution for the majority of regression tasks.

Statistical regression (or simply regression) is a basic approach to modeling a regression problem, entailing the creation of a mathematical model that approximates the target variable. Also known as *curve fitting*, this model is basically a combination of previously-normalized features, optimized so that the deviation from the target variable is as small as possible. The combination itself is most commonly linear, but can be non-linear. In the latter scenario, non-linear variants of the features are also included, while combinations of features are also commonplace.

To avoid overfitting, complex regression models stemming from non-linear combinations are limited in terms of how many components make it to the final model. In order to distinguish this non-linear approach to regression, the method involving these non-linear components alongside the linear ones is usually referred to as a *generalized linear model* as well as a *generalized regression model*.

Despite its simplicity, statistical regression works well and it is still the default choice for many data science practitioners. Of course you may need to put some effort into tweaking it, to obtain decent performance. Also, you may need to develop combinations of features to capture the non-linear signals that often exist in the data at hand.

The key advantages to this kind of regression are interpretability and speed. The absolute value of the coefficient of the feature (or feature combination) in the regression model is directly related to its significance. This is why the feature selection process is often tightly linked to the modeling, for regression applications when statistics are involved.

Implementing statistical regression in Julia

Let's see how we can implement this great regression model in Julia, by making use of the GLM package. (Until another decent package exists, we strongly recommend you stick with this one for all regression-related tasks.) Let's start by shaping the data into a form that the programs of the package will recognize, namely data frames:

```
In[40]: using DataFrames
In[41]: ONP = map(Float64, ONP[2:end,2:end]);
    data = DataFrame(ONP)
In[42]: for i = 1:(nd+1)
        rename!(data, names(data)[i], symbol(var_names[i][2:end]))
    end
```

Now that we've loaded everything into a data frame called data and renamed the variables accordingly, we are ready to start with the actual regression analysis. Let's load the corresponding package as follows:

```
In[43]: using GLM
```

Next, we need to create the model, using the fit() function:

```
In[44]: model1 = fit(LinearModel, shares ~ timedelta +
    n_tokens_title + n_tokens_content + n_unique_tokens +
    n_non_stop_words + n_non_stop_unique_tokens + num_hrefs +
    num_self_hrefs + num_imgs + num_videos + average_token_length +
    num_keywords + data_channel_is_lifestyle +
    data_channel_is_entertainment + data_channel_is_bus +
    data_channel_is_socmed + data_channel_is_tech +
    data_channel_is_world + kw_min_min + kw_max_min + kw_avg_min +
    kw_min_max + kw_max_max + kw_avg_max + kw_min_avg + kw_max_avg
    + kw_avg_avg + self_reference_min_shares +
    self_reference_max_shares + self_reference_avg_sharess +
    weekday_is_monday + weekday_is_tuesday + weekday_is_wednesday +
    weekday_is_thursday + weekday_is_friday + weekday_is_saturday +
    weekday_is_sunday + is_weekend + LDA_00 + LDA_01 + LDA_02 +
    LDA_03 + LDA_04 + global_subjectivity +
    global_sentiment_polarity + global_rate_positive_words +
    global_rate_negative_words + rate_positive_words +
    rate_negative_words + avg_positive_polarity +
```

```
min_positive_polarity + max_positive_polarity +
avg_negative_polarity + min_negative_polarity +
max_negative_polarity + title_subjectivity +
title_sentiment_polarity + abs_title_subjectivity +
abs_title_sentiment_polarity, data[ind_,:])
```

We need to train the model using the training set only, hence the `ind_` index that's used as the final parameter. The result is a `DataFrameRegressionModel` object that contains the coefficients of the variables used (in this case, all of them), along with some useful statistics about each one of them.

The statistic that's most important is the probability (right-most column), since this effectively shows the statistical significance of each factor of the model. So, the variables that have a high probability can probably be removed altogether from the model, since they don't add much to it, and may stand in the way of the other variables. If we were to use the common cutoff value of 0.05, we'd end up with the following model:

```
In[45]: model2 = fit(LinearModel, shares ~ timedelta +
    n_tokens_title + n_tokens_content + num_hrefs + num_self_hrefs
    + average_token_length + data_channel_is_lifestyle +
    data_channel_is_entertainment + data_channel_is_bus +
    kw_max_min + kw_min_max + kw_min_avg +
    self_reference_min_shares + global_subjectivity, data[ind_,:])
```

Even though this is more compact and its coefficients generally more significant, there is still room for further simplification:

```
In[46]: model3 = fit(LinearModel, shares ~ timedelta +
    n_tokens_title + num_hrefs + num_self_hrefs +
    average_token_length + data_channel_is_entertainment +
    kw_max_min + kw_min_avg + self_reference_min_shares +
    global_subjectivity, data[ind_,:])
```

This one is much better. All of its coefficients are statistically significant, while it's even more compact (and doesn't take too many lines to express!). We can get the coefficients or weights of this model as follows:

```
In[47]: w = coef(model3)
```

Of course, this is not enough to apply the model to the data; for some peculiar reason, there is no `apply()` function anywhere in the package. So, if you want to use the actual model on some test data, you need to do it using the following code that we provide for you. First, let's get the testing set into shape, since we only need ten of its variables:

```
In[48]: PT3 = convert(Array,data[ind, [:timedelta, :n_tokens_title,
    :num_hrefs, :num_self_hrefs, :average_token_length,
    :data_channel_is_entertainment, :kw_max_min, :kw_min_avg,
    :self_reference_min_shares, :global_subjectivity]])
```

Now, let's find the prediction vector by applying the corresponding weights to the variables of the testing set, and adding the constant value stored in the first elements of the w array:

```
In[49]: pred = PT3 * W[2:end] + W[1]
```

Finally, we can assess the performance of the model using our familiar `MSE()` function:

```
In[50]:   MSE(pred, TT2)
Out[50]:  1.660057312071286e8
```

This is significantly lower than the one we got from the random forest, which shows that this is a robust regression model. Nevertheless, there may still be room for improvement, so feel free to experiment further with this (by using meta-features, other feature combos, etc.).

Statistical regression tips

Although statistical regression is probably the easiest supervised learning model out there, there are a few things that you need to be aware of before using it. In order for this method to work well, you need an adequate amount of data points, significantly larger than the number of components you plan to use in the final model. Also, you need to make sure that your data doesn't have outliers; if it does, be sure to use an error function that isn't heavily influenced by them.

There are various ways to parametrize the model to make it better. The creator of the package even includes a few other models as well as some distribution functions as options for modeling the data, using the generalized version of the linear regression model. We encourage you to explore all these option further through the package documentation: http://bit.ly/29ogFfl.

OTHER SUPERVISED LEARNING SYSTEMS

Boosted trees

These are similar to random forests, in the sense that they are also tree-based supervised learning systems, comprising a series of decision trees. The reason we didn't describe them previously is that they are similar enough to other tree-based systems, plus there are other classification methods that are more interesting and more widely used. Boosted trees are implemented in Julia in the `DecisionTree` package, like the other tree-based methods.

Support vector machines

Support Vector Machines (SVMs) were popular in the 1990s and many people still use them today, although they do not have any edge over existing methods in terms of performance or speed. However, their approach to supervised learning is unique as they manage to warp the feature space in such a way that the classes are linearly separable. They then find the straight line (support vector) that is as far from the class centers or borders as possible, turning learning into a straightforward optimization problem. The basic SVMs work only for binary problems, but there are generalized ones that handle multi-class problems.

So, if you have a complex dataset, are not willing to find the right parameters for a neural network, find that your data is not compatible with Bayesian networks (which will be discussed shortly), and have exhausted all other alternatives, then you may want to give this method a try. Currently there are a couple of Julia packages called `LIBSVM` and `SVM` that aim to make all this possible.

Transductive systems

All the supervised learning systems we have seen so far are induction-deduction based, i.e. they create and apply rules that generalize what they see in the training set. Once the rules are created in the training phase, they are easily applied in the testing phase.

Transductive systems make use of a completely different approach, where no rules are generated. In essence, they are systems that work on-the-fly, without any training phase. Instead of creating some abstraction of reality, they operate based on what is there, looking at similar (nearby) data points for every point of the test set whose target value they need to predict.

Usually transductive systems use some kind of distance or similarity metric to assess how relevant the other data points are. This makes them prone to the curse of dimensionality issue, but they work fine on well-engineered datasets where this problem is alleviated. They are generally fast, intuitive, and easy to use. However, they may not handle complex datasets well, which is why they are not often used in production. Overall they are good for cases where you are willing to use all available data for your prediction, instead of relying on a previously generated model.

Examples of transductive systems are the k Nearest Neighbor (kNN) method we saw in the beginning of the book, all of its variants, the Reduced Coulomb Energy (RCE) classifier, and Transductive Support Vector Machines (TSVMs). The final instance is a special type of SVM that makes use of both clustering and supervised learning to estimate the labels of the test set.

Deep learning systems

Deep learning systems (also known as deep belief networks or Botlzman machines) are popular supervised learning methods these days. They promise to handle all kinds of datasets with minimal effort on the user's part. They were developed by Professor Hinton and his team, and are basically beefed-up versions of conventional neural networks, with many more layers and a significantly larger number of inputs.

We recommend you spend some time getting familiar with ANNs, the various training algorithms associated with them, their relationship with regression models, and what their generalization represents on a feature space, before proceeding to deep learning. That's because although deep learning is an extension of ANNs, there are so many different flavors of ANNs to begin with, that the transition from one system to the other is definitely not an easy leap. Once you have mastered ANNs you can proceed to deep learning, though you may want to buy a specialized book for it first!

Despite their obvious advantage over all other methods of this kind of machine learning (and AI as well), deep learning systems are not suitable for most applications. They require a whole lot of data points, take a long time to train, and it is practically impossible to interpret their generalizations. They are handy when it comes to image analysis, signal processing applications, learning to play Go, and any other domain where there exist a plethora of data points and enough interest to justify the use of a great deal of resources.

To work around the resource use issue, there have been some clever hacks that allow conventional machines to work these supervised learning systems, through the use of graphics processing units (GPUs) working parallel to conventional CPUs during the training phase. You can try them out in Julia by making use of the `Mocha` package (http://bit.ly/29jYj9R).

Bayesian networks

Just like a neural network, a Bayesian network is also a graph that provides a kind of order to the dataset it is trained on, and makes predictions based on that. The main difference is that a Bayesian network employs a probabilistic approach, based on the Bayes theorem, instead of a purely data-driven strategy. This makes them ideal for cases where the data clearly follows a distribution and can be modeled statistically as a result.

In a Bayesian network there are nodes representing different variables and edges representing direct dependencies between individual variables. The implementation of Bayesian networks in Julia is made easy through the use of the `BayesNets` package. You can learn more about the theory behind this supervised learning system through Dr. Rish's tutorial on the topic, available at http://bit.ly/29uF1AM. We recommend trying Bayesian Networks out once you finish reading this book, since they make use of graph theory, which we'll look into in the next chapter.

SUMMARY

- Supervised learning covers both classification and regression methods and is the most widely-used methodology of data science, since most of the insights come from its methods.

- There are various supervised learning methods out there. The ones we focused on in this chapter were: tree-based, network-based, and statistical regression.

  o **Tree-based**: These are methods based on tree-like machine learning systems such as decision trees, regression trees, and random forests.

    - Decision trees are simple yet effective classification systems that make use of a number of binary choices, using the data on a selection of features, until they reach one of the target labels with high enough certainty. They are easy to use and interpret.

    - Regression trees are the regression counterparts of decision trees.

    - Random forests are series of trees working together to tackle classification or regression problems. A random forest is better than any single tree in it and can also be useful for determining the value of particular features in the dataset.

  o **Network-based**: These are methods that involve the creation of a network (graph) with each part carrying information related to the model built through the training phase. These are generally more complex than tree-based methods, which also involve graphs to represent their generalizations. The most common network-based models are neural networks, while Extreme Learning Machines are also gaining ground.

- Artificial neural networks (ANNs) provide a sophisticated approach to supervised learning by emulating the function of brain tissue in order to derive useful features and use them for predicting unknown data points. They are applicable for both classification and regression. ANNs are implemented in Julia in various packages, the best of which is `BackpropNeuralNet`. Unlike other classifiers, ANNs need special pre-processing of the target value, so that it is compatible.

- Extreme Learning Machines (ELMs) are similar to ANNs, but they have a much swifter training phase, as they reduce the whole process into a straightforward optimization task that is solved analytically. Also, they exhibit decent out-of-the-box performance, while their parameters (number of hidden layers, number of nodes in each layer) are fairly easy to tweak. ELMs are implemented in Julia in the `ELM` package.

  o **Statistical regression** (also known as a **generalized regression model**): This is a classic approach to regression, using different linear or non-linear combinations of the available features in order to minimize some error function that depicts the difference between the predicted target value and the actual value. They are generally very fast and easy to interpret. The best package out there is the generalized linear model package (`GLM`).

- Other supervised learning systems include support vector machines (SVMs), transduction systems, deep learning systems, and Bayesian Networks.

  o Boosted decision trees provide an ensemble approach to tree-based classification, somewhat similar to random forests. You can find a good implementation of them in Julia in the `DecisionTree` package.

  o SVMs are clever approaches to supervised learning (particularly binary classification), that warp the feature space and find the optimum boundaries among the classes.

o   Transduction systems are distance- or similarity-based supervised learning systems, usually focusing on classification. They make their predictions by making direct connections between the unknown data points and the known ones, bypassing the generalization stage. They don't build models and are generally fast, but difficult to interpret.

o   Deep learning systems are the most sophisticated supervised learning systems out there. They are enhanced versions of conventional ANNs, with significantly more layers and input nodes, requiring a large amount of data in order to work well. They are used for specific domains, such as image analytics, where conventional approaches perform poorly. Although they take a while to train and are resource-hungry, they are good at emulating the function of the human brain and constitute the highest-level AI technique that has become mainstream.

o   Bayesian networks provide a network-based approach to supervised learning, relying on both graph modeling of a problem and on Bayesian statistics. They are generally more time-consuming than other methods, but they perform quite well, particularly in cases where the features used are independent to each other.

CHAPTER CHALLENGE

1.   You have a data sample consisting of 200 data points and 100 features, most of which are independent. Which supervised learning system would you use? Why?

2.   What's the best classification system out there, for a well-engineered dataset consisting of information-rich features that are statistically independent of each other? Why?

3.   What's the best classification system to use for a huge dataset with very messy data? Why?

4. Can a robust supervised learning system make data engineering unnecessary? Explain.

5. What's the best supervised learning system to use if interpretability is of great importance for your project? Why?

6. What's the relationship between statistical regression and neural networks, for regression problems?

7. What's the main limitation of transduction systems for supervised learning? How would you overcome it?

8. Why doesn't everyone use deep learning networks if they are so great?

9. You are working with a dataset that is updated every minute. What kind of supervised learning system would you use to make sure that your predictions are never stale?

10. Can you make use of a deep learning network for something other than its predictions? How?

11. How could you calculate the probabilities of a prediction made by an ELM?

Although the conventional approach to analyzing data works in the majority of cases, there are times when a different kind of modeling works better. This may be due to the nature of the data, its dimensionality, or even the interpretability factor (which is crucial in many cases). There is an abundance of information on this topic, and a lot to learn to master it. For the purposes of our book, we will limit ourselves to only some of the applications of graph analysis, along with the tools for implementing them in Julia.

We'll be making use of two packages throughout this chapter, `Graphs` and `LightGraphs`, so make sure that you have both installed on Julia before we get started. We won't be delving too deep into the `LightGraphs` package; this introduction is mainly for the purpose of acquainting you with its unique feature of saving a graph object in a compact format as a file.

We'll also be providing you with a couple of auxiliary functions for converting between the two corresponding graph types (see the IJulia notebook). Also, be sure to load the `normalize.jl` script into memory as we'll be using the `normalize()` function.

There is enough material in graph theory and Julia's implementation of it for a whole additional book. If you want to learn more about it, please refer to the references. In this chapter we will cover the following topics:

- Importance of graphs

- Overview of graph theory

- Graph statistics

- Shortest distance in a graph

- Detection of cycles and maximal cliques in a graph

- Connected components of a graph

- Minimum spanning trees (special graphs used in machine learning).

IMPORTANCE OF GRAPHS

Although graph theory has been around for many years, only recently has it become popular in the data analytics sphere. This could be because graphs are heavy on math–particularly the abstract type. Also, the database technology has been traditionally focused on table-based data structures and graphs are completely different from this paradigm. Fortunately, people are coming around to the value of graphs, and are gradually developing more tools for them (particularly on the database side). Also, databases like neo4j have come out of the shadows and entered the mainstream, even featured in some online courses. Before that, they were esoteric and known only by the very few who were specialists in the graph analysis subfield.

We have seen in the previous chapters how dimensionality can cause major performance issues, especially when distances are used. Also, the diversity (variety of the types of data, such as numeric or nominal) of features doesn't make things easier, while the computational overhead of the feature space is not a trivial challenge. Needless to say, this isn't intuitive, since we, as human beings, are accustomed to more direct ways of associating things.

Graphs follow this intuitive approach, simplifying things through the use of an abstract representation of all the connections (and lack thereof) among the various elements of a dataset. These elements can be data points, features, classes (in the case of classification), or anything else that makes sense when modeling the problem at hand.

Believe it or not, you have already used graphs during this book (unless you skipped the most juicy chapters!). Graphs are everywhere in data science, even if they are not made apparent. In fact, it is hard to imagine data analytics in general without graphs. Just to clarify, the graphs we are talking about are graphical representations of relationships, not plots like the ones we explored in Chapter 7. Yet, graphs can be plotted so that we understand them better (in fact, that's one of their perks: easy two-dimensional plotting). You can view a typical graph in Figure 12.1.

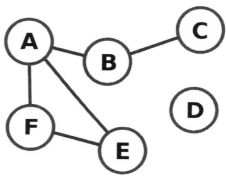

Figure 12.1 An example of a typical graph.

For now, all you need to know about graphs is the following:

- Graphs (also called networks) are abstract representations of objects and the connections among them. They are composed of nodes (also called vertices) and edges.
    - Nodes are the "stop points" of a graph, often represented by circles, and depicting data points, features, etc. In Figure 12.1 they are points A, B, C, etc.
    - Edges are the (usually) straight lines that connect nodes. They depict various types of relationships: distances, similarities, etc. In Figure 12.1 they are the lines connecting A, B, C, E, and F.

- Nodes and edges have associated properties including name, some numeric variable, and more.

- There are numerous ways of plotting a graph, since you can move nodes around as you wish, as long as you maintain the connections within the graph. For large graphs, the nodes are typically located at points on the periphery of a circle, with all the edges as curves connecting the corresponding points.

- Graphs are described as "connected" if each of their nodes are connected to one or more nodes.

- Edges can be directed or undirected (i.e. one-way vs. two-way streets).

- You can represent a graph in either a connection or adjacency matrix, or as a set of edges and a list of the corresponding weights.
  - o A connection or adjacency matrix is a square matrix of size N, where N is the total number of nodes. Its elements represent the strength of connection between the members of each of node, which is termed "weight." If weight is zero, then the corresponding nodes are not connected to each other. This matrix is usually sparse (i.e. mostly zeros).
  - o The set of edges shows which nodes are connected. In the example of Figure 12.1, the set of edges looks something like this:

```
A, B
A, E
A, F
B, C
E, F
```

If there were weights corresponding to these connections, they would be part of the set as well, making the whole data structure a dictionary of sorts. This representation of a graph is particularly useful for graphs having few connections among their nodes. That's it! All of the fundamentals of this incredibly complicated theory are distilled into the above points. If you want to learn more about the math behind these concepts, we recommend checking out the comprehensive tutorial created by Professor Harju of the University of Turku, Finland: http://bit.ly/29kRzJx. This tutorial may also be useful in understanding the corresponding algorithms, which we will be using in this chapter (although we won't be describing them in any detail). Due to the vastness of the topic, in this chapter we'll be focusing on undirected graphs only.

CUSTOM DATASET

Unlike the previous chapters where all your code could be set up with just a couple of lines, here we'll have to do some extra work (nothing too challenging). The reason is that the original datasets are not useful in illustrating the points we need to make in this chapter, so that you get acquainted with the set of techniques related to graph analysis.

So, for starters we'll be introducing a new dataset that's simple enough to draw on a piece of (electronic) paper. This way there will be no confusion about what's happening in each algorithm, while examining the edges of the corresponding graph won't be time-consuming.

Without further ado, here is the dataset. It describes the relationships among a group of friends: Alice, Bob, Christine, Dan, Eve, Frank, and George. Imagine that they all use a social medium of your choice (perhaps the website from the startup in the case study of Chapter 5) and that this website has established some kind of reliable metric that expresses how close they are to each other, in terms of interests, background, affinity for the Julia language, etc. This metric takes values between 0 and 1. The data we have looks like something like this:

```
Alice -- Bob, 0.00956345
Alice -- Christine, 0.952837
Alice -- Eve, 0.775323
Alice -- George, 0.0875062
Bob -- Christine, 0.546019
Bob -- Eve, 0.573757
Bob -- Frank, 0.43756
Bob -- George, 0.665684
Christine -- Dan, 0.445205
Christine -- Frank, 0.248718
Christine -- George, 0.977219
Dan -- Frank, 0.732508
Dan -- George, 0.149959
Eve -- Frank, 0.284119
Frank -- George, 0.990848
```

This can be easily coded in two ways: either as an array of edges (relationships between pairs of friends) with a corresponding weights array (similarity weight), or as a 7 x 7 matrix with a weight value wherever there is a connection between two friends. Here we will use the first option as it's more straightforward and user-friendly. Feel free to try out the other approach if you want.

Whatever the case, we have a couple of functions that allow us to translate the data structures of one approach to that of the other. So, if we were to assign numbers to the various friends (according to the order they are listed), and get rid of the "--" string, we would end up with something like this:

```
1, 2, 0.00956345
1, 3, 0.952837
1, 5, 0.775323
1, 7, 0.0875062
2, 3, 0.546019
2, 5, 0.573757
2, 6, 0.43756
2, 7, 0.665684
3, 4, 0.445205
3, 6, 0.248718
3, 7, 0.977219
4, 6, 0.732508
4, 7, 0.149959
5, 6, 0.284119
6, 7, 0.990848
```

We can now split this numeric array into two arrays: one for the indexes of the people in the group, and one for the weights signifying the strength of their bonds. The first array will include the first two columns and the second array the last column.

In order to avoid any confusion, it is important to code the two arrays with the appropriate type. Although Julia will not create any fuss about it during the coding phase, the functions of the graph analysis packages most certainly will, since they expect the data in a specific way. So, make sure that the indexes are coded as integers while the weights as floats.

Also, keep in mind that these weights represent similarity in this example (in reality, they can represent whatever you want). If we were to examine how different one member of the group is from another, we would need to use some other metric (such as the inverse of w, or any other function that grows as w diminishes).

STATISTICS OF A GRAPH

This is the graphical counterpart of data exploration, but it's much more straightforward. Since a graph is simple as a data structure, the main things we can learn about a graph are:

- The number of nodes (aka vertices) and edges

- The identities of the nodes and edges

- The nature of the graph (directed or not)

- The number of neighbors of a node (termed the degree of the node)

- The identity of each node's neighbors

- The degree of a graph

- Other characteristics which lend themselves to more specialized applications.

Let's see how we can calculate these on our simple graph (g) of Alice's social circle, using the `Graphs` package:

```
In[1]:   num_vertices(g)
Out[1]:  7
In[2]:   num_edges(g)
Out[2]:  15
In[3]:   vertices(g)
Out[3]:  1:7
In[4]:   edges(g)
Out[4]:  15-element Array{Graphs.Edge{Int64},1}:
```

```
edge [1]: 1 -- 2
edge [2]: 1 -- 3
edge [3]: 1 -- 5
edge [4]: 1 -- 7
```

There are a few more of these, which we are omitting here as we don't want to fill the pages with stuff you can view on the IJulia notebook.

```
In[5]:   Graphs.is_directed(g)
Out[5]:  false
In[6]:   out_degree(1, g)
Out[6]:  4
```

This basically means that there are four edges stemming from node 1 (Alice).

```
In[7]: Graphs.out_neighbors(1, g)
```

This yields a somewhat elaborate `TargetIterator` object, which contains all the edges that correspond to node 1. These are basically all the neighbors of the node.

To find the degree of a graph, we calculate the degrees of all of its nodes and take the largest value:

```
In[8]: n = num_vertices(g)
    d = Array(Int64, n)
    for i = 1:n
     d[i] = out_degree(i, g)
    end
    dg = maximum(d)
Out[8]:  5
```

CYCLE DETECTION

Cycles are paths comprising three or more nodes that are connected to each other in a ring fashion. The nodes of a cycle need not be connected to all of the other members of the cycle, though there sometimes exist multiple connections among a cycle's elements.

Take for example your closest friends. Some of these may be friends with other members of your group, while others may know just you and one other person. As long as you can trace a ring-like connection among you and your friends, this connection constitutes a cycle in a social network. This is actually how Facebook knows who to recommend to you as potential friends. You may be friends with Tracy, who is friends with Joe, who is Mike's best buddy, who is also your friend, yet you are not connected to Joe directly. Facebook sees this and based on your connections (and probably other factors too), recommends that you reach out to Joe, while it does the same for Joe regarding you.

If a graph doesn't have any cycles, it is called acyclical. A special case of acyclical graphs are the ones that are also directed graphs. These graphs are often referred to as DAGs (directed acyclical graphs) and are common in graph theory. So, finding out whether there are cycles in a graph is a simple way to deduce whether it's a DAG (since we usually already know if it's directed).

Cycles are interesting in the context of social networks, but they are also extremely valuable artifacts in feature analysis. If you represent all your dataset's features as nodes in a graph and connect them through a similarity metric (the value of this metric can be the weight of the corresponding edge), then you have a clear representation of how everything is connected in your feature set.

Cycles in this graph represent redundancy in your feature set (i.e. three or more features being similar to each other) and therefore it would be best if we eliminate them. If feature A is closely connected to feature B, while both are closely connected to feature C, then one of them could go. Of course you would want to take other things into account, such as each feature's connectivity to the target variable (i.e. through its DID score in the case of classification or its cosine similarity in the case of regression). For now we'll just look at the cycle aspect of the graph, using Julia to sort things out.

Julia the cycle detective

Let's look at how Julia can help simplify the feature selection process so that you can explain to everyone in a straightforward manner. As before, we'll be making use of the Graphs package. Before we look into feature analysis, though, let's see how the cycle detection function works on a simple graph:

```
In[9]: test_cyclic_by_dfs(g)
Out[9]: true
```

It gets even easier than that. Just plug in the graph object to the `test_cyclic_by_dfs()` function and you'll quickly know whether there is a cycle in the graph or not. Now let's see how we can apply this in a more useful scenario. First, let's work the data of the `OnlineNewsPopularity` dataset and obtain the correlation matrix of its numeric features:

```
In[10]: ONP =
    readcsv("D:\\data\\OnlineNewsPopularity\\OnlineNewsPopularity.c
    sv");
```

It is useful to have the number of features in a variable, so:

```
In[11]: nd = size(ONP, 2) - 2
```

We can opt to normalize the whole thing in order to calculate the similarity (in case we'll go with an alternative metric later on):

```
In[12]: ONP = normalize(map(Float64,ONP[2:end,2:end]), "stat")
In[13]: F = ONP[:,1:(end-1)];
In[14]: CM = cor(F)
```

Now we can go ahead and build the graph corresponding to the feature correlations. To do this, we'll need the connectivity matrix, which we can initialize as follows:

```
In[15]: M = Array(Bool, nd, nd)
```

Of course, we'll need to populate it. We'll be using the threshold of 0.7 to signify a strong similarity, although other thresholds can also be used:

```
In[16]: for i = 1:(nd-1)
   M[i,i] = true
   for j = (i+1):nd
    M[i,j] = M[j,i] = (abs(CM[i,j]) .> 0.7)
   end
  end
```

Next, we can get the edge list going, using the custom CM2EL() function:

```
In[17]: E = CM2EL(M)
```

Finally, we can build the actual graph:

```
In[18]: g2 = simple_graph(nd, is_directed=false)
In[19]: for i = 1:size(E, 1)
   e = E[i,:]
   Graphs.add_edge!(g2, e[1], e[2])
  end
```

Like in the previous example, we can perform some detective work using the corresponding function that identifies the cycles in a graph:

```
In[20]: test_cyclic_by_dfs(g2)
Out[20]: true
```

So, this analysis verifies the fact that there is redundancy in the features, as we realized during our data exploration in the early part of the book.

By the way, if you feel that this cycle detection function is a let-down, that's because it is! On its own, there is limited value it can provide. However, it can be useful in that if you know that there is a cycle in your graph, you will have a reason to perform the next kind of a analysis, seeking out the connected components of the graph.

CONNECTED COMPONENTS

A connected component is a fancy term for a set of nodes in a graph, where you can get from node A to node B, for any A and B belonging to that set of nodes. So, if you were to draw the whole graph, a component of it would look like a bunch of nodes that are linked to each other in some kind of fashion. Obviously, you cannot traverse from any A to B if that A and B belong to different components. If a graph has exactly one connected component, then every node of it is accessible from any other node in the graph (i.e. it is connected to them directly or indirectly), and is therefore called a connected graph.

Basically, connected components are sets of sub-graphs, each one of which is fully connected to the others. One such graph may be composed of a single node. Needless to say, it's great to see lots of these micro-graphs when analyzing the feature similarity of a dataset.

Once Julia detects a cycle in a graph, it is time to connect the dots and go deeper into the graph itself, using the `connected_components()` function. Since this function exists in both graph packages, it is necessary to specify which one you want to use:

```
In[21]:  Graphs.connected_components(g)
Out[21]: 1-element Array{Array{Int64,1},1}:
    [1,2,3,5,7,6,4]
```

In this case it looks like all of the nodes are jumbled up (so it wouldn't be easy to infiltrate Alice's group of friends!). This makes the said graph a connected one. Let's see how our features graph from the OnlineNewPopularity dataset fares:

```
In[22]:  Graphs.connected_components(g2)
Out[22]: 43-element Array{Array{Int64,1},1}:
    [1]
    [2]
    [3]
    [4,5,6]
    [7]
```

In this case we have a lot of connected components, due to the fact that most of the features are unrelated to the rest of the feature set (or we could have set up a very high threshold). Most of these are omitted here, but if you check the notebook file, you'll be able to verify this. Also, towards the end of the list of connected components lies [56, 59], denoting a connection between these two features. Let's take a closer look using the correlation matrix array we calculated previously:

```
In[23]:  CM[56,59]
Out[23]: 0.714527589349792
```

CLIQUES

The cliques are closely related to cycles as they are sets of nodes in a graph that are all connected to each other. So, when investigating this property of a graph, they are usually examined together. The cliques are common in social networks and logistics problems; we are generally interested in the largest one of them. This is because there are often many cliques, and the smaller ones don't reveal much. The largest ones, however, are unique, containing more information related to their members.

So, if we have determined that there is a cycle in a graph, the next logical step would be to check for the actual nodes that make cycles possible, namely the clique(s) present in the graph. For example, if there is a clique that Alice belongs to, this means that we can identify her closest friends (or the people who are most similar to her, and are also similar to each other) by examining this clique. Clearly there is some marketing opportunity in this, as well as a more personalized experience for her given that all of the members of her group are on our website.

Let's now check our simple graph for cliques and try to make sense of Alice's social circle. To do this we'll need to use the `maximal_cliques()` function, specifying the package as a prefix, like before:

```
In[24]:  Graphs.maximal_cliques(g)
Out[24]: 5-element Array{Array{Int64,N},1}:
     [4,7,3,6]
     [2,7,3,6]
     [2,7,3,1]
     [2,5,6]
     [2,5,1]
```

What does all this tell us? Well, if Alice wanted to go out with as many of her friends as possible, without making the communication among them awkward, she would have to pick the third cycle (since it is tied with the most members). Moreover, she would be sure that each person would be friends with at least two other people, so it would not be weird for them whenever she would go to the restroom! As for Bob, he can do the same with two groups of friends (the first two cliques), so if he is sick and tired of Alice, he can hang out with other members of the gang!

Although finding the maximal clique in a graph is useful overall, it doesn't yield any interesting information when applied to a feature graph, so we won't be examining how it applies to our other graph example.

SHORTEST PATH IN A GRAPH

More often than not, the edges of a graph have weights, so finding the shortest route from A to B becomes a different kind of problem. Now, the objective is not just getting there, but getting there quickly. To make this happen we will make use of the Dijktra algorithm, which is popular in computer science among other fields. Apart from graph theory, it has applications in finding the best way to schedule your tasks (project management) and getting you to the closest Julia event in your city (or any city for that matter) through a GPS-based app. There are other minimal distance calculation algorithms out there, the most important of which have been implemented in the Graphs package. We encourage you to experiment with them, once you are comfortable with the Dijktra algorithm.

We won't go into depth on the math of this technique, but we encourage you to investigate it through a specialized document such as Melissa Yan's presentation at MIT: http://bit.ly/29zFogk.

When calculating the distances involved in the shortest path investigation, we interpret the weight of an edge as the distance between the corresponding nodes.

So, if our weights represent similarity, we'll need to adjust them for the shortest path algorithms to work properly.

Let's now see how we can calculate the distance of the shortest path between two points in a graph using Julia. First of all, let's invert the weights to get a measure of how dissimilar the various members of the group are:

```
In[25]: ww = 1 - w
```

We could have used any number of functions to accomplish this. We refrained from using the obvious one (`1/w`) since this would yield extreme results in cases of nodes having a very low weight. In general, if you want to preserve the scale of the weights when inverting them, you can apply the function `c + maximum(w) - w`, where `c` is a positive constant of your choice. Also, if the weights are very disperse, you can apply a sigmoid to them first and then reverse them. Be creative!

Once we have all the weights sorted out, we need to define a starting point. In this case, we'll make Alice the starting point (node 1). To find the shortest path to Alice from the various parts of the graph, we'll apply the `dijkstra_shortest_paths()` function, after specifying that it's from the `Graphs` package:

```
In[26]: z = Graphs.dijkstra_shortest_paths(g, ww, 1)
```

The result is a DijkstraStates object that's loaded with information about the shortest paths to Alice's node (set as the last input of the function). To get some more comprehensive information from all this, let's access the two most relevant parts of this data structure, `parents` and `dists`:

```
In[27]:  z.parents
Out[27]: 7-element Array{Int64,1}:
    1
    7
    1
    6
    1
    7
    3
```

Hopefully you were not expecting a list of the names of each person's actual parents, otherwise you'd be disappointed right now. Clearly, the term "parent" has a different meaning here; it refers to the node that is right before the examined node, as we travel from the source node (in this case, 1) to that node. Also note that the source node is a parent of itself.

So, if you were Bob (node 2) and wanted to get a message across to Alice as swiftly as possible, your best option would be to go through node 7, since apparently Alice and Bob are not close (i.e. the distance between them is high, as shown by the corresponding element of the ww array). To find the actual smallest distance between anyone in the graph and the source node, we'll use the dists part of the aforementioned data structure:

```
In[28]:    z.dists
Out[28]:  7-element Array{Float64,1}:
    0.0
    0.40426
    0.047163
    0.346588
    0.224677
    0.079096
    0.069944
```

From this it becomes clear that the closest person to Alice (apart from herself) is Christine (node 3). This is to be expected, as there is a direct link between the two (edge 1---3), while the similarity weight is very high. On the other hand, the person furthest from Alice is Bob (node 2), since the direct link between them has a low similarity weight and a high distance weight. To go from one to the other, you would be best served by going through other people in the group.

MINIMUM SPANNING TREES

A tree is basically an acyclical graph designed for a specific task. We have already seen classification trees that emulate the decision process for associating a data point to a particular class. If we were to do the same but using other data points instead of a class, we would end up with a spanning tree. If we were to minimize the total (or the average) weight of the connections of this tree, we would have a minimum spanning tree. So, fancy terminology aside, a minimum spanning tree (MST) is an optimal graph connecting all the data points of a dataset, where the overall weight is as small as possible.

One important application of MSTs is in logistics. If you wanted to create a road network with an exceptionally small budget, but you had to abide by the requirement that all the major buildings must be connected somehow (i.e. you could drive from one to any other, even if you had to take a scenic route), an MST would solve your problem.

In this case, the nodes would be the buildings you want to connect, and the edges would be the actual roads you would construct. The people in the area may not be too happy about this since, they might have to drive a lot and there might be just one route to get from the library to the courthouse, but the overall cost of the project would be minimal. This example may be a bit extreme, but it would make sense for a new subway project where you want to cover as many places as possible, without having any redundancy among the train lines used (at least for the initial phase of the project).

MSTs can also be useful in other applications, including classification. MSTs are one of the most intuitive parts of graph theory; as such, they hold a lot of potential for the development of future techniques in data science. We encourage you to delve deeper into this topic, through reliable references such as this web page by Princeton University: http://bit.ly/29pnIol.

Finally, there also exist graphs called *maximum* spanning trees. However, since all maximum spanning trees can be expressed as MSTs (e.g. by reversing the weights of the edges), we won't be examining those in this chapter. A maximum spanning tree would be applicable if the weights of a graph expressed distance and the nodes features of a dataset, in which case you would want to perform a feature selection that yields a set of features as different as possible. Such a selection would be a connected component of the maximum spanning tree of the features graph.

There are two ways to calculate the MST of a graph. These are expressed through two efficient algorithms: Prim's and Kruskal's. Both are relatively easy (almost intuitive) and have been implemented in Julia through the `Graphs` package.

Julia the MST botanist

Julia can also be useful for creating MSTs out of graphs. Going back to Alice's group, it may be the case that someone in the group wants to make a certain message known to everyone else at a time when it so happens that social media is down. So, how would that person go about communicating this message, keeping the awkwardness to a bare minimum (i.e. connecting everyone in the group through the shortest dissimilarity on average)? That's where Julia's MST functions come in handy. Here we'll be using the `kruskal_minimum_spantree()` function, along with the distance weights, since this MST algorithm is easier to use:

```
In[29]: E, W = kruskal_minimum_spantree(g, ww)
```

You can examine the actual tree on your own by checking out which edges of the original graph are connected (array `E`). Right now we'll focus on the average weights (array `W`), as this is a common metric associated with MSTs:

```
In[30]:  mean(W)
Out[30]: 0.15093016666666667
```

So, even though there are some people in Alice's group who can't stand each other, the average distance (awkwardness) of this whole communique can be fairly small through the use of an MST that connects everyone.

Saving and loading graphs from a file

We can make that graph we crafted available for future analytics. The best part is that it can be compressed, so it won't take much space. To make this happen we'll use the `save()` and `load()` functions from the `LightGraphs` package. First, we'll need to transform the graph to a type that this package can recognize:

```
In[31]: gg = G2LG(g)
```

Now we can proceed with the actual saving operation, using the `save()` function:

```
In[32]: save("graph data.jgz", gg, "AliceGang", compress=true)
Out[32]: 1
```

The output denotes the number of graphs saved. Also, the name for the graph (`AliceGang`) is not essential, so you can omit it if you want (if you do, it will be named something generic like "`graph`"). However, if you plan to store more graphs in a file, you may want to give them descriptive names so that you can distinguish them from each other after you load them. Speaking of loading a graph data file:

```
In[33]: gg_loaded = load("graph data.jgz", "AliceGang")
```

Since we knew the name of the graph in the data file, we asked for that particular graph. If we didn't, we could just load it into a temp file and access the graph afterwards. This is relatively easy since the object that the `load()` command yields if no name is given as a second parameter is a dictionary.

Also keep in mind that the loaded graph is going to be a LightGraphs object, so if you want to use it with functions from the `Graphs` package, you'll need to convert it, using the custom `LG2G()` function:

```
In[34]: g_loaded = LG2G(gg_loaded)
```

Should you wish to compare the original graph with the loaded one, you can check the edges using something like this:

```
Int [35]: hcat(edges(g_loaded), edges(g))
```

GRAPH ANALYSIS AND JULIA'S ROLE IN IT

Although the field of graph analysis is still relatively new and Julia even newer as a technology, it is clear that there is a good match between the two. There are certain signs (or features, if you will) that clearly point toward the possibility of a powerful synergy. Specifically:

- As more and more people become aware of the value of networks of all sorts, the availability of graph datasets will grow, making graph analysis more relevant. This is good news for Julia, since it is particularly good at working with complex datasets and finding insightful connections before other analytics platforms can even finish loading the data.

- Graph analysis generally attracts competent data scientists, the ones that are usually head-hunted by Facebook, Twitter, Microsoft, and other well-known companies. If just 1% of these professionals decide to give Julia a chance, the language will grow significantly more robust, as the packages developed will be made by people who are adept at writing clean code and documenting it well.

- As Julia's popularity grows in the graph analysis field, database developers may take notice and develop a IDEs for them. We expect in the near term that forward-thinking companies like Turi will take notice, because Julia can handle extremely novel data structures. This is due to Julia's intimate connection with C-based languages (e.g. C++, through the `Cxx` package).

Beyond these points, it becomes clear to anyone who uses Julia for this kind of task that even though other data science languages can fudge their way into this field through the use of C under the hood, it is the more powerful languages that can truly handle it and allow for innovation in the tools. So, for those people who are not particularly keen on writing C, C++ or Java code, Julia is pretty much the best option out there for graph analysis applications.

It is difficult to overstate how empowering this is, since a robust language allows programmers to experiment more freely, without having to rely on a bunch of third-party scripts that you may never have a chance to examine and understand fully. This may lead to a more fast-paced evolution of the graph analytics field.

SUMMARY

- Graphs are useful for modeling certain kinds of problems, although they could be used for a variety of datasets.

- Graphs are dimensionless, as they constitute abstract representations of data, with emphasis on the relationships in the data. The relationships can be among data points, features, classes, or any other aspects of the data at hand.

- Graphs can be directed or undirected. These correspond to cases where the relationships among the nodes are one-way or two-way, respectively.

- Graphs are defined by their list of edges (this includes the direction of each relationship) and the corresponding weights (if any), or by the connectivity (or adjacency) matrix.

- There are several statistics we can calculate for a given graph `g`, the most important of which are the following:

  o The number of nodes – `num_vertices(g)`
  o The number of edges – `num_edges(g)`
  o The nodes themselves – `vertices(g)`
  o The edges themselves – `edges(g)`
  o Whether a graph is directed – `Graphs.is_directed(g)`
  o The degree of a node x – `out_degree(x, g)`
  o The neighbors of a node x – `Graphs.out_neighbors(x, g)`
  o The degree of a graph –the maximum value of the list of the degrees of all the nodes of the graph.

- Cycle detection involves finding whether there is a path starting from a node and ending up in the same node. This is important for feature selection, among other things. You can apply cycle detection on a graph `g` using the function: `test_cyclic_by_dfs(g)`.

- Graphs that don't have any cycles and are directed in nature are called directed acyclical graphs, or DAGs for short.

- A connected component is a set of nodes that are all accessible from each other (i.e. there is a path through which you can go from A to B, for any A and B in the set of nodes). You can uncover all of the connected components of a graph `g` through use of the function `Graphs.connected_components(g)`.

- Cliques are sets of nodes in a graph that are all connected to each other. As there are often several such cases in a graph (particularly a social one), we are usually interested in the largest ones, called maximal cliques.

- A maximal clique is the largest possible clique in a graph. Usually there are several such maximal cliques, depending on what part of the graph we are looking at. We can obtain a whole list of these maximal cliques of a graph `g` through the function `Graphs.maximal_cliques(g)`.

- The shortest path in a graph, connecting node `x` to some other node, is often useful as it allows for efficient traversing through the graph. You can identify these paths and their distances in graph `g` for node `x` through the use of the Dijktra algorithm, implemented by the function `Graphs.dijkstra_shortest_paths(g, ww, x)`, where `ww` is the vector of the weights corresponding to the various edges of the graph, expressing some kind of dissimilarity or distance. The resulting object contains several pieces of information related to the shortest paths to node `x`. The most important components of this object are:

  o Parents: a list of the parent of each node, in relation to `x`. This is the closest node from the node examined, that you would have to go through in order to reach `x`. Remember that node `x` is a parent of itself.

o   Dists: the list of the distances corresponding to each path.

- Minimum Spanning Trees (or MSTs) are acyclical graphs that connect all the nodes of a given graph, minimizing the overall weight. You can calculate the MST of a graph using one of two algorithms, Prim's or Kruskal's. The latter is the easier to work with in Julia and is implemented through the function: `kruskal_minimum_spantree(g, ww)`. The outputs of this are two objects, `E` and `W`, representing the list of edges and the corresponding weights of the MST, respectively.

- You can save and load graphs using the `LightGraphs` package as follows:

  o   Saving a graph `g`: `save(fn, g, gn)`, where `fn` is the filename of the data file where the graph `g` is going to be saved, and `gn` (an optional parameter) is the name to be used for referring to that graph in the data file.

  o   Loading a graph `g`: `load(fn, gn)`, where `fn` is the filename of the data file where the graph is stored, and `gn` (an optional parameter) is the name of the graph to be retrieved. The output of this is a LightGraphs graph object. If you don't use that parameter, you'll end up with a dictionary, containing all the graphs stored in that data file.

- Transforming a graph from one type to another is helpful if you want your graph to be accessible from both the `Graphs` and the `LightGraphs` packages. This is possible through the `G2LG()` and `LG2G()` custom functions, which convert a Graphs graph to a LightGraphs one, and vice versa.

- Julia can play an important role in the graph analytics field, due to its high performance and the fact that it allows for easy access and understanding of the algorithms used for each task.

CHAPTER CHALLENGE

1.   Why are graphs useful for data science?

2. How would you use graph analysis to establish the credibility of a feature set?

3. Can everything be modeled and analyzed as a graph? Why?

4. Is it possible to use MSTs as a classification system? Explain.

5. Can you use graph analysis right off the shelf on a dataset? Why?

6. Write a program that creates the *maximum* spanning tree of a given graph. (Hint: if you use a function from a graph package as a dependency, the required program is going to be very small.)

7. Does the data file of the saved graph (gg) contain all of the information of the graph? Why?

CHAPTER 13
Reaching the Next Level

If what they say about learning is true, this chapter is where you'll get to know what you know (and perhaps more importantly, what you don't know). This is because this chapter will teach you to become self-sufficient in Julia, when it comes to data science applications.

That's not to say that you'll be a know-it-all after finishing this chapter! However, if you can work through everything we recommend in this chapter, you'll have gained an impressive level of competency in the language. You won't need to rely on this or any other book for your Julia-related endeavors in data analytics, and you'll be empowered to use Julia more freely.

Although this chapter is accompanied by an IJulia notebook, we recommend that you don't use it unless you need a little help. Instead, try first to create your own notebook and write all the necessary code from scratch.

This chapter covers the following topics:

- The Julia community and how to learn about the latest developments on the language

- What you've learned about using Julia for data science through a hands-on project

- How you can use your newly-acquired skills to contribute to the Julia project, making make Julia more relevant in the data science world.

JULIA COMMUNITY

Sites to interact with other Julians

Although the Julia community is relatively small, there are people out there who use Julia and are open to interacting with other users of this technology. Fortunately, they tend to be quite experienced in Julia, as well as in other computer languages, since it's rare that someone starts programming with Julia as their first programming language.

Most Julians understand that the world has not yet adopted this language, so if they do any programming for their day job, they most likely use other, more established platforms. This is helpful because they'll usually be able to answer your questions about whether functions in other languages have equivalents in Julia, or at least point you to the right direction. That's not to say that there are no knowledgeable people in other programming communities. You can find experienced programmers everywhere, though the population density of such individuals tends to be higher in Julia groups.

So, if you want to interact with other Julians, this Google group is a good place to start: http://bit.ly/29CYPoj. If Spanish happens to be your language of choice, there is a version of this group in Spanish: http://bit.ly/29kHaRS.

What if you have a very specific question about a Julia script, one of the built-in functions, or you can't find a way to deal with an error on your code? Well, that's what StackOverflow is for, with the `julia-lang` tag being the go-to option for organizing questions related to this language.

There are also Meetup groups, which are a great way to meet other Julia users in person. You can find a list of all of them here: http://bit.ly/29xJOCM. Currently Julia is popular in the United States and a few other countries, so if you are privileged enough to live in a city where there is an active Julia meetup, do check it out.

Code repositories

As Julia is an open-source project, all of the code for it and the majority of its packages is available on GitHub. You can find a list of all supported packages in this site: http://pkg.julialang.org, along with the links to the corresponding GitHub repositories. In Appendix C, we have a list of all the packages used in this book along with their GitHub links.

Videos

As videos have quickly become the most popular medium for sharing information, the Julian creators have taken advantage of this and have a specialized channel on YouTube: http://bit.ly/29D0hac. Beyond this channel, there are several other videos created by individual Julia users. If you happen to speak Portuguese, check out this great video by Alexandre Gomiero de Oliveira: http://bit.ly/28RMlbW. If you prefer something in English, this channel by Juan Klopper is a good place to start: http://bit.ly/28NS27K. Always be on the lookout for new Julia videos, since there are new ones popping up regularly.

News

If you find that YouTube is too slow in delivering the latest developments of this language, then try looking for a reliable blog to keep you up to date. You can read the official blog maintained by the creators of the language (http://julialang.org/blog), or this meta-blog that gathers Julia-related posts from various blogs: http://www.juliabloggers.com. The entries of this blog contain all kinds of articles, along with links to the original sources.

If you like small snippets of news, then the Twitter medium may be best for you. In this case, check out tweets with the hashtag #JuliaLang, and #JuliaLangsEs for the Spanish ones.

PRACTICE WHAT YOU'VE LEARNED

Now it's time to apply what you have learned to a hands-on project. Before you start, we recommend you review the notebook from Chapter 5 one more time, to make sure that you understand the whole process and how Julia fits into it. Also, you may want to go back to all the questions or exercises of this book that originally puzzled you, and try to tackle them once more. Once you are ready, you can gather all your notes and start looking at your task below.

Although it would be great if you could apply as much of your new know-how as possible, you won't need to use every single tool in your toolbox in order to complete this task. An example of a minimalist solution to this project is available in this chapter's corresponding IJulia notebook, while a high-level approach to how you could tackle this project is in Chapter 5. Your solution is bound to be different than the suggested one and that's fine; our solution is there just as an aid in case you get stuck. Also, you may find some of the auxiliary functions in that notebook handy, so feel free to use them for this and any other application.

In this project, your task is to analyze the `Spam Assassin` dataset that we saw briefly in the beginning of this book, ultimately creating a system that will be able to distinguish a spam email from a normal (or "ham") email based upon its subject. You can use whatever method you see fit. Provide the necessary code for your analysis (along with any other relevant material) and validate your results.

The dataset comprises three folders of emails, labeled "spam," "hard-ham," and "easy-ham." Most of the data in each file will be irrelevant to this task, as you need to focus on the subject only. (Once you finish the task, you can tweak your system so that it makes use of additional data, for additional practice.)

We recommend you do some data engineering to gather all the relevant data across all the files, and store it in additional files that you can use for further analysis. Also, since all of this is text data, you'll need to create your own features before you can apply any Stats or ML algorithms. We also recommend you use an

IJulia notebook for all your code, your results, and any additional comments throughout this project.

You'll quickly notice that some files contain emails written in another language, so you won't be able to make much of them due to their encoding. We suggest you skip them and work with the remaining part of the dataset. If you find the programming involved too frustrating at this point, and you find yourself stuck, you can either use some other data science tool you are more familiar with (see Appendix D), or you can go ahead and work with the `titles_only.csv` delimited file. We created this file to help you along in the process of tackling this project (the delimiter is a comma, something made possible through the removal of all special characters from the `subject` data).

Some features to get you started

If this whole project seems daunting to you, that's fine; most text-based project are like that. However, without going into natural language processing (NLP) methods, we can discuss some methods of solving such a problem with Julia, applying the data science process. So, if you just don't know where to start, here are several features you can try using to build a baseline model.

- The presence of the following words or phrases:
  - sale
  - guaranteed
  - low price
  - zzzzteana
  - fortune
  - money
  - entrepreneurs
  - perl
  - bug
  - investment
- The presence of very large words (more than 10 characters)
- The number of digits (i.e. numeric characters) in the subject.

Finding useful features is a good exercise in creativity (an essential quality in data science) as well as for refining your understanding of how prediction works in machine learning. Some features may be great for predicting one class, other features may be good for predicting another, while others may be good as aids of other features. Also, you may use functions like the sigmoid (`sig()` in the notebook) to make your numeric features more powerful (i.e. able to provide higher distances between the classes you are trying to distinguish).

Since this particular problem is relatively simple, if you apply yourself during feature creation, it is possible to obtain a perfect class separation (discernibility of 1.0). Of course, this does not guarantee a great performance for this kind of problem, since there is a significant imbalance between the classes. Remember that your aim is to be able to pinpoint the spam emails, so predicting the ham ones is good, but not as important.

Also, keep in mind that you can build a good model even if you don't have the most complete feature set, so don't spend all of your time on this part of process. We recommend you build a basic feature set using the low-hanging fruits first, create a model based on that, and then go back and enrich your features. Also, be sure to perform as many of the techniques we described in the book as possible. After all, the objective of the project is to get some hands-on experience in using data science methods in Julia.

Some thoughts on this project

Although this is real-world data, we made an effort to keep the whole thing as simple as possible. Ideally, you would make use of other relevant data apart from the subject text, such as the IP of the sender, time of correspondence, and the actual content of the email. Were you to take all of this data into account, you would surely have better performance in your system, but the whole project might take a long time to complete (you may need to create a series of new features specializing on the body text, for example). Also, if you were to work on such an application in the real world, you would probably have access to some blacklist where known spammers would be mentioned, making the whole process a bit easier.

The objective of this project, however, is not to build the perfect spam detection system, but rather to make use of Julia for a data science project and have something to use as a reference for your future projects. Also, such a project can be a great opportunity to exercise your discernment and intuition, qualities that although crucial to data science are rarely acknowledged in the majority of relevant books out there. Among other things, these qualities are imperative for figuring out which validation metrics you would apply on this problem, which words or phrases would you use as features, and what other aspects of the linguistic structure you could express as numeric features.

Once you have finished this project and you are satisfied with the outcome, you can try your hand at more sophisticated datasets (Kaggle would be a good place to start) and gradually expand your Julia expertise. Also, once you obtain more experience, you can dig deeper in the `Spam Assassin` dataset and see how you can improve your prediction system further. Perhaps you can perform some clever feature selection too, so that the whole thing is even faster. The sky is the limit!

FINAL THOUGHTS ABOUT YOUR EXPERIENCE WITH JULIA IN DATA SCIENCE

Refining your Julia programming skills

Unfortunately there is only one way to do this and there is no instant gratification: practice writing Julia programs. The various challenges in http://www.codeabbey.com are a great place to find programming problems, although it's unlikely that you'll find many answers with solutions in Julia. If you want something more focused on Julia, the first 10 problems of the *99 problems in Haskell* are available in this site, along with some proposed solutions: http://bit.ly/29xKI2c.

Once you reach the level where you can create bug-free code (at least for the majority of cases!), you can start looking at how you can make the code more efficient. One good way for monitoring that is the `@time` meta-function, which you can insert in front of the code you want to benchmark, in order to get some measurement of the resources it takes (CPU time and RAM). It would also be helpful if you got to know the different data types, and see how the expert Julians handle them for optimal efficiency in their code. You'll find out that Julia is a high-performance language with even mediocre code, and can be even more efficient when you optimize your coding style.

Contributing to the Julia project

You can contribute to the Julia project in the following ways:

Easy ways:

- Share your experience of Julia with other people.

- Share articles you find about the language to raise awareness of Julia among your contacts.

- Report any issues with the language or packages of it to the Julia developers' community.

- Donate to the project (there is a donate button at the bottom of the community page of the language's official site: http://julialang.org/community).

More hands-on ways:

- Create functions or packages that may be useful to other Julia users and share the corresponding scripts online (via your personal website, or through a public one like Dropbox or GitHub).

- Edit existing packages and resolve issues or limitations they have.

- Solve programming challenges in Julia and make the solutions available to everyone through a blog.

- Start using Julia for your everyday work (even if it is in parallel with your existing platform).

Ways involving some commitment:

- Attend the annual Julia conferences (currently in Boston and Bangalore, in June and in September or October, respectively).

- Promote Julia-related events, articles, and books on your site, blog, or Meetup event.

- Create learning material for the language and make it available to other people (or translate existing material to your native tongue).

- Buy more copies of this book and give them to friends as presents!

Okay, you don't have to do the last one if your friends are not particularly interested in the topic (and you want to keep them as friends). However, you can still buy these extra copies and hand them out to your colleagues or to members of your local data science Meetup group!

Future of Julia in data science

It is difficult to make predictions about this matter, especially at this point when there isn't a ton of information to base those predictions on. However, if the latest trends in the Julia language are any indication of its growth and increased applicability, we can expect to see more of it in the future, particularly in data science related applications.

At the end of the day, no matter how conservative people are when it comes to embracing a new tool, eventually its usability will overcome the inertia of its potential users. A good example of this is Linux, which has been a great alternative to other operating systems since the early 90s, even though people were not initially willing to adopt it.

Now, however, the majority of computers (and other electronics) make use of this OS in one way or another, while more and more people are switching to it as their main OS. Perhaps something similar will happen with Julia. It may not happen this year, or the next, but just like Python came to be the status quo due to its simplicity and ease of use, so can Julia gradually become a major player in the data science field.

Will Julia replace R, Python, and other languages? That's unlikely; there will always be people (and companies) that will use these tools even when they don't have any clear advantage over the alternatives–simply because these people have invested a lot in them. Consider the case of the Fortran language, which has been gradually replaced by Java, C, C++, and other low-level languages. Still, there are people out there who use Fortran and will probably continue doing so even when it has become entirely irrelevant. Of course, R and Python are far more adaptive and high-level than Fortran. Yet, it is likely that in the future, working with these platforms would be a matter of preference rather than of any actual advantage– just as some people prefer to work with C# instead of Java or C++.

Besides, Julia doesn't have an aggressive approach towards existing technologies, which is why there several APIs for bridging the gap between them and Julia (see Appendix D). So, it is unlikely that there will be a "fight to the death" between Julia and the R / Python duo, but rather some symbiosis of sorts. Perhaps Julia will lead the way in data engineering tasks and prove self-sufficient in the majority of other applications, with R being the go-to platform for statistical analyses, Python being the choice for some specialized models, and all of them running in parallel. At the end of the day, true data scientists just want to get the job done and couldn't care less about the tools used, just like good developers are happy to use whatever language they see fit for building the application they need.

It is our wish that you become the kind of data scientist who takes advantage of new technologies such as Julia to make the field richer and more valuable to everyone. Perhaps you can one day be a contributor to this technology, making things easier for the Julia-oriented data scientists to come.

You can download the latest versions of Julia at this site: http://bit.ly/2a6CtMi.

Just like other pieces of software, it has a stable version and an experimental one (nightly builds). We highly recommend that you go with the former, as the latter can be buggy and does not necessarily give you any significant advantages. So, unless you want to test a new package at the next popular version of the language while it is being developed, you have no reason to play around with the nightly builds.

Also, make sure that you download the installer that corresponds to your computer's OS and its internal data transference bandwidth (64 bits for most computers today and 32 bits for the older ones). Once you download the installer, just run it and follow these instructions: http://bit.ly/29qh7XQ.

Although Julia exists as a package in the Linux system, this is bound to be an earlier version of the language. To get the latest (stable) version, you'll need to access the corresponding repositories: ppa:staticfloat/juliareleases and ppa:staticfloat/julia-deps for Ubuntu-based systems.

The vanilla flavor of Julia (which is the one shown first on the official website) is basic but you can still do a lot with it. This form of the language is called REPL (which stands for Read, Evaluate, Print and Loop), and is particularly handy for basic tasks and for running scripts you have already written in a text editor or an IDE.

Speaking of IDEs, the Julia creators promote Juno and offer it as a bundle with Julia. Juno is currently somewhat unstable, even though Atom itself works fine.

For getting IJulia on your system, things get a bit trickier. Although the package itself is fine, one of its dependencies (Zero MQ, or ZMQ in the Julia universe) may or may not build properly on your system. To avoid any unnecessary back-and-forths with this, we strongly recommend you avoid the conventional approach to packages for this one and do the following instead:

1. Install ipython on your computer

2. Install ipython-notebook on your computer

3. Run Julia

4. Add the `IJulia` package

5. Build the package (`Pkg.build("IJulia")`).

Afterward, you can access the IJulia environment on your browser using the following commands:

```
using IJulia
IJulia.notebook()
```

Site	Description
www.julialang.org	Julia's official website. A great resource for the latest Julia version, tutorials, news, and other relevant info.
https://en.wikibooks.org/wiki/Introducing_Julia	An excellent reference book for Julia.
http://learnjulia.blogspot.com	A great blog for Julia updates.
http://media.readthedocs.org/pdf/julia/latest/julia.pdf	Official documentation for Julia.
http://learnxinyminutes.com/docs/julia	A useful overview of the main commands of the language, based on simple examples.
https://www.linkedin.com/grp/home?gid=5144163	The most popular Julia group on LinkedIn.
http://julia.meetup.com	A list of the various Meetup groups for Julia users.
www.junolab.org	The homepage of the Juno, a dedicated IDE for developing, running and debugging Julia scripts.
bogumilkaminski.pl/files/julia_express.pdf	A fast-paced tutorial on the Julia language, based on examples.
http://bit.ly/28RMlbW	The best video tutorial out there, specifically designed for aspiring Julia users, without any assumptions on their programming background. Unfortunately it's only in Portuguese.
https://groups.google.com/forum/#!forum/julia-users https://groups.google.com/forum/#!forum/julialanges	Google+ groups for Julia users. The first is in English, while the second is in Spanish.

Site	Description
https://www.youtube.com/user/JuliaLanguage.	The official YouTube channel for Julia.
http://www.juliabloggers.com	A blog post aggregator for Julia-related topics. This is the best resource for Julia news.
http://learnjulia.blogspot.com/2014/05/99-problems-in-julia-programming.html	An interesting collection of some basic programming problems solved in Julia.
http://www.tutorialspoint.com/execute_julia_online.php	A great place to create and run Julia scripts online (no registration needed).
http://samuelcolvin.github.io/JuliaByExample/	An excellent resource for getting basic things done in Julia.
http://www.jlhub.com/julia	An index of all the built-in functions of Julia, categorized and with examples where necessary.
http://quant-econ.net/jl/index.html	An introduction to Julia and how it is applicable for econometrics applications.
http://pkg.julialang.org	The list of official packages available for the latest Julia versions.
http://docs.julialang.org/en/release-0.4	Official documentation on the specifics of the Julia language.
https://twitter.com/JuliaLanguage	Julia's official Twitter channel.

Package	Location	Description
JLD	https://github.com/JuliaLang/JLD.jl	Julia data file format package
StatsBase	https://github.com/JuliaStats/StatsBase.jl	Statistics functions – general
HypothesisTests	https://github.com/JuliaStats/HypothesisTests.jl	Statistics functions – hypothesis testing
PyPlot	https://github.com/stevengj/PyPlot.jl	Plotting package from Python
Gadfly	https://github.com/dcjones/Gadfly.jl	One of the best plotting packages out there
Clustering	https://github.com/JuliaStats/Clustering.jl	Clustering techniques
DecisionTree	https://github.com/bensadeghi/DecisionTree.jl	Decision trees and random forests
BackpropNeural Net	https://github.com/compressed/BackpropNeuralNet.jl	Basic neural network trained using the algo of backpropagation
Graphs	https://github.com/JuliaLang/Graphs.jl	Complete graphs package
LightGraphs	https://github.com/JuliaGraphs/LightGraphs.jl	Relatively fast graph algorithms
PyCall	https://github.com/stevengj/PyCall.jl	Calling Python scripts from Julia

Package	Location	Description
RCall	https://github.com/armgong/RJulia	Calling R scripts from Julia
DataFrames	https://github.com/JuliaStats/DataFrames.jl	Great package for integrating data frames in Julia
ELM	https://github.com/lepisma/ELM.jl	The go-to place for Extreme Learning Machines
Distances	https://github.com/JuliaStats/Distances.jl	Useful package for various distance related functions
GLM	https://github.com/JuliaStats/GLM.jl	Generalized Linear Model package
TSNE	http://lvdmaaten.github.io/tsne	An official package to implement the t-SNE algorithm
MultivariateStats	https://github.com/JuliaStats/MultivariateStats.jl	A great place to get PCA and other useful statistics functions
MLBase	https://github.com/JuliaStats/MLBase.jl	An excellent resource for various support functions for ML applications

APPENDIX D
Bridging Julia with Other Platforms

Jumping from one programming language to another is usually a hassle, particularly if you are not an expert in one of the languages. The situation can get even more challenging when you are dealing with peculiar data that must be transferred to the other platform in order to process or visualize it. This issue is often tackled by putting everything into a data file that both platforms can access. However, this still requires considerable time, especially if you are dealing with large datasets.

Bridging two platforms together is usually the best way to resolve this matter, which is made possible with some specialized packages. Julia can be bridged with various platforms, the most relevant of which to data science are Python and R. It is also possible to bridge Julia with C, C++, and Fortran, but this is something beyond the scope of this book. What's more, there are packages in Python and R that can make this a two-way street, making Julia even more relevant. In this appendix we'll look into how this is done.

BRIDGING JULIA WITH R

RUNNING A JULIA SCRIPT IN R

Although R is great for plots and running statistical models, it is not the best platform for scripts that involve loops, which are often encountered in data engineering. Fortunately you can outsource this part of the data science pipeline to Julia using the `rjulia` package (which has the `devtools` package as a dependency). Depending on your operating system, you can make use of this as follows:

Installation of `rjulia` package:

Linux OS:

```
install.packages("devtools") # if you haven't installed the
    devtools package already
install_github("armgong/rjulia", ref="master")
```

Windows OS:

```
install.packages("devtools") # if you haven't installed the
    devtools package already
installeddevtools::install_github("armgong/rjulia", ref="master",
    args ="--no-multiarch")
```

Here is how you can apply the rjulia package in R:

```
library(rjulia)
julia_init() # the rjulia package will find your julia home folder
    automatically
julia_eval("2 + 2") # a very basic example
```

The output of this should be 4 and be in a data type native to the R environment.

RUNNING AN R SCRIPT IN JULIA

In the rare case where you would want to use an R code snippet while in Julia, you can summon it using the RCall package. Here is the code you need to use to get this up and running:

```
In[1]: Pkg.add("RCall")
In[2]: using(RCall)
```

If everything is running smoothly you should see a confirmation message like the following:

```
R installation found at C:\Program Files\R\R-3.2.2
```

Since it is unlikely that you will ever need to make use of this package, we won't elaborate on this.

Bridging Julia with Python

RUNNING A JULIA SCRIPT IN PYTHON

Although Python often poses as a true programming language, in essence it is a scripting language with OOP capabilities. If you want to run a long loop in this language, you may face a lengthy wait time. That's one of the reasons it is often useful to have Julia on the side: to do all the stuff that Python wouldn't ever be able to handle in a reasonable time frame. To make this happen you need to use the Julia module, as follows:

At the command prompt / shell type:

```
pip install Julia
```

While in Python type the following:

```
import Julia
J = julia.Julia()
J.run("1 + 1")
```

This should yield the output 2 and be in a data type that is native to Python.

RUNNING A PYTHON SCRIPT IN JULIA

Although unlikely, it is possible that you may need to run a Python script while in Julia (probably to make use of some package that hasn't been developed in Julia yet). You can accomplish this by making use of the `PyCall` package, just like in the following example:

```
In[1]: using PyCall
In[2]: @pyimport numpy.random as nr
In[3]: nr.rand(3,4)
Out[3]: 3x4 Array{Float64,2}:
    0.564096 0.12906  0.828137 0.238906
    0.783359 0.682929 0.929377 0.155438
    0.511939 0.713345 0.182735 0.453748
```

The output values you see are bound to be different than these. However, there is something else in the output that is particularly important: the data type of the output. Even though this came from a function in the `numpy` package of Python, the output is still a Julia data type, fully compatible with other data structures in the environment this is run on.

APPENDIX E
Parallelization in Julia

When we talk about parallelization in Julia, we refer to the use of different CPUs (or GPUs) either within your computer or a computer cluster. This can be done using the base package and with just a few lines of code, making it a powerful tool. Parallelization is particularly useful in stochastic processes (e.g. Monte-Carlo simulations), linear algebra calculations, and any other processes that can be broken down into independent components. Even optimization has a lot to benefit from this technique, particularly if you are going deep into AI territory.

Parallelization is extremely important in data science too, as it allows you to process data in an effective manner. However, not all data analysis processes require parallelization. It is usually applied in problems that can be broken down in self-sufficient parts to be effectively parallelized, saving you valuable time and making the most of your resources.

To perform parallelization, you need to do the following, in this particular order:

1. Add new processors to Julia (i.e. give Julia access to your computing resources, namely processors and/or threads).

2. Create one or more mapper functions that will be run on each processor, and make them available to all of the processors.

3. Create a wrapper function that will also act as a reducer or aggregator.

4. Test each mapper to make sure that it provides the desired result.

5. Run the wrapper function on two or so processors to ensure that it works as expected.

6. Make any changes if necessary.

7. Run the wrapper function on all of your processors.

For this whole process to be efficient, it is important to split the data processing work equally among the processors. This way you can minimize the waiting in the wrapper function.

A mapper function can be any function that is preceded by the term "@everywhere" in its definition. This makes it available to all the processors, and its outputs are universally accessible. To make the whole parallelization process easier, you can define the mapper to have the whole dataset as its input, along with an index that limits the data that will be processed by it. This will make the memory requirements of the wrapper lighter and the whole process somewhat faster.

As for the wrapper, it needs to make sure that the data processing tasks are split equally among the mappers and that their outputs are combined appropriately afterwards. Splitting the tasks can be a bit tricky, since not all tasks are parallelizable in an obvious way. That's why it is best to start with small data first (which can be analyzed without parallelization) and see if the wrapper's results are the same as its non-parallelized counterpart.

Here are some helpful functions and commands that are used in a parallelization setting:

Basic:

- **CPU_CORES** – this fundamental command allows Julia to access the BIOS information of your machine and retrieve the total number of cores available in its hardware.

- **nprocs()** – yields the number of processors available through Julia at this moment (this is subject to change).

- **addprocs(n)** – adds n processors to Julia (n is an integer). The output of this function is an array containing the numbers of the added processors. Alternatively, you can give Julia access to n processors when firing it up by typing in the command line: `julia -p n`. For best performance, we recommend you use as many processors as the total number of cores in your machine's CPU.

- **procs()** – yields an array of all the available processors (i.e. their reference numbers).

More advanced:

- **@parallel** – performs a certain command, usually a loop, in parallel. Indexing is not maintained in this case, so this command is most useful for simulations.

- **@everywhere** – makes the function that follows available in all the processors accessible to Julia. This is essential for parallelizing a custom function.

- **pmap()** – this function is related to `map()`, but instead of mapping a function to the various elements of an array, it does so across all available processors. The equivalent function in R is `sapply()`.

As this is an advanced topic, we won't go into more detail here. However, if you wish to learn more about this, we recommend studying the examples in Alex Shum's post on the topic (probably the best resource on this topic across the web): http://bit.ly/29lPygg. Should you want a hands-on view of parallelization, you can check out the YouTube video created by Jeff Bezanson (one of Julia's creators): http://bit.ly/29lPNaZ.

APPENDIX F
Answers to Chapter Challenges

CHAPTER 2

1. Juno would be your safest bet, if you haven't used Julia before. Otherwise, you can utilize the same advantage by using IJulia with the latest Julia kernel (shown at the top right part of the IJulia screen).

2. JuliaBox is the most well-known option. If, however, you don't have a Google account or you don't wish to give Google access to your code, you can use the one at tutorialspoint.com.

3. <u>IDE over REPL:</u> Reasons include: ability to load/save scripts (.jl files), more user-friendly interface, easier to organize your code, easier to clean up code, code is retained if Julia crashes, built-in features such as file explorer, color-coding of the code makes scripts easier to understand.

    <u>IJulia over other IDEs:</u> Reasons include: scripts are much easier to share with non-programmers, plots are usually in the same area as the code, code can be exported as a variety of formats (e.g. .jl scripts, .ipynb notebooks, .html pages, .pdf documents), easier to use if you are coming from a Python or Graphlab background, formatting capabilities for relevant text.

4. <u>Internal reasons:</u> Auxiliary functions allow you to organize your thoughts in a more high-level and functional way. They make the whole process of building a solution much more efficient, and make debugging much more straightforward and quick.

    <u>External reasons:</u> Auxiliary functions allow other users of your code to grasp its functionality faster, and they make your code more reusable (the auxiliary functions can be used by themselves in other applications). They also make

your main function much simpler (allowing for high-level understanding of what's going on).

5. It's a function that combines (wraps) several auxiliary functions to accomplish a greater objective. If there is only one wrapper function, it is often referred to as the *main function*. Wrapper functions are common in complex applications and in various packages.

6. **sqrt()**: It yields the square root of a number. It takes a non-negative variable of type number as an input. It also works on arrays of such numbers, as well as complex numbers (variables that are of type number but not of type real).

    indmin(): This provides you with the index of the minimum value of a numeric array. It takes an array as an input, of any dimension. It also works on other collection types.

    length(): This identifies the number of elements of a collection or the number of characters in a string. It takes an array, dict, range, or abstractstring as an input, and always yields a single integer.

7. Assuming that y and z are of the same size, the expression always yields a float between 0 and 1 (inclusive). The first part of the expression (`sum(y==z)`) basically yields a number between 0 and n, where n is the number of elements in y. This same number is the value of the latter part of the expression (`length(y)`). The expression is the ratio of the two, so it must be between 0 and 1.

8. For a filename `Array A.csv` in path `d:\data\`, use the command `writecsv("d:\\data\\Array A.csv", A)`.

9. Pick the most important variables, say A, B, and C, and a name for your data file, say "workspace - Friday afternoon." Then load the `JLD` package:

    ```
    using JLD
    ```

    Afterward, run the following command:

```
f = open("workspace - Friday afternoon.jld", "w")
@write f A
@write f B
@write f C
close(f)
```

You may need to change the first command slightly, if you wish to add a path, as in the previous question.

10. `Max()` works on a pair of numbers and takes two inputs of type number. `Maximum()` is the generalization of `max()`, applicable on a series of numbers; it takes a single input: the array containing these numbers. For finding whether a or b is larger (where `a, b <: Number`), you need to use the former: `max(a, b)`.

11. Use `Pkg.add("NMF")` as follows:

```
Pkg.update()
using NMF
```

12. No. kNN, like any other classifier, is unable to work with text data. The distance calculation that lies at its core only works with numeric data. Nevertheless, kNN could be used in text analytics with the right data engineering, as we'll see in Chapter 6.

13. The fastest way to do this is to change the reference to the `distance()` function in the `kNN()` function to that of the Manhattan distance, if you already have that knowledge. If not, you can edit the `distance()` function by replacing the line

```
dist += (x[i] - y[i])^2
with the following:
dist += abs(x[i] - y[i])
```

Since you might need to revert to the original distance calculation when working with different datasets, you may want to keep the original line as a comment (i.e. add a "#" in front of it).

CHAPTER 3

1. Yes, I have!

2. Julia functions are your best choice in most cases. However, if you have a function implemented in C, you may want to make use of it since in many cases it may improve performance slightly.

3. A dictionary structure (dict) would be most suitable.

4. It does make sense if you know what you are doing and don't plan to share your functions with other users. If you accidentally use these functions with inputs of irrelevant types, however, this may cause Julia to throw exceptions or errors. Also, the performance of the function is bound to be suboptimal.

CHAPTER 4

1. Yes, using the multiple dispatch characteristic of Julia. So, if function `awesome_fun(A::Array)` is designed to calculate the entropy of an array `A`, you can extend it by writing another function `awesome_fun(f::ASCIIString)` that calculates the entropy of the contents of a file `f`. This way, you can run `awesome_fun()` on either one of these two cases seamlessly.

2. The `hdist()` function takes abstractstring type inputs and `a` and `b` are character variables.

3. Yes. Multiple dispatch.

4. The answer is:

```
function word_counter(text::AbstractString)
    words = split(text, " ")
    word_count = length(words)
    return word_count
end
```

```
text = "Data science is the coolest field today."
println(word_counter(text)) # yields the number 7
```

5. The answer is:

```
function non_space_characters_prop(text::AbstractString)
    chars = split(text, "")
    N = length(chars)
    n = sum(chars .!= " ")
    return n / N
end
text = "Data science is the coolest field today."
non_space_characters_prop(text) # yields the number 0.85
```

6. Here the main function is `digit_freq()`. Functions `convert_to_string()` and `find_most_popular_item()` are auxiliary.

```
function convert_to_string(A::Array{Float64, 1})
    temp = string(A)
    return temp[2:(end-1)]
end
function find_most_popular_item(D::Dict)
    ind = indmax(values(D))
    temp = collect(keys(D))
    return temp[ind]
end
function digit_freq(A::Array{Float64, 1})
    temp = convert_to_string(A)
    freqs = Dict{Char,Int64}()

    for character in temp
      if character in "1234567890"
       if haskey(freqs, character)
         freqs[character] += 1
       else
         freqs[character] = 1
       end
      end
    end
    digit = find_most_popular_item(freqs)
    return digit
end
```

For large enough samples of numbers, it is expected that '1' will be the most common digit (Benford's law).

CHAPTER 5

1.   This is the part of the data science pipeline that has to do with getting the data ready for analysis. It involves data preparation, exploration, and representation. Often referred to as "data wrangling," it is one of the most necessary aspects of data science.

2.   It is important as it makes the data ready for data exploration, taking care of the missing values, pinpointing potential issues, cleaning it, normalizing it, and in many cases removing at least some of the outliers.

3.   The data science pipeline is geared towards complex and/or messy data, with the goal of creating a data product and/or actionable insights about the future. Other data analysis pipelines focus more on creating some summary or interesting conclusion, usually related to the past or present. Also, the data in other data analysis pipelines is relatively simpler and cleaner.

4.   We can clean it up a bit and transform it into something like this:

Variable `Text`: "the customer appeared to be dissatisfied with product 1A2345 released last may"

Variable `RelatedProduct`: 1A2345

5.   It entails the understanding of the dataset through examination of the variables' distributions, how they are related to each other, and their relationship to the target variable. All this is done by looking into the geometry of the feature space and the application of various visuals.

6.   The main process involved is encoding the data into the most appropriate kind of data types. In many cases, it also involves the featurization of the data (especially in the case of text data).

7. This is anything related to the discovery of patterns and connections within the data, usually directly applicable to the data learning phase that ensues.

8. This entails getting the computer(s) to learn from the dataset we have prepared in the previous stages. This involves the intelligent analysis of that data and the use of regression, classification, clustering, and other techniques to derive some kind of generalization or applicable insight.

9. This is the process of deploying the model created in the previous stage into production. This is usually done through the development of an API, an application, or a dashboard; it aims to make the model accessible to an audience different from the data science and engineering teams (often the clients of the organization owning this product).

10. During this phase a number of visuals and reports are created. The target audience is management, and sometimes other parts of the organization owning this pipeline. This is different from the data product, which is more often than not made available to a broader audience, either at a price or for promotional purposes. The insight, deliverance, and visualization phase also encompasses the results and insights from the data product (e.g. how successful it was, what feedback was received by the users) and is essential for the evaluation of the whole data science project. It is a return to the starting point, in a way, often spawning a new cycle for the project.

11. It is highly non-linear since there are often detours from the "normal" flow, as new tasks come about, or things don't go as expected.

12. An app that calculates your average calorie consumption based on your movement throughout the day, a recommender system on a social medium, or a risk evaluation system for potential clients.

13. These tend to be more polished and convey more high-level information.

14. Yes, since every one of them contributes to either transforming, analyzing, or distilling the data as it is gradually transmuted into information. Omitting

certain ones may be possible in some cases (e.g. when all the data is tidy and ready to be analyzed), but this is quite rare.

CHAPTER 6

1. Data engineering is important since it allows you to identify the most information-rich aspects of your data and prepare them for further analysis.

2. Data frames are capable of handling missing values (coded as NA). Also, it is possible to host all kinds of data types in the same data frame.

3. By opening the file and parsing it using the JSON package:

```
f = open("file.json")
X = JSON.parse(f)
close(f)
```

4. There are three main strategies:

    a) You can process it on a cluster or cloud environment.

    b) You can process it natively by breaking it down to manageable pieces.

    c) You can load the whole thing into an SFrame, after installing the corresponding package.

5. It entails the following processes, based on the kind of data we have:

    a) For numeric data: eliminate missing values, handle outliers.

    b) For text data: remove unnecessary characters, remove stop words (in the case of text analytics).

6. Because they allow you to do more efficient resource management, and also represent your data in a way that makes sense to both the user and to the Julia functions used in the stages that ensue.

7. We'd do this by normalizing them, ideally to (0, 1). However, a normalization to [0, 1] would also be very good, assuming there are no outliers in the dataset. Alternatively, a normalization using the mean and the standard deviation is also a feasible option.

8. The abstractstring type is the obvious choice. However, various subtypes of integer would be useful, particularly if you are planning to do a frequency analysis. The Boolean type is also useful if you want to perform a lexicon analysis or something along these lines. In all cases, a sparsematrixCSC data type will come in handy, especially if you are dealing with a dataset having a large vocabulary.

9. A bitarray, a Boolean array, or an array of Int8 type would work.

10. `OnlineNewsPopularity`: Correlation

    `Spam`: Jaccard Similarity, Mutual Information, or Similarity Index

CHAPTER 7

1. Remove one of them, taking into account its correlation to the other variables and its similarity to the target variable.

2. Never. You can only disprove it, with a certain degree of confidence.

3. If the target variable is ordinal and each class is equally different from its neighboring classes. Since this is rarely the case, it's best not to use correlation in classification problems.

4. Be sure to perform data preparation first, creating as many plots as you can. An observation could be something like "variable A appears to be closely related to variable B," "variable C seems to be a very good predictor for the target variable," "variable D has a few outliers," "variables need to be normalized," etc.

5. Yes, although it works best on variables following the normal distribution. Since this rarely happens, it is often used regardless.

6. No. In order to draw statistically significant conclusions you need a larger sample.

7. Use a scatter plot.

8. Visualizing the whole dataset, transforming it into a smaller dimensionality, without much distortion. Based on this, you can deduce that this method allows for better depiction of meaningful patterns, such as clusters, and assessment of classification difficulty.

CHAPTER 8

1. Yes, as the number of features is very high for most data analytics methods. Any one of the described methods would work. If labels are available, use the methods based on feature evaluation, as they would be considerably faster and less prone to memory overflow problems for this particular dataset.

2. Yes, as the number of features is still somewhat high for many data analytics methods. Any one of the available methods would work, though PCA would be preferable for performance reasons.

3. A method based on feature evaluation, as the dataset is too small for PCA to work properly.

4. Possibly, though not as a first choice. If the attempted data analytics methods don't work well, or if some of the features are shown to be redundant based on the data exploration stage, try applying one of the data analytics methods.

5. No. Data science projects usually involve a large number of features, making the total number of possible feature combinations extremely large. Applying such a method would be a waste of resources, while the additional benefit of the optimal reduced feature set may not improve the performance of the data

analysis much more than the result of a sub-optimal feature reduction method.

6. The use of additional information residing in the target vector (i.e. what we are trying to predict).

7. In this case the ICA method would be best, as it yields statistically independent meta-features.

8. Any one of the more sophisticated approaches would work. If you don't mind playing around with parameters, the GA-based method would be best.

CHAPTER 9

1. It is possible, but only if there is a discreet variable in the dataset and it is used as the target variable. After the stratified sampling, you can merge the two outputs together and use the new matrix as your sample dataset.

2. Stratified sampling would maintain the signals of the minority class(es) to some extent. Using basic sampling might result in a sampling with the smaller class(es) poorly represented.

3. Randomization. As any statistics book would stress, this is key for any decent sampling, as it is the best way to deal with potential biases in the sample.

4. Yes, although it's not a method you would see in any data science book. To normalize the total cost to be between 0 and 1, first find the maximum possible cost (assume that all elements of each class are misclassified in the worst possible way, i.e. yielding the highest misclassification cost). Then take the ratio of the total cost of a given classification with the maximum cost.

5. No, unless you break the problem into three smaller ones, each having a binary result (e.g. "class 1" and "Any other class"). Then you can create an ROC curve for each one of these sub-problems.

6. You can use KFCV for any problem with a target variable that doesn't have many different values. So, although this is designed for classification problems only, you could theoretically use it for regression too, if the number of distinct values in the target variable were relatively small.

CHAPTER 10

1. Distances are important in clustering and any other distance-based algorithms. This is due to the fact that they directly influence the function and the results of these algorithms. Picking the right distance metric can make or break the clustering system, yielding either insightful or nonsensical outputs.

2. Use DBSCAN or some variant of it.

3. Those metrics rely on the presence of a target variable, containing information independent from the data points in the feature set. Applying these metrics on clustering would be confusing, if not entirely inappropriate.

4. Only numeric data can be clustered, although non-numeric data could be clustered if it were transformed to binary features first. All data must be normalized before being used in clustering, in order to obtain unbiased results.

5. Partitional clustering is not limited to two or three dimensions, while the objective is a meaningful grouping of the data at hand. t-SNE aims to limit the dimensionality to a manageable amount without significantly distorting the dataset structure, so that it can be visualized well. Theoretically the output of t-SNE could be used for clustering, although that's not often the case.

6. Technically no, since its output is not directly applicable in the rest of the pipeline. However, it is useful in datasets having a certain level of complexity, as it allows us to understand them better and make more interesting hypotheses for these datasets.

7. High dimensionality can be a real issue with clustering, as the distance metrics generally fail to provide a robust way to express the dissimilarities of the data points (particularly when it comes to the diversity of these dissimilarities). However, this issue can be tackled effectively by making use of dimensionality reduction methods, such as PCA.

8. You can multiply this feature by a coefficient c that is greater than 1. The larger the coefficient, the more pronounced the feature will be in the clustering algorithm.

CHAPTER 11

1. Try either a random forest, a Bayesian network, or an SVM. If it's a regression problem, statistical regression would also be an option. If the dimensionality is reduced to a manageable number of features, a transductive system would also work. The fact that the original features are independent of each other would make any tree-based approach ideal, though a Bayesian network would also benefit.

2. Any one of the tree-based systems would do. Bayesian networks would also work well in this case. Depending on the amount of data available and the dimensionality, ANNs and transductive systems would also be viable options.

3. Neural networks, since they can handle noisy data well, are ideal for large datasets, and excel at the task of classification.

4. No. Even a robust supervised learning system would benefit a lot from intelligent data engineering.

5. Tree-based systems and, in the case of regression applications, the generalized statistical regression model.

6. Neural networks are an extension of the statistical regression, where everything is automated. Each node in the second layer can be seen as the

output of a statistical regression model, making a 3-layer ANN an ensemble of sorts, comprising statistical regression systems.

7. Dimensionality. The use of feature selection or of meta-features instead of the original features would solve the problem effectively.

8. Deep learning systems are not panaceas. They work well for certain types of problems, where data points are abundant, and where resource allocation is generous. It would be overkill to use them for every problem encountered, especially if interpretability is a requirement.

CHAPTER 12

1. They help us model and visualize complex datasets in a simple and intuitive way, and can also tackle certain datasets (e.g. social network data) that are practically impossible to model with conventional data science techniques.

2. If we denote each feature as a node and its similarities to (or distances from) other features as the corresponding edges, we can graph the whole feature set. Then we can see how independent the features are using basic graph analysis. Also, if we correlate the features with the target variable (using an appropriate metric), we could evaluate the various features. All this analysis can help us get an idea of the robustness of the feature set.

3. Possibly, depending on the data. Certain datasets should be modeled this way, but sometimes conventional techniques work well enough or better than graphs. Graph analysis generally works best in cases where the relationship among the data points or features or classes are important.

4. Without a doubt. In fact, we already implemented such a system in MATLAB several years back. However, this never reached the public domain as there were other more pressing innovations that took precedence. Anyway, an MST based classification system could be implemented as follows:

a) Inputs: Use a feature set for training, labels for training, a feature set for testing, or a distance metric.

b) Training: Create an MST for each class based on the data points of the training set and their distances (calculated using the given distance metric), and calculate the average edge weight.

c) Create an MST, compare the average edge weight of the new MST, compare it with the original MST of that class, assign the class label based on the case with the biggest improvement (lower difference in the average edge weights). Repeat this process for each data point in the test set and for each class.

It would be best to try building it yourself before checking out the provided code (MSTC.jl). Nevertheless, you are welcome to use the code provided, as long as you reference it properly.

Despite its simplicity, the MST-based classifier is powerful due to its holistic nature (even though this is not so apparent at first). However, it inherits the shortcomings of all distance-based classifiers, and it doesn't scale well.

5. No. You need to do a lot of preprocessing first, and model the data in such a way that the graph makes sense.

6. The answer is:

```
function MST2(g, w) # MAXimum Spanning Tree
   E, W = kruskal_minimum_spantree(g, -w)
   return E, -W
end
```

7. No, because there is additional information related to the graph that is not contained in the graph object of either package. Most importantly, the weights data is not stored in the graph data file.

CHAPTER 13

See corresponding IJulia notebook.

Index

Made in the USA
San Bernardino, CA
26 August 2016